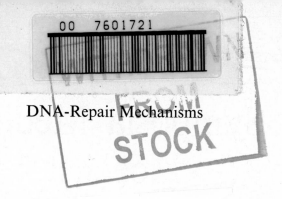
DNA-Repair Mechanisms

Symposia Medica Hoechst

Herausgegeben von der
Medizinischen Abteilung
der Farbwerke Hoechst AG

DNA-Repair Mechanisms

Symposium, Schloß Reinhartshausen/Rhein
October 4th/5th, 1971

Chairman: **Dr. H. Altmann**
Seibersdorf bei Wien

With 157 figures
and 22 tables

F. K. SCHATTAUER VERLAG · STUTTGART–NEW YORK

14

© 1972 by F. K. Schattauer Verlag GmbH, Stuttgart, Germany
Printed in Germany

Composing and printing: Universitätsdruckerei Mainz GmbH

ISBN 3 7945 0292 2

Contents

Participants

ALTMANN, Dr. H.

Institut für Biologie, Reaktorzentrum Seibersdorf, 2444 Seibersdorf, Österreich

ANTONI, Prof. Dr. F.

Institute of Medical Chemistry, Semmelweis University of Medicine, Puskin u. 9, Budapest VIII, Hungary

AVERBECK, Dr. D.

Christie Hospital & Holt Radium Institute, Paterson Laboratories, Manchester M20 9BX, Great Britain

BECK, Dr. J.

Kinderklinik der Johannes-Gutenberg-Universität, 65 Mainz

BOOTSMA, Prof. Dr. D.

Medische Faculteit Rotterdam, afd. Celbiologie en Genetica, Dr. Molewaterplein 50, Rotterdam, Nederland

BOYLE, Dr. J. M.

Christie Hospital & Holt Radium Institute, Paterson Laboratories, Manchester M20 9BX, Great Britain

CHANDRA, Prof. Dr. P.

Institut für Therapeutische Biochemie der Johann-Wolfgang-Goethe-Universität, Ludwig-Rehn-Str. 14, 6 Frankfurt a. M.

EBERL, Dr. R.

II. Medizinische Abteilung, Rheumastation Krankenhaus Wien-Lainz, Wolkersbergenstr. 1, 1130 Wien, Österreich

EDGREN, Dr. M.

Department of Tumor Biology, Karolinska Institutet, 10401 Stockholm, Sweden

ERNST, Dr. D.

Gesellschaft für Strahlenforschung mbH München, Institut für Strahlenbotanik, Herrenhäuser Str. 2, 3000 Hannover

FOX, Dr. M.

Christie Hospital & Holt Radium Institute, Paterson Laboratories, Manchester M20 9BX, Great Britain

HOFER, Dr. H.

Institut für Biologie, Reaktorzentrum Seibersdorf, 2444 Seibersdorf, Österreich

JUNG, PD Dr. E.

Universitäts-Hautklinik, Voßstr. 2, 6900 Heidelberg

KALTHOFF, Dr. K.

Institut für Biologie I der Albert-Ludwigs-Universität, Katharinenstr. 20, 7800 Freiburg i. Br.

KAPLAN, Prof. Dr. R. W.

Institut für Mikrobiologie der Johann-Wolfgang-Goethe-Universität, Siesmayerstr. 70, 6 Frankfurt a. M. 1

KIEFER, Doz. Dr. J.

Strahlenzentrum, Institut für Biophysik, Leihgesterner Weg 217, 63 Gießen

KLEPPE, Dr. K.

Department of Biochemistry, Bergen University, Bergen, Norway

KRÄMER, Dr. D. M.

Am Rosengarten 4, 65 Mainz

LINDAHL, Prof. Dr. T.

Karolinska Institutet, Kemiska Institutionen II, 10401 Stockholm, Sweden

LUCAS, Dr. C. J.

Centraal Laboratorium van de Bloedtransfusiedienst van Het Nederlandsche Roode Kruis, Plesmanlaan 125, Amsterdam-W., Nederland

MENNIGMANN, Prof. Dr. H. D.

Institut für Mikrobiologie der Johann-Wolfgang-Goethe-Universität, Siesmayerstr. 70, 6000 Frankfurt a. M. 1

MOUTON, Dr. R. F.

No. 3 Résidence Chevreuse, 91 Orsay, France

NORMAN, Prof. Dr. A.

University of California, Department of Radiology, The Center for the Health Sciences, Los Angeles, California 90024, USA

OKAZAKI, Prof. Dr. R.

Institute of Molecular Biology, Faculty of Science, Nagoya University, Chikusa-Ku, Nagoya, Japan

ORMEROD, Dr. M. G.

Chester Beatty Research Institute, Institute of Cancer Research, Royal Cancer Hospital, Clifton Avenue, Belmont/Sutton/Surrey, Great Britain

PAINTER, Prof. Dr. R. B.

University of California, School of Medicine, Laboratory of Radiobiology, San Francisco, California 94122, USA

PARTSCH, Dipl.-Ing. G.

Institut für Biologie, Reaktorzentrum Seibersdorf, 2444 Seibersdorf, Österreich

POHLIT, Prof. Dr. W.

Institut für Biologie, Abt. für Biophysikalische Strahlenforschung, Paul-Ehrlich-Str. 15+20, 6 Frankfurt a. M.

REGAN, Dr. J. D.

Oak Ridge National Laboratory, Biology Division, Oak Ridge, Tenn. 37830, USA

RÉVÉSZ, Prof. Dr. L.

Department of Tumor Biology, Karolinska Institutet, 10401 Stockholm, Sweden

ROBERTS, Dr. J. J.

Chester Beatty Research Institute, Pollards Wood Research Station, Nightingales Lane, Chalfont St. Giles/Buckinghamshire, Great Britain

SLOR, Prof. Dr. H.

Tel Aviv University, Medical School, Department of Human Genetics, Tel Aviv, Israel

STENMAN, Dr. S.

III Department of Pathology, University of Helsinki, Haartmansgatan 3, Helsinki, Finland

STRAUSS, Prof. Dr. B.

Department of Microbiology, 5724 Ellis Avenue, Chicago, Ill. 60637, USA

TRAUT, Prof. Dr. H.

Westfälische Wilhelms-Universität, Institut für Strahlenbiologie, Hittorfer Str. 17, 4400 Münster (Westf.)

WACKER, Prof. Dr. A.

Institut für Therapeutische Biochemie der Johann-Wolfgang-Goethe-Universität, Ludwig-Rehn-Str. 14, 6 Frankfurt a. M.

Introduction

H. Altmann

Many diseases have a genetical background. But the occurrence of new mutations in man is rare, if we expect that the mutation rate per locus and generation is approximately 0.00004 (4×10^{-5}) (1). Sutton calculated that the total frequency of point mutations is of the order of 10^{-5} to 10^{-6} per protein per generation (2). The determination of the turnover rate resulted in the calculation that, if DNA would be 35 years in one cell which has a normal DNA repair of skin cells, every DNA base would be replaced within this time (3). Therefore mammalian cells must have very active DNA-repair systems, so that about 2.3×10^9 single-strand breaks, which can occur per μg DNA in 1 hour, lead to such low mutation frequency. On the other hand, if DNA-repair mechanisms are too efficient, this may be a block for human evolution. At present there are still open questions to the known DNA-repair mechanisms.

Normal mammalian cells can repair damage induced in their DNA by either UV-light, ionizing radiation, or chemicals including alkylating agents. The best-known repair mechanisms are those acting on pyrimidine dimers produced in DNA by UV-light. Most experiments were performed with different E. coli strains, and three mechanisms to repair DNA after UV-irradiation were investigated. Photoreactivation is the simplest mechanism to monomerize pyrimidine dimers, but this DNA-repair system is not present in human cells. The dark-repair system, also known as excision repair, cannot act only on pyrimidine dimers, but also on damaged DNA constituents after ionizing radiation or alkylating agents. Post-replication repair involves a recombinational process, and gaps opposite to the pyrimidine dimers are repaired by this mechanism.

Excision repair requires endonucleases which make a nick close to the damaged part of DNA, exonuclease activities to remove the damaged part and a polymerase to resynthesize the region of this chain. A polynucleotide ligase joins up the 3'OH-5'P ends and the repair is then complete.

The second step in this reaction chain is done by the same enzyme which can effectively work also in the reverse direction either as exonuclease or polymerase. Kelly et al. (4) concluded that the Kornberg polymerase I from E. coli shows neither exclusive exonuclease nor endonuclease activity, and cannot only clip single nucleotides, but also excise short oligo-nucleotides. It seems that in bacteria most of the excised oligo-nucleotides contain 2–8 nucleotides, but normally 20–500 nucleotides per dimer are removed, possibly dependent on the ligase activity in different cells. In mammalian cells it seems that only about 3 nucleotides are excised after base damage by the exonuclease activity of the polymerase.

Two different DNases with exonuclease activity have been found in mammalian tissues. DNase III attacks single- and also double-stranded DNA from the 3' end (5). In contrast DNase IV degrades DNA from 5' termini on (6). DNase IV liberates pyrimidine dimers as parts of oligo-nucleotides very quickly, while DNase III shows a low reaction rate to release dimers (7).

DeLucia and Cairns (8) have isolated a set of E. coli mutants which carry lesions in the structural gene for DNA polymerase I. Polymerase II was discovered by Kornberg's son, included also in a second repair mechanism. This second mechanism is also required for recombination. Gross, Grunstein and Witkin (9) found that E. coli cells which lack both repair mechanisms are inviable. Replication of DNA with unexcised pyrimidin dimers leaves gaps opposite to the damage. Recombinational repair does not work very accurately and for nearly all UV-induced mutants non-exact recombinational repair is responsible (10). Recombinational repair of X-ray-induced chain breaks is a slow repair mechanism in E. coli and needs about 40 minutes at 37° C, while the other DNA-repair system acts so quickly that this mechanism cannot be analyzed by sedimentation (11). Also in yeast (12) and mammalian cells two forms of dark DNA-repair mechanism could be detected (13).

The nuclease activity of the recombinational repair is inhibited by caffeine (14), while excision of pyrimidine dimers is insensitive to caffeine. Recombination and excision repair seem to have a common enzymatic mechanism, but some steps may be specific. The same DNA ligases seem to be involved in replication, excision repair and possibly also in rejoining of DNA strands after recombination. Excision repair enzyme activities differ only slightly during the cell cycle (15). Recombination-repair mechanisms can be induced in irradiated cells (16). Certain unusual survival curves in several organisms have been explained on the basis of an induced repair mechanism (17). For the induction process, RNA and protein synthesis after irradiation should be necessary for recombination and survival. Westergaard (18) could demonstrate, in the eukaryotic organism Tetrahymena, a correlation between excision-repairable damage to DNA and an induced DNA-polymerase activity dependent on the presence of all four deoxyribonucleoside triphosphates, Mg^{++} and primer DNA. Deoxyribonucleoside triphosphates are necessary for normal DNA synthesis and repair replication, but WERNER (19) reported that these two processes seem to draw their precursors from separate pools. Bacterial cells seem to differentiate between thymin and thymidin, using them separately for DNA replication or DNA repair. After the addition of antiserum against E. coli DNA polymerase I, a DNA-synthesizing activity was still present and also required the four deoxyribonucleoside triphosphates, Mg^{++} and a double-stranded DNA primer (20). It seems, therefore, that both processes, semiconservative DNA synthesis and repair replication, need the same precursors. Only the way of synthesizing nucleotides, especially after high irradiation doses, may be different. Enzymes involved in the preformed pathway are generally more resistant than those from the de novo synthesis pathway (21).

It may be of practical importance to know inhibitors against DNA-repair components or against the semiconservative DNA synthesis. Hydroxyurea has been shown to possess promising antineoplastic and antiviral properties (22). In determination of DNA repair, hydroxyurea is known as specific and reversible inhibitor of semiconservative DNA synthesis, possibly owing to inhibition of nucleoside diphosphate reductases (23). Also formamidoxine, which is structurally related to hydroxyurea, has similar inhibitory effects (24). 1-β-D-arabinofuranosyl cytosine also interfers with polymerization of DNA, but not at the ribonucleoside diphosphate reductase level (25). 6-(p-hydroxyphenylazo)uracil seems to induce blockage of DNA replication at the polymerization step. In bacterial cells infected with virulent phage the synthesis of phage DNA proceeds normally, while residual host semiconservative DNA synthesis is completely blocked without affecting DNA repair. Therefore it should be a useful tool for identifying the real DNA replicase (26). On the other hand, N-ethyl-isatin-β-thiosemicarbazone has a wide spectrum of specific antiviral activity against RNA and DNA viruses including RNA-tumor viruses and is effective in humans (27). Many investigations are dealing with the effects of metabolic inhibitors on rejoining of broken DNA single strands. Cycloheximide and 5-fluoro-deoxyuridine cannot suppress the rejoining of DNA in mammalian cells if treatment was done at the time of irradiation, but pretreatment with these substances shows remarkable inhibitory effects (28). KLEIJER and BOOTSMA (29) found that KCN (10^{-3} M) and dinitrophenol (10^{-4} M) block rejoining of single-strand breaks by inhibition of the ATP supply, EDTA (10^{-1} M) by binding of Mg^{++} ions, iodoacetate by inhibition of several enzymes, and crystal violet ($40\,\mu g/ml$) by binding to DNA.

Energy dependence of DNA repair and cellular recovery is perhaps important in fractionated radiotherapy (30). Several antibiotics, like bleomycin, phleomycin, actinomycin D, induce DNA breaks in nonirradiated cells.

Bleomycin, which has antitumor activity, shows a very similar effect to that of X-rays. HeLa cells are most sensitive to this antibiotic in late G_1, less sensitive in the late S and least sensitive in the early G_1 stage (31). Caffeine is the most often investigated inhibitor in DNA-repair experiments. It inhibits also the repair of radiation-induced chromosome breaks in root-tip cells, and YAMAMOTO suggests that the repair of radiation-induced chromosome breaks is a process not greatly different from DNA-excision repair (32). Caffeine has a high binding affinity for single-stranded but not double-stranded DNA and binds also with UV-irradiated DNA (33). In mammalian systems caffeine inhibits phosphodiesterase (34). The reversal of caffeine inhibition by cAMP could be detected (35). Also sulfonylurea agents are inhibitors of adenosine – 3′ : 5′ – cyclic monophosphate phosphodiesterase (36). Another group of natural products, which sometimes contaminate our food, are mycotoxins. These toxins are DNA-repair inhibitors and longterm feeding tests have been reported to provoke liver degeneration and tumors (37). Environmental contaminants, like Hg compounds, SO_2, carcinogenic carbohydrates, nitrosoamines and pesticides should also be tested with respect to a possible DNA-repair inhibitor action. DNase I that has endonuclease activity between 5′P and 3′OH to yield oligonucleotides is inhibited by several hydroxybiphenyls. It appears that these substances inhibit by hydrogen bonding too and by intercalation between the bases of DNA (38).

It has been generally assumed that photochemical damage is restricted to those cells on the surface of the organism which are exposed to UV-light or light of longer wavelength in the presence of photosensitizers. These substances can be photoexcited and most bind the DNA in different types of C_4 cycloaddition reaction (39).

Psoralen and some of its derivatives have a photosensitizing action on viruses, bacteria and mammalian cell cultures, producing lethal and mutagenic effects. Furocumarins appear to act as photosensitizers not by involving energy transfer but by producing DNA cross-links (40). Mutagenesis could also be detected in E. coli by visible light alone, without an added dye (41). Pyrimidine dimers can also be found in man surface cells as a result of the generation of electronically excited molecules without UV-light. An open question is, »can metabolic products in excited states, occurring in each organism, produce pyrimidine dimers, or single-strand breaks?« This could be an explanation of the high repair activity in nonirradiated cells. LAMOLA (42) used the decomposition of trimethyl-1,2-dioxetan in the presence of E. coli DNA to show the production of »photodimers« without UV-light.

Irradiation of H. influencae transforming DNA with UV-light of 313 nm in the presence of acetone or acetophenone leads to inactivation of the transforming activity. If acetophenone was used as sensitizer only pyrimidine dimers, mainly thymidine dimers, could be found, whereas with acetone additional radicals are formed, which produce also DNA single-strand breaks (43). With radical scavengers a chemical protection against single-strand breaks is possible (44).

A free radical is a chemical compound that has an odd number of electrons and is therefore generally highly reactive. Radicals can be detected during metabolic steps in different cells and may be involved in the production of at least some types of cancer (45). It is interesting that radiation-protective drugs are effective in lengthening the mean life span of mice. HOWARD J. CURTIS of the Brookhaven National Laboratory favors the hypothesis that aging in mammals results from mutations in the animals' somatic cells. He has shown a remarkable correlation between aging and chromosome alterations in liver cells (46).

PRICE, MODAK and MAKINODAN (47) reported (1971) that there is an age dependent change in DNA of mouse tissue. DNA polymerase catalyzed greater incorporation of nucleotides into nuclei of old than young mouse neurons, astrocytes, Kupffer cells and heart muscle fibers. DNA strand breaks with diminished DNA repair and/or increased lysosomal enzyme activities were discussed as possible reasons. In our experiments on DNA repair with leukocytes of L.E. patients we also found lower values for repair capacity in the cells of older patients.

MATSUDAIRA and NAKAGAWA (48, 49) got experimental evidence for differences in the repair capacity between normal and tumor cells. But CLEAVER reported at the Baltimore Symposium (5. Int. Symp. on Molecular Biology »Molecular and cellular repair processes«, June 3–4, 1971, Baltimore, USA) that he could not find any differences between normal und tumor cells from different sources. We discussed that it is not necessary to find a reduced repair capacity in malignant tumors compared with healthy tissues, but in the initial state of the tumor development a reduced DNA repair in immunocompetent cells can lead to a reduced immunoreaction involving possibilities for tumor growth. BARDOS et al. (50) have reported increased priming activity of DNA isolated from a variety of malignant tissue compared with DNA from normal tissue. It has been known for a long time that the incidence of Down's syndrome increases with maternal age (51). Down's syndrome associated with chromosome abnormality is one of the congenital diseases which predispose the affected person to the development of leukemia (52). TORADO and MARTIN (53) observed an increased susceptibility of trisomic cells to transformation by SV_{40} viruses. Similarly, an increased chromosomal radiosensitivity in cells with trisomy 21 could be found. The increased level of chromosome aberrations occurred only on the level of exchange type, but the number of simple chromosome scissions and terminal deletions was not changed (54).

Genetic diseases with an increased rate of chromosome breakage frequently lead to malignant diseases. But it seems that irregular chromosome changes in tumor cells are not the cause but the product of a malignant transformation of the cell. Virus-induced chromosomal breaks closely resemble those that can be obtained by application of antimetabolites and DNA-base analoga. The mechanism through which viruses cause chromosomal mutations is unknown. Direct enzymatic action of virus protein, virus-dependent liberation of lysosomal enzymes and virus-induced inhibition of DNA repair are in discussion. Although the mechanism is not known, it is of potential importance for cell death, carcinogenesis, aging, teratogenesis and somatic and germ cell mutations. Inhibition of one part of the DNA repair might easily involve at the beginning small invisible deletions or point mutations. Frameshift mutations in the lysosomal gene of bacteriophage T_4 were investigated by demonstration of the insertion of four bases and the preferential occurrence of base addition in acridine mutagenesis (55). SMITHIES et al. (56) described deletions in immunoglobulin polypeptide chains as evidence for breakage and repair in DNA.

In rheumatoid diseases structurally changed immunoglobulins are synthesized, and in lupus erythematosus also antibodies against DNA are produced. In whole white blood cells of L.E. patients we could detect a reduced DNA repair, but till now there is no evidence if it is really a reduced repair capacity of immunocompetent cells or a shift from lymphocytes to terminal cells which show less DNA repair (57). On the other hand, no reduction of DNA repair could be detected in fibroblasts of L.E. patients (58). L.E. may be considered as prototype of an immune complex disease (ICD). Some viruses have the ability to protect the organism against immune complex diseases while others enhance the disease process.

Investigations of the different repair steps in lymphocytes have shown that there exists an endonuclease that attacks alkylated DNA but not normal or UV-irradiated DNA (59). The disease most often investigated with respect to DNA repair is xeroderma pigmentosum. The defective enzyme is an endonuclease, because cells of X.P. can repair DNA strand breaks after ionizing radiation. The connection between unrepaired DNA and carcinogenesis in X.P. is still unclear because many malignant cells have no direct effect in DNA repair (58). RNA-dependent DNA polymerase of oncogenic RNA viruses can be detected by its capacity to copy synthetic RNA-DNA hybrids (60). Recently an RNA-dependent DNA polymerase could be found in X.P. skin cells which is absent in normal cells. It was assumed that virus infective X.P. cells and the transformation of cells are possible in connection with defective DNA repair (61).

The time is not far that we can choose appropriate genes to cure genetical-dependent defects in mammalian cells and incorporate strange DNA by recombination processes in the cells so treated (62). Therefore research on DNA repair will be a fascinating field also in the future.

References

(1) WEINSTEIN, B. I.: In: Nucleic Acids, Proteins and Cancer; p. 8. Maruzen Co., Tokyo 1968.
(2) SUTTON, H. E.: Teratology *4:* 103 (1971).
(3) PAINTER, R. B.: 1. Europ. Biophys. Congress, Baden, 10–17.9.1971, Vol. *II:* 123 (1971).
(4) KELLEY, R. B., M. R. ATKINSON, J. A. HUBERMAN, A. KORNBERG: Nature *224:* 495 (1969).
(5) LINDAHL, T., J. A. GALLY, G. M. EDELMAN: J. Biol. Chem. *244:* 5014 (1969).
(6) LINDAHL, T., J. A. GALLY, G. M. EDELMAN: Proc. Natl. Acad. Sci. *62:* 597 (1969).
(7) LINDAHL, T.: Europ. J. Biochem. *18:* 407 (1971).
(8) DeLUCAI and CAIRNS: Nature *230:* 11 (1971).
(9) GROSS, J. D., J. GRUNSTEIN, E. M. WITZKIN: J. mol. Biol. *58:* 631 (1971).
(10) BRESCH, C., R. HAUSSMANN: In: Klinische und molekulare Genetik; p. 173. Springer, Berlin-Heidelberg-New York 1970.
(11) TOWN, CH. D., K. C. SMITH, H. S. KAPLAN: Science *172:* 851 (1971).
(12) FABRE, F.: Molec. gen. Genetics *110:* 134 (1971).
(13) ELKIND, M. M., C. KAMPER: Biophys. J. *10:* 237 (1970).
(14) DOMON, M., A. M. RAUTH: Rad. Res. *39:* 207 (1969).
(15) CABELA, E., H. ALTMANN: 4. UN Int. Conf. on the Peaceful Uses of Atomic Energy. Genf, 6.–16.9.1971.
(16) HOLLIDAY, R.: Nature, New Biology, *232:* 233 (1971).
(17) CALKINS, J., W. TODD: Int. J. Rad. Biol. *14:* 487 (1968).
(18) WESTERGAARD, O.: Biochim. biophys. Acta *213:* 36 (1970).
(19) WERNER, R.: Nature *230:* 570 (1971).
(20) LOEB, L. A., J. P. SLATER, J. L. EWALD, S. S. AGARWAL: Biochem. biophys. Res. Commun. *42:* 147 (1971).
(21) PARTSCH, G., H. ALTMANN: Radiation and radioisotopes for industrial microorganisms. IAEA, p. 53 (1971).
(22) NII, S., H. S. ROSENKRANZ, C. MORGAN, H. M. ROSE: J. Virol. *2:* 1163 (1968).
(23) MOORE, E. C.: Cancer Res. *29:* 291 (1969).
(24) ROSENKRANZ, H., R. HJORTH, H. S. CARR: Biochim. biophys. Acta *232:* 48 (1971).
(25) SKOOG, L., B. NORDENSKJÖLD: Europ. J. Biochem. *19:* 81 (1971).
(26) BROWN, N. C.: Proc. Natl. Acad. Sci. *67:* 1454 (1970).
(27) LEVINSON, W., B. WOODSON, J. JACKSON: Nature, New Biology *232:* 116 (1971).
(28) TSUHOI, A., T. TERASIMA: Molec. gen. Genetics *108:* 117 (1970).
(29) KLEIJER, W. J., D. BOOTSMA: Europ. Biophys. Congress, Baden 10.–17.9.1971, Vol. *II:* 129 (1971).
(30) REVESZ, L., B. LITTBRAND: Europ. Biophys. Congress, Baden 10.–17.9.1971, Vol. *II:* 155 (1971).
(31) TERASIMA, T., M. YASUKAWA, H. UMEZAWA: Gann *61:* 513 (1970).
(32) YAMAMOTO, K., H. YAMAGUCHI: Mut. Res. *8:* 428 (1969).
(33) GRIGG, G. W.: Mol. gen. Genetics *107:* 162 (1970).
(34) ROBINSON, G. A., R. W. BUTCHER, E. W. SUTHERLAND: Ann. Rev. Biochem. *37:* 149 (1968).

(35) WACKER, A., H. FELLER, P. CHANDRA, T. K. R. REDDY: Z. Naturforsch. *26b:* 166 (1971).
(36) BROOKER, G., M. FICHMAN: Biochem. biophys. Res. Commun. *42:* 824 (1971).
(37) MOUTON, R. F., P. FROMAGEOT: FEBS-Letters *15:* 45 (1971).
(38) GOTTESFELD, J. M., N. H. ADAMS, A. M. ELBRADY, V. MOSES, M. CALVIN: Biochim. biophys. Acta *228:* 365 (1971).
(39) KRÄMER, D. M., M. A. PATHAK: Photochem. Photobiol. *12:* 333 (1970).
(40) COLE, R. S.: Biochim. biophys. Acta *217:* 30 (1970).
(41) WEBB, R., M. M. MALINA: Science *156:* 1194 (1967).
(42) LAMOLA, A. A.: Biochim. biophys. Res. Commun. *43:* 893 (1971).
(43) MENNIGMANN, H. D., F. W. POUS: 1. Europ. Biophys. Congress, Baden 10.–17. 9.1971, Vol. *II:* 233 (1971).
(44) GINSBERG, D. M., H. K. WEBSTER: Rad. Res. *39:* 421 (1969).
(45) PRYOR, W. A.: Scient. Amer., p. 70, August 1970.
(46) CROWLEY, C., H. J. CURTIS: Proc. Natl. Acad. Sci. *49:* 626 (1963).
(47) PRICE, G. B., S. P. MODAK, T. MAKINODAN: Science *171:* 917 (1971).
(48) MATSUDAIRA, H., CH. NAKAGAWA, S. BANNAI: Int. J. Rad. Biol. *15:* 575 (1969).
(49) MATSUDAIRA, H., CH. NAKAGAWA, T. HISHIZAWA: Int. J. Rad. Biol. *15:* 95 (1969).
(50) BARDOS, T. J., J. L. AMBRUS, Z. F. CHIELEWICZ, A. G. PENNY, C. M. AMBRUS: Cancer Res. *25:* 1238 (1965).
(51) VOGEL, F.: In: Chemical Mutagenesis in Mammals and Man (Ed.: VOGEL, F. and G. RÖHRBORN) p. 42. Springer, Berlin-Heidelberg-New York 1970.
(52) JACKSON, E. W., J. H. TURNER, M. R. KLAUBER, F. D. NORRIS: J. chron. Dis. *21:* 247 (1968).
(53) TODARO, G. J., G. M. MARTIN: Proc. Soc. exp. Biol. *124:* 1232 (1967).
(54) SASAKI, M. S., A. TONOMURA: Jap. J. hum. Genet. *14:* 81 (1969).
(55) IMADA, M., M. INONYE, M. EDA, A. TSUGITA: J. mol. Biol. *54:* 100 (1970).
(56) SMITHIES, O., D. M. GIBSON, E. M. FAMING, M. E. PERCY, D. M. PARR, G. E. CONNELL: Science *172:* 574 (1971).
(57) ALTMANN, H., I. DOLEJS, R. EBERL: 1. Europ. Biophys. Congress, Baden, 10.–17.9.1971, Vol. *II:* 143 (1971).
(58) CLEAVER, E.: J. Invest. Dermatol. *54:* 181 (1970).
(59) STRAUSS, B. S., M. COYLE, B. ROBBINS: Cold Spring Harbor Symp. Quant. Biol. *33:* 277 (1968).
(60) SPIEGELMAN, S., A. BURNY, M. R. DAS, J. KEYDAR, J. SCHLOM, M. TRAVNICEK, K. WATSON: Nature *228:* 430 (1970).
(61) MÜLLER, W. E. G., ZEN-ISCHI JAMAZAKI, R. K. ZAHN, G. BREHM, G. KORTING: Biochem. biophys. Res. Commun. *44:* 433 (1971).
(62) HILL, M., J. HILLOVA: Nature, New Biology *231:* 261 (1971).

Session I

Chairman: L. Révész

DNA Repair in Lymphocytes and Some Other Human Cells *

A. Norman

Rasmussen and Painter (1) provided the first evidence for DNA repair in mammalian cells when they showed by autoradiography that radiation induced the uptake of labelled thymidine into the DNA of cells that were not in the normal phase of DNA synthesis. This unscheduled DNA synthesis, as it is now generally called, is illustrated in Fig. 1 which shows an autoradiograph of human spermatogenic cells that had been irradiated with ultraviolet light and then incubated for two hours with tritiated thymidine (^{3}HTdR). The ultra-violet light has induced the incorporation of ^{3}HTdR into the nuclei of the spermatogonia and spermatocytes, probably also into the spermatid nuclei,

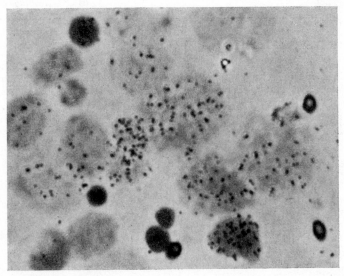

Fig. 1. Unscheduled DNA synthesis in human spermatogenic cells. The large nuclei with many grains over them are in spermatogonia and spermatocytes. The small, dark, sparsely labelled nuclei are in spermatids. Three unlabelled sperm heads (small ovals with light centers) are also evident.

---

* Supported in part by the USAEC and the California Institute for Cancer Research.

but not into sperm heads. It is clear from this example that unscheduled DNA synthesis (UDS) cannot be demonstrated in every cell type, but it has been demonstrated in human cells from a variety of both normal tissues and malignant tumors.

Ionizing radiation, ultraviolet light, and the alkylating agent methyl methanesulfonate induce UDS in human peripheral blood lymphocytes and polymorphonuclear leukocytes. UDS can be demonstrated by autoradiography in all stages of the mitotic cycle except S phase in populations of lymphocytes that have been induced to transform and proliferate by the mitogen

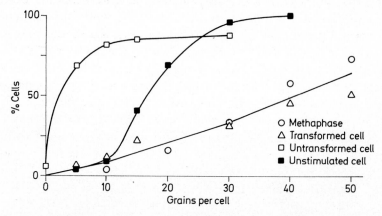

Fig. 2. Unscheduled DNA synthesis in a population of proliferating lymphocytes. The open symbols are for cells that had been incubated for 72 hrs with PHA, then irradiated with ultraviolet light and incubated for 1 hr with ³HTdR. The closed symbols show the comparable results with lymphocytes which had not been stimulated by PHA. The ordinate shows the per cent cells with grains over their nuclei equal to or less than the grains per cell on the abscissa.

phytohemagglutinin (PHA). The rate of UDS is greater by a factor of two to three in the transformed and proliferating cells than in cells that had not been exposed to PHA (see Fig. 2). The presence of a vigorous UDS in metaphase chromosomes should help dispel the notion that chromosomes are metabolically inert during this period of maximum condensation. The presence of UDS cannot be demonstrated autoradiographically during the period of normal DNA synthesis, but it can be inferred from experiments demonstrating that repair replication and the repair of single-strand DNA breaks are induced by radiation during the period of normal DNA synthesis.

The proportion of cells in normal DNA synthesis is very small in lymphocyte populations – about one in a thousand – when they are drawn from the peripheral blood. For that reason, it is possible to study the rates of UDS using liquid scintillation counting rather than the more tedious grain counting in autoradiographs to measure the amount of ^{3}HTdR incorporated into the lymphocyte DNA. The rates of UDS during the first hour following exposure of the lymphocytes to ionizing radiations can be represented adequately by a simple enzyme model for which the substrates are ^{3}HTdR and the radiation-induced lesions in the DNA (2). In terms of the model, the effect of anoxia is to decrease twofold the concentration of lesions; the action of PHA doubles the concentration of enzymes prior to the onset of normal DNA synthesis. Applications of the model to data acquired in additional studies (3–5) have yielded estimates of a number of parameters characterizing the rate limiting

Table 1. The rate limiting step in the rejoining of single-strand DNA breaks and in unscheduled and normal DNA synthesis in human lymphocytes.

| Parameter | Rejoining of single-strand DNA breaks | Unscheduled DNA synthesis | | Normal DNA synthesis |
		ionizing radiation	ultraviolet light	
Activation energy (kcal/mole)	19 ± 0.4	16–18	18–25	21–24
Temperature at maximum rate (°C)	near 40	near 42	42–44	37–40
Half-life of rate controlling step (min)	—	14	63	—
Enzyme molecules/cell	—	$1\text{–}2 \times 10^4$	5×10^4	—
Maximum rate of repair or synthesis	10^4 breaks/cell/min	10^4 nucleotides/cell/min	10^4 nucleotides/cell/min	10^7 nucleotides/cell/min

step during the first hour following exposure of the lymphocytes to either ionizing radiations or ultraviolet light. Some of these estimates are shown in Table 1.

Recently we have concluded a study of the kinetics of single-strand break repair in lymphocyte DNA (6). The number of breaks were calculated from measurements of the sedimentation velocity of the DNA on alkaline gradients. Some of the parameters characterizing the rate limiting step are also shown in Table 1. It can be seen that the activation energy and temperature of maximum rate are similar in the rate limiting steps for the rejoining of strand breaks and for UDS stimulated by ionizing radiation. Moreover, the number of breaks per rad and the maximum rate of rejoining of single-strand breaks are similar respectively to the number of lesions per rad and the maximum rate of incorporation of nucleotides per cell in UDS. It seems likely, therefore, that UDS stimulated by ionizing radiation and the rejoining of single-strand breaks share the same rate limiting step. However, three different enzymatic steps appear to limit the rates of UDS induced by ionizing radiations, UDS induced by ultraviolet light, and normal DNA synthesis.

Chromosome aberrations induced by physical, chemical and biological agents in human lymphocytes have been the subject of intense study during the past two decades. If we adopt the simple model that the chromosome is basically a double-stranded DNA molecule or a linear array of such molecules, we expect a close relationship between the breakage and repair of DNA and the production of chromosome aberrations. However, no simple relationship exists (7). For example, on the simple model a double-strand break in DNA should result in a terminal deletion in the chromosome. The number of double-

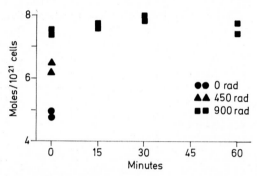

Fig. 3. The effect of varying the time between two 450 rad doses on unscheduled DNA synthesis. The lymphocytes were incubated for a total of 2 hrs in ^{3}HTdR. The effect of a single dose of 450 rad is also shown.

strand breaks in lymphocytes is proportional to the dose of ionizing radiation, and the yield is about one double-strand break per cell per rad. The yield of terminal chromosome deletions is also roughly proportional to dose, and the yield is of the order of 10^{-3} deletions per cell per rad. There is a discrepancy of three orders of magnitude, therefore, between the yield of aberrations and yield of double-strand breaks instead of the one to one correspondence expected on the simple model. Moreover, there is no evidence for a repair of double-strand DNA breaks that would account for such a discrepancy. Again, on a simple model, chromosome exchange aberrations should result from the interaction of single-strand breaks. However, single-strand breaks show a half-life of about 14 minutes at low X-ray doses, whereas split-dose experiments on the yield of dicentrics suggest a half-life of about an hour. The interaction of radiation-induced breaks is not evident in the experiments on UDS.

Fig. 3 shows the results of varying the time between doses. As can be seen, the effect of two 450 rad doses is just equal to that of one 900 rad dose regardless of the time interval between the doses. These results may mean nothing more than that the great majority of breaks are repaired without interacting to give rise to chromosome exchange aberrations. They illustrate the point, however, that there is no obvious simple relationship between the breakage and repair of DNA and the production of chromosome aberrations.

Sperm can be considered as terminal cells with short lifetimes. The absence of UDS is not unexpected, therefore. (It would be interesting to learn whether DNA damage in the sperm is repaired in the fertilized ovum.) The polymorphonuclear leukocytes are also terminal cells with a short lifetime. The number of enzyme molecules involved in the rate limiting step of ultraviolet light-induced UDS is an order of magnitude smaller than the number in lymphocytes (5).

Table 2. Unscheduled DNA synthesis in peripheral blood lymphocytes from old and young humans.

	Age of donor	Metaphase frequency	Average grains in metaphase chromosomes	Average grains in transformed cells	Average grains in untransformed cells
Donor I	81 years	2/1000	18	19	13
Donor II	76 years	1/1000	12	10	10
Donor III	25 years	150/1000	29	23	16

The lymphocytes were exposed to a UV dose of 25 ergs/mm² and then labelled for 1 hr with ³HTdR. The cells were then cultured for 72 hrs with PHA and, during the last 12 hrs, with colcemide.

If a decrease in the number of repair enzymes is characteristic of cells as they approach the end of their life span, then we may expect to find a reduced UDS in cells obtained from old donors. Table 2 shows a comparison of UDS in lymphocytes obtained from three donors 25, 79, and 81 years old. The most marked change with age is in the fraction of cells which can be induced by PHA to enter the mitotic cycle. The data also show a consistently smaller uptake of ³HTdR in the cells that respond to PHA by transforming than in those which remain untransformed. This functional division of cells by their response to mitogens and other agents is simply a reflection of the fact that the peripheral blood lymphocytes consist of mixed populations of biologically heterogeneous cells. One more point is worth noting: a dose of 25 ergs/mm² of ultraviolet light resulted in good labelling of the lymphocytes without inhibiting markedly – at least in the young donor – the proliferation of the lymphocytes. We have used this technique successfully to label the DNA of lymphocytes in experiments on the transfer of mitogenic stimulation between lymphocytes. Whether there is a significant loss of repair enzymes with advancing age remains to be confirmed, and the relation of such loss to the recently reported accumulation of DNA-strand breaks with aging (8) or the increased aneuploidy with age of donor in peripheral blood lymphocytes (9) remains to be discovered.

The incidence of cancer in man is a very strong function of age. We have examined some thirty samples of spontaneous tumors obtained from seventeen patients and have not been able to detect a significant decrease in UDS induced by either ultraviolet light or ionizing radiation (10). We have also carried out some preliminary measurements on the inhibition of UDS by a number of

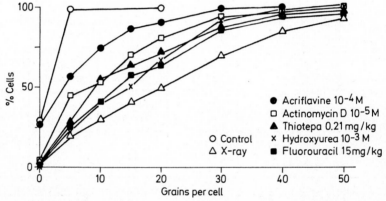

Fig. 4. The inhibition of unscheduled DNA synthesis in a spontaneous human tumor. The cells from an endometrial tumor received a dose of 21 krad of 6 MeV electrons and were then incubated for 1 hr with ^{3}HTdR in the presence of the indicated drugs. The graph shows the per cent of cells (on the ordinate) with a grain count over their nuclei equal to or less than the grains per cell (on the abscissa).

drugs. Fig. 4 shows the results of one such experiment on cells from an endometrial tumor. Table 3 summarizes the preliminary results in a number of tumors. The inhibition of UDS and of the fraction of cells in S by some drugs is evident. We have been carrying out a more detailed study on the action of acriflavine. This drug can inhibit UDS when added after irradiation and when it is bound to DNA in the ratio of one acriflavine molecule per fifty DNA base pairs. It also remains bound to lymphocyte DNA even after repeated washings and prolonged incubation. We hope that further studies will help elucidate the action of inhibitors which have some potential for clinical use. Meanwhile the data in Table 3 show that it is feasible in selected cases to study in tumor samples the action of drugs both on unscheduled and normal DNA synthesis.

Table 3. Effect of drugs on unscheduled DNA synthesis and on the percent of cells in S.

Agent	Concentration	P.B. ovarian carcinoma 5-26-69		Y.T. breast carcinoma 5-27-69		I.S. endometrial carcinoma 6-2-69		I.S. endometrial carcinoma 6-16-69		A.M. ovarian carcinoma 6-30-69		A.M. ovarian carcinoma 7-8-69	
		Median grains/cell	%S	Grains/cell	%S	Grains/cell	%S	Grains/cell	%S	Grains/cell	%S	Grains/cell	%S
Controls		10	16	1	2	0	1	0	0	3	5	3	7
UV	150 ergs/mm^2	—	—	28	6	11	0	—	—	18	4	29	6
Electrons	21 krad	—	—	—	—	13	0	19	0	8	0	—	—
Acriflavine	10^{-4}M	26	10	13	4	—	—	3	—	—	—	22	6
Acriflavine	10^{-5}M	>50	24	—	—	10	0	—	—	22	4	—	—
Actinomycin D	10^{-5}M	>50	28	—	—	—	—	9	0	—	—	28	7
Actinomycin D	10^{-6}M	>50	20	—	—	15	0	—	—	00	0	—	—
Alkeran	0.14 mg/kg	49	23	—	—	9	0	00	0	13	0	00	00
Caffeine	10^{-3}M	29	12	—	—	10	0	—	—	—	—	21	3
Cyclohexamide	10^{-4}M	>50	15	—	—	—	—	—	—	—	—	16	10
Cyclohexamide	10^{-5}M	>50	28	—	—	22	0	—	—	—	—	—	—
Daunomycin	0.15 mg/kg	>50	26	—	—	26	0	—	—	—	—	—	—
Fluorouracil	15 mg/kg	>50	17	36	8	9	0	15	0	24	3	28	10
Hydroxyurea	10^{-3}M	>50	0	19	4	12	0	12	0	17	0	—	—
Thiotepa	0.21 mg/kg	>50	28	38	5	—	—	7	0	—	—	—	—
Vincristine sulfate	0.075 mg/kg	>50	19	—	—	—	—	—	—	—	—	—	—
Vinblastine sulfate	0.2 mg/kg	>50	36	—	—	3	0	—	—	—	—	—	—

References

(1) RASMUSSEN, R. E., R. B. PAINTER: Nature *203:* 1360 (1964), and J. Cell Biol. *29:* 11 (1966).
(2) SPIEGLER, P., A. NORMAN: Radiat. Res. *39:* 400 (1969).
(3) SPIEGLER, P., A. NORMAN: Radiat. Res. *43:* 187 (1970).
(4) SPIEGLER, P., A. NORMAN: Mutation Res. *10:* 379 (1970).
(5) CONNOR, W. G., A. NORMAN: Mutation Res. *13;* 393 (1971).
(6) DONLON, T. E., A. NORMAN: Mutation Res. *13;* 97 (1971).
(7) NORMAN, A.: Experimental and Theoretical Biophysics, Vol. III (in press).
(8) PRICE, G. B., S. P. MODAK, T. MAKINODAN: Science *171:* 917 (1971).
(9) JACOBS, P. A., W. M. COURT BROWN, R. DOLL: Nature *191:* 1178 (1961).
(10) NORMAN, A., R. E. OTTOMAN, P. CHAN, I. KLISAK: Mutation Res. (in press).

Repair Replication after X and UV Irradiation in Rodent Tumor Cell Lines in Vitro

Margaret and B. W. Fox

Our initial observations – Ayad and Fox (1968), Fox, Ayad, and Fox (1970) – of incorporation of ^{3}H IUdR into the light non-replicating DNA after low doses of X-rays have led to certain contradictions amongst our own and other people's data. The results of the original experiments are shown in Figs. 1 and 2.

^{3}H activity was consistently associated with the light DNA peak and remained associated with it after denaturation. This activity amounted to approximately 10% of that present in the hybrid density peak, and was not reduced when normal DNA synthesis was inhibited by hydroxyurea 10^{-2}M.

These observations were in marked contrast to those of Painter and Cleaver (1967) who reported that repair replication could not be detected after X-ray doses lower than 100,000 rads in HeLa cells. Later Painter (1970) reported the phenomenon after doses of 1,000 rad, and Brent and Wheatley (1971) using synchronized HeLa cells have obtained some evidence for its occurrence after 500 rad and could clearly demonstrate it after 1,000 rad.

In P388F cells, for the amount of ^{3}H activity incorporated into the light DNA peak one would expect to detect some shift in density compared with the light unlabelled DNA peak; however, none was observed. In addition, unless approximately 10% excess DNA is synthesized which has been reported by Savada and Okada (1970) in L5178Y lymphoblasts, then this extensive incorporation would necessitate extensive DNA degradation. We have looked for DNA degradation in P388F cells prelabelled with ^{125}IUdR in order to reduce reutilisation, but in common with other workers – Little (1968), Painter (1968), Dalrymple et al. (1969) and Hill (1969) – have failed to detect any loss of label from DNA irradiated with up to 1,000 rad. These results are shown in Table 1.

A close correlation both quantitatively and qualitatively has been observed between repair replication and unscheduled synthesis (Painter, 1970). We have looked for unscheduled synthesis in P388F cells after X-ray doses up to 1,000 rad. Using doses of ^{3}H TdR and exposure times which would have

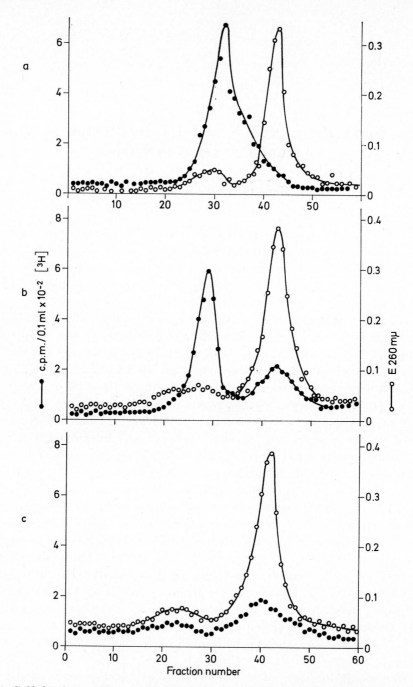

Fig. 1. CsCl density gradient profile (pH 7.0) of DNA from P 388 F cells after growth for 3 hours in unlabelled IUdR 2 μg/ml followed by culture for 3 hours in ^{3}H IUdR. DNA was isolated by the Marmur procedure. a) Control, b) 150 rad, c) 150 rad with hydroxyurea 10^{-2}M added immediately after irradiation. ○—○ E 260, ●—● ^{3}H c.p.m.

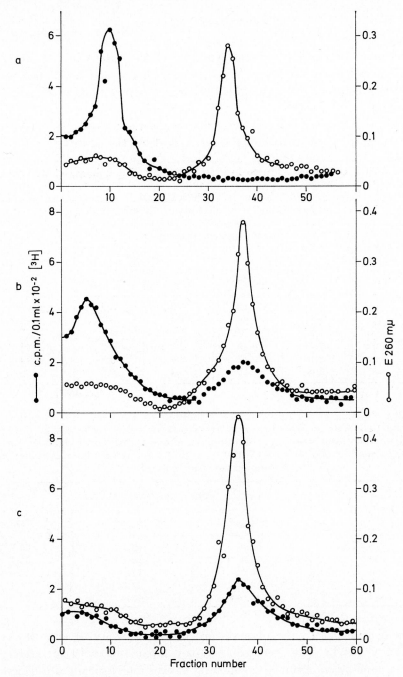

Fig. 2. As for Fig. 1, but DNA was denatured by heat 100° C for 10 min, before banding in pH 7.0 CsCl gradients. ○—○ E 260, ●—● ³H c.p.m.

enabled us to detect unscheduled synthesis to the extent of 1% of the rate of normal synthesis, no differences between control and irradiated cultures could be detected (Table 2; cf. the 10% repair activity observed in the CsCl gradients).

A feature of the original data was that there was no increase in amount of activity incorporated into the light DNA peak as the X-ray dose increased.

Table 1. P388F cells were cultured in ^{125}IUdR for 2 cell doublings, 24–28 hours, then washed and resuspended in medium containing unlabelled IUdR. After irradiation, samples were taken at hourly intervals, washed 2 times in saline containing unlabelled thymidine, then extracted with cold and hot PCA.

Time after irradiation (hrs)	% total activity recovered				S. A. of DNA $\times 10^{-4}$	
	Control		500 rad			
	Medium	cold PCA	Medium	cold PCA	C	500r
0.5	1.4	0.15	0.91	0.2	1.9	2.3
1.0	1.1	0.33	1.3	0.2	4.2	2.5
1.5	1.5	0.20	1.7	0.3	2.7	2.4
2.0	2.4	0.15	2.1	0.2	3.1	3.0
3.0	2.1	0.13	2.4	0.3	2.8	3.0
4.0	2.0	0.14	2.4	0.3	3.2	2.6

Table 2. Percentage labelled cells in P388F cultures after irradiation with various doses of X-rays. Cells were incubated prior to irradiation in ^{3}HTdR 1.0 μCi/ml S. A. 22 Ci/mM for 1 hour, then after washing in medium containing unlabelled thymidine were re-incubated in medium containing ^{3}HTdR 1.0 μCi/ml for a further 1 hour. Autoradiographs were exposed for 4 weeks.

Dose (rad)	Percentage labelled cells		
	> 250 grains	5–20 grains	Total
C	53.6	12.1	65.7
150	57.9	14.8	72.7
300	55.0	11.0	65.0
500	52.9	11.5	64.4
1000	49.0	10.0	59.0

This is in contrast to the observations of PAINTER (1970) and BRENT and WHEATLEY (1971). The increase in repair replication with increasing dose has been used as an argument against its having a biologically significant role, i.e. it may be merely a response to damage which increases as the amount of damage increases. The absence of a dose response as shown in Table 3 could, however, be used to argue in favour of a biological role for repair replication, but it would necessitate the postulation of a repair system that was already saturated at a dose of 150 rad. This is a somewhat tempting speculation, however, since above doses of 150 rad the X-ray dose-response curve for P 388 F cells becomes exponential.

In view of these discrepancies we have repeated the experiments with P 388 F cells and, in addition, have looked for repair replication in two strains of L 5178 Y cells which have widely differing radiosensitivities.

Recently GOTTLIEB et al. (1970) have reported the presence of a lipid/DNA complex in isolates of DNA from primed lymphocytes labelled with ³H BUdR

Table 3. Summary of data from originally published (1968, 1970) gradients for X-ir-radiated P 388 F cells showing large amounts of »repair« associated with the normal density regions.

Treatment	DNA specific activity c.p.m./OD unit			$\dfrac{\text{Repair}}{\text{Normal}}$ %
	H.L. (hybrid band)	L.L. (light band)	Total	
Control	8570	378	1900	
C + HU	420	—		10.0
150 rad	8700	870	2300	
150 r + HU	410	850		
†C + IUdR	4360	—	825	16.8
†220 r + IUdR	2787	469*	1005	
†C	5800	—	850	9.5
†300 r	4100	383	1100	
C	9160	328	1930	13.8
400 r	7150	970	2110	

* Repair incorporation in this instance was in the heavy position.
† X-ray doses in this instance were matched to give equal survival ∼ 10%.

but not when lymphocytes were labelled with ³H TdR. This complex consistently banded at a slightly lighter density than normal unlabelled light DNA in neutral CsCl gradients, i.e. at 1.685 gm/cm³.

FRIEDMAN and MUELLER (1969) have also reported the presence of a lipid-enriched DNA component in synchronized cultures of HeLa cells. This material was extracted from the interphase of a phenol-water extraction procedure after pulse-labelling the HeLa cells with ³H thymidine. The main part of the DNA had been previously labelled with ¹⁴C thymidine. On centrifugation in neutral CsCl gradients, between 30–60% of the ³H-labelled DNA floated whilst the remainder sedimented at the same density as the bulk of the ¹⁴C-labelled DNA. DNA pulse-labelled in this way gradually became converted into an extractable form, i.e. more and more banded with the ¹⁴C-labelled material as the duration of the ^{3}H thymidine pulse was increased. If hydroxyurea was added to the cultures, the DNA did not become converted to an extractable form, i.e. continued to band at a light density.

It appears likely, therefore, that the DNA species reported by GOTTLIEB et al. (1970) after growth of cells in ^{3}H BUdR and the lipid-enriched fraction reported by FRIEDMAN and MUELLER (1969) represent, as suggested by these authors, DNA bound to the nuclear membrane which can be extracted with varying efficiency by different DNA isolation methods. The species appears to be made more dense by incorporation of ^{3}H BUdR or ^{3}H IUdR so that it bands in a CsCl gradient instead of floating as it does when labelled with ^{3}H thymidine.

Release of low molecular weight material from lysed cells by relatively high doses of X-rays has been described by ORMEROD and LEHMAN (1971). Under the conditions of their experiments, the majority of the DNA floated in CsCl gradients, but as the radiation dose was increased, more and more of the DNA banded within the gradient. These workers have proposed that replicating DNA is attached to the nuclear membrane and that radiation-induced breaks between the attachment points release free DNA segments, which then show the predicted sedimentation characteristics.

In our original experiments, activity remained associated with the light DNA peak after denaturation. The lipid/DNA complex reported by FRIEDMAN and MUELLER (1969) and by GOTTLIEB (1970) was sensitive to denaturation by heat and by 0.15 N NaOH. BURDON, however, recently (1971) has reported a DNA species associated with a lipid fraction which renatures very rapidly, and BRAHIC and FRASER (1971) have reported that up to 10% of Ehrlich-ascites DNA after denaturation was not sensitive to digestion by a nuclease from Neurospora crassa specific for single-stranded DNA. This fraction had an anomalous G.C. content, banded at a density of 1.684 gm/cm^3 in CsCl and probably represents highly repetitive DNA sequences.

It seems possible, therefore, that since in our original experiments formaldehyde was not used, some rapid renaturation could have occurred, either of the complex or of some repetitive DNA sequences, thus accounting for the persistance of activity associated with single-stranded DNA.

In view of these observations and a communication from Dr. PAINTER that he had been unable to repeat our observations in P388F cells, we reasoned that the observed labelling in light peak in our experiments was possibly the result of an artefact due to contamination of the light DNA peak with ^{3}H IUdR-labelled complex.

Initially, therefore, we isolated DNA from cells labelled with ^{3}H BUdR for 6 hours using three different methods:

1. PAS-phenol,
2. SDS-phenol,
3. SDS-chloroform: isoamyl alcohol.

The DNA was extracted from $\sim 1 \times 10^8$ cells in each sample and the supernatant precipitated with ethoxyethanol. The interphases from each extraction were reextracted in each case with PAS and phenol, the supernatant was either precipitated with ethoxyethanol and dissolved in SSC, or these DNA's were dialysed for 2–3 days to remove PAS before banding in CsCl.

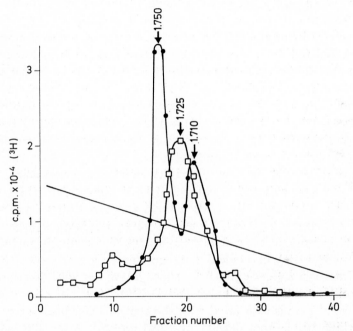

Fig. 3. CsCl density gradient profile (pH 7.0) of DNA isolated by the SDS-phenol method from P 388 F cells after culture for 6 hours in ^{3}H BUdR. ○—○ E 260, ●—● ^{3}H c.p.m.

The yield of DNA obtained by the three different methods varied greatly. Methods 1 and 2 gave an approximately 10 times greater yield than method 3. Equal amounts, 1–2 OD units of DNA isolated by each method were banded in neutral CsCl gradients. DNA isolated by methods 1 and 2 showed highly anomalous banding patterns as shown in Fig 3.

There are two peaks of labelled DNA, one sedimenting somewhat heavier than expected for hybrid DNA at a density of 1.75, the other at a density lighter than the light unlabelled DNA peak, i.e. 1.71 gm/cm³. It should be

noted that in this case »light« unlabelled DNA also sedimented at an anomalous density, i.e. 1.725 gm/cm³. DNA isolated by the Marmur procedure
(method 3) also showed an anomalous banding pattern but to a lesser extent
than that shown by DNA isolated by the other two methods. With decreasing
amounts of complex, the density of the light DNA peak decreased, and
approached that normally seen for light unlabelled DNA.

Interphase DNA when banded in CsCl after methods 1 and 2 showed even
greater amounts of »complex«, the ³H activity in the complex sometimes
exceeding that in the hybrid DNA peak. Complex was consistently isolated
both from the spooled DNA and the interphase when methods 1 and 2 were
used and from the interphase after the Marmur extraction. DNA precipitated
after chloroform isoamyl alcohol extraction showed varying amounts of complex. DNA isolated from the interphase after a chloroform isoamyl alcohol
extraction was subjected to sonnication for 20 sec. The complex was dissociated by sonnication as shown in Fig. 4.

The amount of complex was also markedly reduced by treatment with
phospholipase A but not with amylase (Fig. 5). The material in the complex
was also sensitive to heat denaturation in the presence of formaldehyde as
will be shown later. It would appear, therefore, that in certain circumstances
the presence of this DNA complex could be mistaken for »repair«.

P 388 F cells were cultured in unlabelled IUdR for 3 hours, then in ³H TdR
together with unlabelled IUdR for a further 3 hours after irradiation with
doses of X-rays up to 1 500 rad. After isolation by the Marmur procedure DNA
was banded before and after denaturation (100° C for 10 min in the presence
of 1 M formaldehyde) in neutral CsCl gradients. Fig. 6 shows the pattern
obtained from control cells and from those irradiated with 300 and 500 rad.
The control shows the main unlabelled DNA peak banding at a density of
1.710 gm/cm³. There is associated with the control DNA peak a small amount
of label which bands at a density of 1.685 gm/cm³. After 300 and 500 rad
label was again found associated with the light unlabelled DNA peak but the
peak of the radioactivity was again shifted to the right of the absorbancy peak.
Banding of DNA from cultures irradiated with 1 000 and 1 500 rad produced
similar patterns as shown in Fig. 7.

In this case (Fig. 7) the control shows no activity associated with the light
peak, which bands close to the expected density, whereas the cultures irradiated with 1 000 rad and 1 500 rad show activity which bands under the OD
peak. There is, however, no increase in activity with increasing dose. These
findings demonstrate quite clearly how ³H activity associated with the light
unlabelled DNA peak can be mistaken for »repair« in the initial gradient,
and that the »complex« cannot be routinely isolated by the Marmur procedure.

In these two experiments, all the DNA samples were isolated at the same time using the same number of cells and the same volume of saline EDTA in the initial lysis stage.

The complex did not reproducibly remain associated with the light DNA after rebanding as is shown in Fig. 8. The control DNA shows no activity to

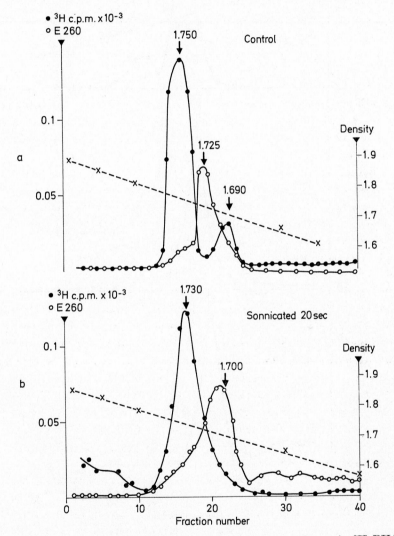

Fig. 4. DNA, from P 388 F cells harvested after growth for 6 hours in ³H BUdR, was isolated from the interphase, after a Marmur extraction, by PAS-phenol. Neutral pH 7.0 CsCl density gradient profile. a) Control, b) DNA sonnicated for 20 sec. ●—● E 260, ○—○ ³H c.p.m.

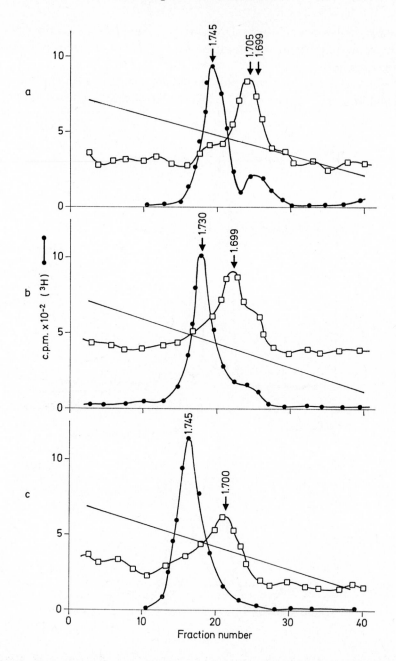

Fig. 5. Interphase DNA labelled as for Figs. 3 and 4 banded in a neutral pH 7.0 CsCl gradient. a) Control, b) after treatment with amylase, c) after treatment with phospholipase A.

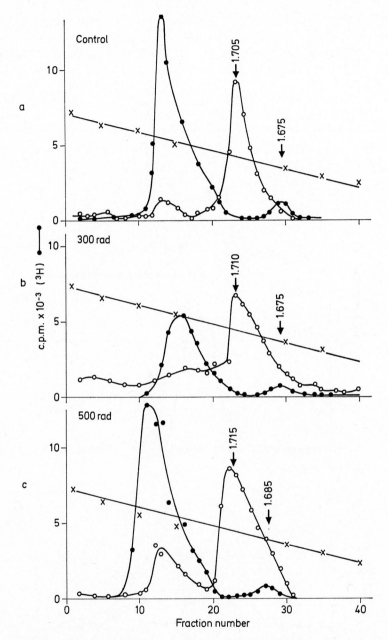

Fig. 6. DNA was isolated by the Marmur procedure from P388F cells after culture for 3 hours in unlabelled IUdR followed by 3 hours in unlabelled IUdR together with ^{3}H TdR neutral CsCl gradients, from a) Control, b) 300 rad, c) 500 rad. ○—○ E 260, ●—● ^{3}H c.p.m.

the right of the normal density DNA peak, the 300 rad sample also shows virtually no activity, but after the 500 rad, significant activity is present banding at a density of 1.685 gm/cm³. It should be noted that the density of the light DNA peak which in the original gradient was 1.710 was on

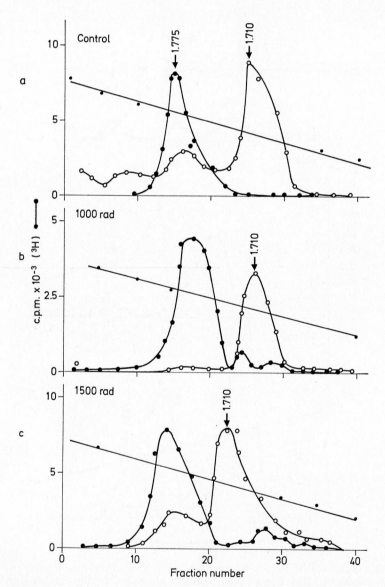

Fig. 7. DNA isolated from cells cultured as described for Fig. 6 and banded in neutral CsCl gradients. a) Control, b) 1000 rad, c) 1500 rad. ○—○ E 260, ●—● ³H c.p.m.

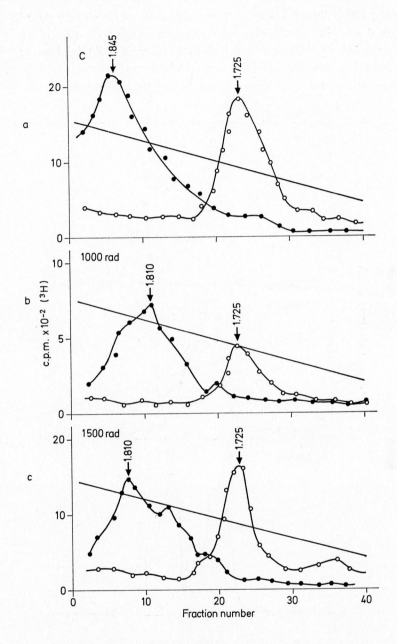

Fig. 8. Reband in neutral pH 7.0 CsCl gradients of normal density regions from gradients shown in Fig. 6. Fractions 20–35 were pooled in each case, dialysed to remove the CsCl and then banded. ○—○ E 260,   ●—● ³H c.p.m.

rebanding 1.690. The instability of the complex on rebanding may be due to differential shearing of the complex during processing for rebanding.

The complex was dissociated by denaturation of DNA by heat (100° C for 10 min) in the presence of 1 M formaldehyde as is shown in Fig. 9. There was no evidence for radiation-stimulated repair replication up to 1500 rad

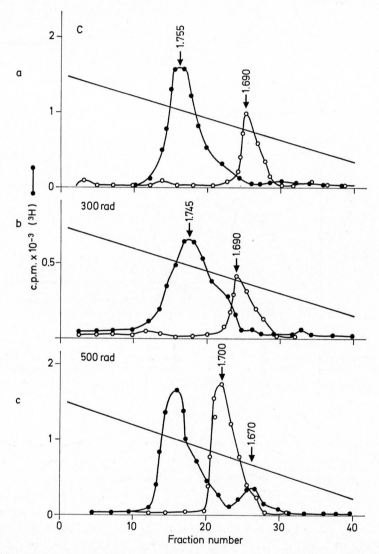

Fig. 9. DNA from cells cultured as described in Fig. 6 was denatured by heat (100° C for 10 min) in the presence of 1 M formaldehyde, then banded in neutral CsCl gradients. a) Control, b) 1000 rad, c) 1500 rad. ○——○ E 260, ●——● ³H c.p.m.

even after rebanding the light DNA regions from these gradients. Thus, neither repair replication nor unscheduled synthesis has been detected in P 388 F cells using doses of up to 1 500 rad. This result is in line with those of PAINTER (1971) in a number of other cell lines, i.e. that radiation doses of less than 10^3 rad do not result in any increase in repair replication over that normally occurring in controls.

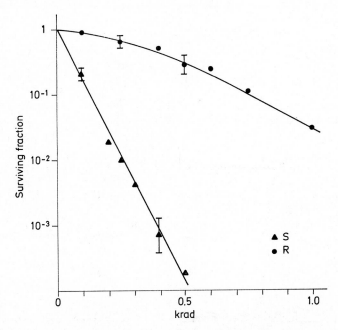

Fig. 10. Sensitivity of two lines of L 5178 Y lymphoblasts to 250 KeV X-rays. Cells were irradiated in suspension, then plated in 0.3% agar for determination of colony forming ability. Colonies were counted after incubation for 7 days: ▲ Sensitive, ● Resistant. Results are mean of 2 experiments.

The biological function of repair replication and unscheduled synthesis particularly after X-irradiation is still the subject of much debate. Clarification of the situation has been hampered by the absence of closely related cell lines which show large differences in X-ray sensitivity. Recently a series of mutants of L 5178 Y mouse lymphoblasts have been isolated which show large differences in radiosensitivity (COURTENAY, 1970). Dose-response curves for two of these cell lines are shown in Fig. 10. The techniques used for examination of the two cell lines for repair replication were the same as those described for P 388 F cells. DNA was isolated by the Marmur procedure from both

sensitive and resistant lines after irradiation with 500 and 1500 rad. On banding
of native DNA in neutral CsCl gradients variable amounts of »complex« were
seen associated with the normal density DNA. DNA's were denatured as
described and again banded in neutral CsCl gradients; the results are shown
in Figs. 11 and 12. The single-stranded DNA from the normal density region

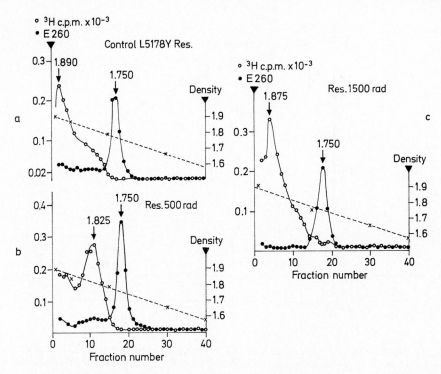

Fig. 11. Single-stranded DNA, denatured by heating (100° C for 10 min) in the presence
of 1 M formaldehyde from irradiation-resistant L5178Y lymphoblasts, banded in pH
7.0 CsCl gradients. Cells were labelled with ³H TdR in the presence of unlabelled IUdR
as described for P388F cells; DNA was isolated by the Marmur procedure. a) Control,
b) 500 rad, c) 1500 rad. ●—● E260, ○—○ ³H c.p.m.

of each of these gradients was rebanded. The results for the resistant line are
shown in Fig. 13 and for the sensitive line in Fig. 14. There is a small amount
of activity present in all four gradients from irradiated cultures. This activity,
however, bands towards the heavier side of the light DNA peak and does not
increase with increase in dose. There is no difference quantitatively in the
amount of activity present in gradients from the two cell lines.

Differences in sensitivity to cell killing by UV between normal skin fibroblasts and fibroblasts from xeroderma pigmentosum patients were correlated with differences in repair replication (CLEAVER, 1968). However, the large differences in sensitivity to X-rays observed between these two lines of L5178Y lymphoblasts could not be correlated with differences in repair replication in these experiments. After UV-irradiation repair replication has been demonstrated in a number of cell lines within the biological dose range although cell lines differ considerably in their capacity to perform this function [see PAINTER (1970) for a review]. We have examined three cell lines for their

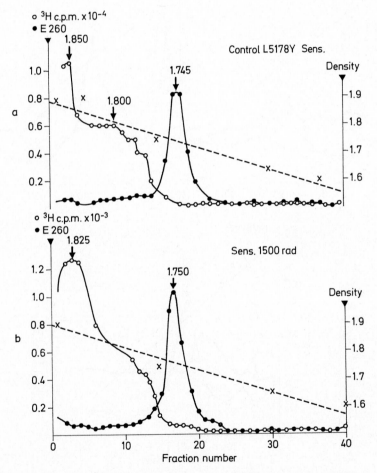

Fig. 12. CsCl gradients of single-stranded DNA from radiosensitive L5178Y lymphoblasts. Conditions of experiment were the same as for Fig. 11. a) Control, b) 1500 rad.
●—● E 260, ○—○ ³H c.p.m.

capacity to perform repair replication, all are of rodent origin. They are as
follows: P388F mouse lymphoma cells, and two cell lines originally derived
from Yoshida ascites tumours of rats (Fox and Fox, 1971). The UV dose-
response curve for P388F cells is shown in Fig. 15. There is no shoulder and a
continuously curving curve is seen. The two Yoshida cell lines were originally
isolated because of their sensitivity and resistance to the alkylating agent

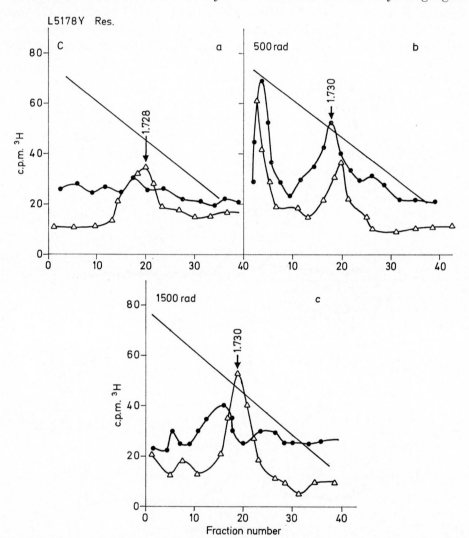

Fig. 13. Rebands of single-stranded DNA from normal density region from resistant
L5178Y cells in pH 7.0 CsCl gradient. a) Control, b) 500 rad, c) 1500 rad. ○—○ E260,
●—● ^{3}H c.p.m.

methylene dimethanesulphonate (Fox and Fox, 1971). The sensitive line was found to be sensitive also to UV, the resistant line showed a similar overall sensitivity to that of the P388F cell line; however, the dose-response curve of the Yoshida resistant line is characterized by a shoulder which is absent from the dose-response curve of the sensitive line and of P388F cells (Fig. 16).

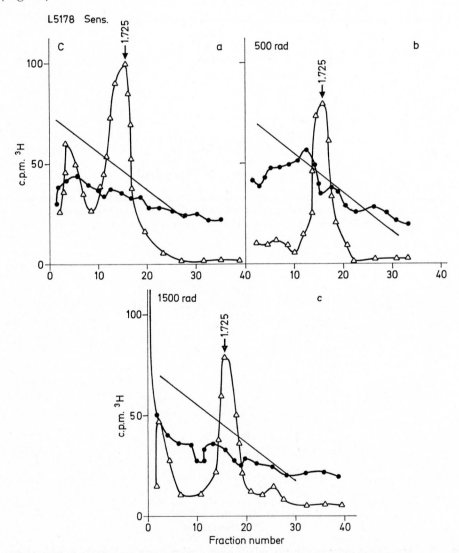

Fig. 14. Rebands of single-stranded DNA from normal density region from sensitive L5178Y cells. a) Control, b) 500 rad, c) 1500 rad. ○—○ E260, ●—● ³H c.p.m.

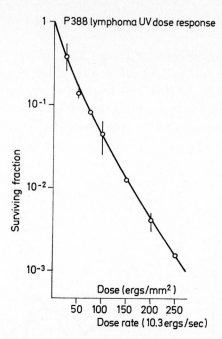

Fig. 15. Dose-response curve for P388F cells after irradiation with UV. Cells were irradiated in phosphate-buffered saline, then diluted into medium and serum before plating in 0.3% agar for determination of colony-forming ability.

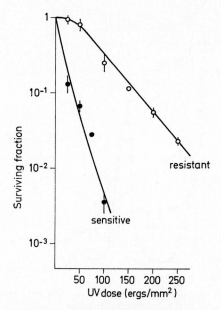

Fig. 16. Dose-response curves for Yoshida cell lines selected for sensitivity and resistance to methylene dimethanesulphonate after irradiation with UV. Cells were plated in agar for determination of colony-forming ability.

Differences in sensitivity of Chinese Hamster cells to inactivation by UV have been correlated with differences in the amount of unscheduled synthesis by CLEAVER (1969). Approximately 30% less unscheduled synthesis occurred in the sensitive cell line than in its resistant counterpart. Xeroderma cells which show greatly increased sensitivity to UV D_0 9 ergs/mm² compared with 29 ergs/mm² also show greatly reduced repair replication and unscheduled DNA synthesis (CLEAVER, 1970). It seems, therefore, that there is strong evidence that repair replication contributes to survival of UV-irradiated cells. To test the generality of this assumption, we have compared repair replication after UV irradiation in the two Yoshida cell lines which show a fivefold difference in sensitivity to UV.

Table 4. Unscheduled synthesis induced in P388F cells by exposure to UV irradiation. Cells were prelabelled with ³HRdR 1.0 μCi ml (22 Ci/mM) for 1 hour, centrifuged, washed 2 times in saline containing unlabelled TdR, then suspended in PO_4-buffered saline for UV irradiation. After irradiation they were resuspended in fresh medium containing ³HTdR 0.2 μCi/ml, and incubated for a further 1 hour before fixation and staining for autoradiography.

| | Percentage labelled cells | | | | | |
| | 2 weeks exposure | | | 4 weeks exposure | | |
	H.L. > 200 g	L.L. 11–15 g	Total % +	H.L. > 200 g	L.L. 10–15 g	Total % +
C	52.0	8.6	60.6	58.6	13.2	71.8
50 ergs/mm²	31.9	55.7	87.6	54.0	42.5	96.5
200 ergs/mm²	49.5	45.4	94.9	55.4	41.5	96.9

Evidence for repair after UV irradiation was sought in P388F cells and in the two Yoshida lines in a similar way. Cells were cultured in unlabelled IUdR for 3 hours, resuspended in phosphate-buffered saline for irradiation, then cultured in complete medium containing ³HTdR, unlabelled IUdR and hydroxyurea 10^{-2} M for a further 3 hours before harvesting. DNA was isolated by the Marmur procedure and banded in neutral CsCl gradients before and after denaturation as before.

Unscheduled synthesis is clearly demonstrable in P388F cells, almost 100% of cells were labelled after a dose of 200 ergs/mm² and 2 weeks' exposure of the autoradiographs (Table 4). Assuming that control cells undergoing normal DNA synthesis accumulated 500 grains in 2 weeks, calculated from exposure of control slides for 48 hours, then unscheduled synthesis, 10–15 grains/cell after 14 days, is $\sim$.02% of that in control cultures.

DNA was isolated from P 388 F cells exposed to a dose of 200 ergs/mm² and cultured in hydroxyurea 10^{-2} M after irradiation. This DNA was compared with DNA from control hydroxyurea-treated cultures after denaturation and banding in a neutral CsCl gradient. The specific activity of the denatured normal density DNA from control cultures was 67.5 c.p.m./OD and that from cultures given 200 ergs/mm² was 422 c.p.m./OD, i.e. there is an increase by a factor of 6 at this dose of UV. In neutral gradients of native DNA, a small shoulder of activity under the normal density DNA was visible after 200 ergs/mm².

The data for the two Yoshida cell lines are summarized in Table 5. In the initial gradients of native DNA from cultures grown in the presence of hydroxyurea after UV irradiation a clear difference was seen between the amount of repair replication occurring in the UV sensitive and resistant

Table 5. Specific activities of normal-density DNA of Yoshida cells sensitive and resistant to UV irradiation.

Cell line	UV dose	S.A. of normal density DNA c.p.m./OD unit
Yoshida resistant	0	173.4
	100 ergs	367.8
	200 ergs	547.8
Yoshida sensitive	0	165.5
	100 ergs	287.3
	200 ergs	327.8

Specific activities were calculated from initial gradients of DNA denatured by heat (100° C for 10 min) in the presence of 1 M formaldehyde. Cultures were grown in unlabelled IUdR 2 μg/ml for 3 hours prior to irradiation and then in unlabelled IUdR in the presence of ³HTdR 0.2 μCi/ml S.A. 22 Ci/mM plus hydroxyurea 10^{-2} M for 3 hours before harvesting. DNA was isolated by the Marmur procedure, the supernatant after the final chloroform : isoamyl alcohol extraction was dialysed for 3 days against SSC before banding.

lines after doses of 100 ergs/mm² and 200 ergs/mm². After denaturation (heat + 1 M formaldehyde) the difference was even more obvious. The specific activity of the normal-density DNA of the sensitive cell line increased by a factor of 2 over that of control after irradiation with 200 ergs/mm² whereas the specific activity of the normal-density DNA of the resistant cell line was greater than of the control by a factor of 3 at this dose level.

The two Yoshida cell lines thus appear to behave in a manner similar to that reported by CLEAVER (1968, 1970) for cells derived from xeroderma cells compared with normal skin fibroblasts. The sensitive cell line does, however, show some capacity for repair of UV damage whereas xeroderma cells are reported to lack this ability completely. A further similarity lies in the fact that both Yoshida cell lines show similar sensitivity to cell killing by X-rays and the monofunctional alkylating agent MMS, and it has been reported recently that xeroderma and normal fibroblasts show equal amounts of unscheduled synthesis after X-rays (CLEAVER, 1969) and repair replication after MMS (CLEAVER, 1971).

In conclusion, therefore, P388F and L5178YS and L5178YR cells have been tested for repair replication and unscheduled synthesis after X-rays. No differences could be detected between the two L5178Y lines in spite of the large difference in X-ray sensitivity. Repair replication was not demonstrable after doses of up to 1500 rad. P388F cells show unscheduled synthesis after 50 and 200 ergs/mm² UV irradiation and repair replication has been demonstrated after a dose of 200 ergs/mm². The two Yoshida cell lines studied show similar sensitivities to X irradiation and the monofunctional alkylating agent MMS but have an approximately fivefold difference in sensitivity to UV. Repair replication was easily demonstrated in the Yoshida cell line resistant to UV after 100 and 200 ergs/mm². In the sensitive cell line it was significantly less. The two Yoshida cell lines thus behave in a very similar way to xeroderma and normal fibroblasts.

References

AYAD, S. R., M. Fox: Int. J. Radiat. Biol. *15:* 445 (1969).
BRAHIC, M., M. J. FRASER: Biochim. biophys. Acta (Amst.) *240:* 23 (1971).
BRENT, T. P., G. A. WHEATLEY: Int. J. Radiat. Biol. *19:* 339 (1971).
BURDON, R.: Personal communication (1971).
CLEAVER, J. E.: Nature *218:* 652 (1968).
CLEAVER, J. E.: Proc. Nat. Acad. Sci. (Wash.) *63:* 428 (1969a).
CLEAVER, J. E.: Int. J. Radiat. Biol. *16:* 277 (1969b).
CLEAVER, J. E.: Int. J. Radiat. Biol. *18:* 557 (1970).
CLEAVER, J. E.: Mutation Res. *12:* 453 (1971).
COURTENAY, V. D.: Radiat. Res. *38:* 186 (1969).
DALRYMPLE, G. V., J. L. SAUNDERS, A. J. MOSS, M. L. BAKER, K. P. WILKINSON: Biochim. biophys. Res. Commun. *35:* 300 (1969).
FOX, M., S. R. AYAD, B. W. FOX: Int. J. Radiat. Biol. *18:* 101 (1970).
FOX, M., B. W. FOX: Chem. Biol. Interact. (in press) (1971).
FRIEDMAN, D. L., G. C. MUELLER: Biochim. biophys. Acta (Amst.) *174:* 253 (1969).
GOTTLIEB, A., L. TAYLOR, F. SEINSHEIMER: Biochemistry *9:* 4322 (1970).
HILL, M.: Int. J. Radiat. Biol. *15:* 483 (1969).
LITTLE, J. B.: Int. J. Radiat. Biol. *13:* 591 (1968).
ORMEROD, M. G., A. R. LEHMAN: Biochim. biophys. Acta (Amst.) *228:* 331 (1971).
PAINTER, R. B.: In: Effects of radiation on cellular proliferation and differentiation; p. 91. I.A.E.A., Vienna 1968.
PAINTER, R. B.: Current Topics in Radiat. Res. *7:* 46 (1970).
PAINTER, R. B.: Proc. 1st European Congress of Biophysics; p. 123. Baden/Vienna 1971.
PAINTER, R. B., J. E. CLEAVER: Nature *216:* 369 (1967).
SAWADA, S., S. OKADA: Radiat. Res. *41:* 145 (1970).

Different Forms of Repair of Alkylated Mammalian Cell DNA

J. J. ROBERTS

In order to be certain that so-called DNA repair phenomena are involved in the recovery of cells from the effects of alkylation it is necessary to establish that alkylation of DNA results in a particular biological effect on cells. The ideal would be to find that repair of DNA is accompanied by the elimination or modification of specific mutagenic effects of alkylation in mammalian cells. Mammalian cell genetics is only beginning to approach this degree of sophisti- action. Alkylation of DNA is probably involved in carcinogenesis but there is no precise definitive evidence to support this view at present. There are many indications, however, that reaction with DNA leads to cell death. Thus, at concentrations of mustard gas permitting high survival of cells in culture the only detectable biochemical effect is an inhibition in the rate of DNA synthesis (1), and this inhibition is a consequence of alkylation of DNA *per se* and not due to the inhibition of enzymes involved in DNA synthesis. Inhibi- tion of DNA synthesis leads to an extended S phase and subsequent mitotic delay (Fig. 1). That the mitotic delay is the result of the inhibition in rate of DNA synthesis following alkylation of DNA was confirmed by showing that G_2-treated cells divide normally and then, following a depression in DNA synthesis in the succeeding cell cycle, undergo a mitotic delay (2). Mustard gas- induced cross-links either interstrand or intrastrand, presumably interfere with semiconservative replication of DNA. Thus cells become blocked in the S phase and continue to synthesize DNA at a reduced rate. Since RNA and protein synthesis are unaffected cells enlarge to form giant cells. Eventually, some of these cells which have been treated with low concentrations of mustard gas divide. That these effects are a consequence of a direct reaction with DNA is supported by the levels of alkylation of DNA, RNA and protein molecules follow-

Abbreviations:	MMS	methyl methane sulphonate
	MNU	N-methyl-N-nitrosourea
	MNNG	N-methyl-N'-nitro-N-nitrosoguanidine
	BudR	5-bromo-2'-deoxyuridine
	TdR	thymidine

ing treatment of cells with mustard gas. At the D_0 dose of mustard gas for HeLa cells less than 1 molecule of protein (mol. wt. 1×10^5) in 2000 but every molecule of DNA of mol. wt. 3×10^8 daltons was alkylated. Hence protein enzymes involved in the replication of DNA are not likely to have been inhibited by these concentrations of mustard gas. Indeed no inhibition of thymidine kinase could be achieved even with appreciably higher concentrations of mustard gas than were required to inhibit DNA synthesis.

Chemical, biochemical and biological observations indicate that cells recover from the otherwise lethal effect of DNA alkylations thus implying the existence

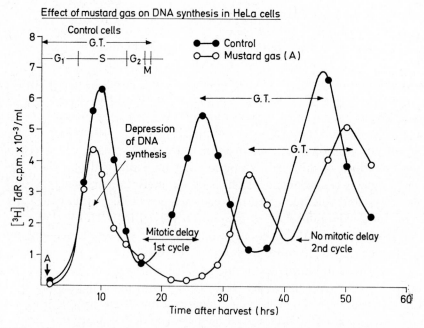

Fig. 1. The effect of treatment with mustard gas during the G_1 phase of the cell cycle (arrowed A) on subsequent DNA synthesis in a synchronous population of HeLa cells. The cells were treated with mustard gas (0.075 μg/ml in ether 0.05%) and the extent of DNA synthesis in treated and untreated cells measured at various times thereafter by the uptake of [³H]TdR into cold TCA-insoluble material in a 1 ml aliquot of cells. ●—● Control; ○—○ 0.075 μg/ml mustard gas.

of a mechanism(s) for repairing lesions in DNA. As can be seen in Fig. 1 (and also in Fig. 5, which shows the effects of half mustard gas on DNA synthesis) those cells which do divide after the initially extended S phase and subsequent mitotic delay do not exhibit any extension of the S phase or mitotic delay in the following cell cycle but divide thereafter with a normal generation time. This implies that the damage which resulted in the depression of DNA synthesis was repaired during the delay period.

Cells given a pulse treatment of mustard gas early in the G_1 phase of the cell cycle showed less subsequent depression of DNA synthesis than those treated just prior to the onset of DNA synthesis, and this was interpreted as being due to the repair of DNA lesions during the G_1 phase (2). Variations in the colony-forming ability of cells treated at different times during the cell cycle accorded with this view. Maximum sensitivity was at the G_1/S interphase, while early G_1- and G_2-treated cells were the least sensitive.

The chemical evidence for repair came from measurements on the extent of reaction of ^{35}S-labelled mustard gas with HeLa cell constituents and in particular from a consideration of the number of cross-links in DNA. At the D_o dose of this agent for HeLa cells it can be calculated that there are approximately 1500 DNA interstrand cross-links per cell. Since theoretically one cross-link could be regarded as adequate to stop the replication of DNA these cross-links must have been circumvented or eliminated. Indeed we have found that the products of alkylation are partially excised from DNA of mustard-treated HeLa cells (1), while REID and WALKER observed a time-dependent removal of cross-links from mustard-resistant mouse L cells (3). We have recently confirmed this finding using an alternative method for determining and quantitating the amount of cross-linking of DNA (4), in HeLa cells treated with mustard gas. One strand of DNA was given a density and radioactive label by growing cells in the presence of BUdR and [^{3}H] TdR simultaneously. Cross-linking of »heavy« labelled DNA to »light« unlabelled DNA then produced a »hybrid« labelled species. The decrease in the proportion of this species in HeLa cell DNA isolated various times after alkylation indicated that cross-links in DNA are lost. The nature of the initially excised material is not yet known but by analogy with the established mechanism of removal of UV-induced lesions it is reasonable to suppose it consists of oligonucleotides containing alkylguanine residues.

It should be noted, however, that the loss of chemical groups from DNA may not be entirely due to the action of an excision enzyme since it is known that alkyl purines are lost hydrolytically from alkylated DNA (5). However, whatever the mechanism for the removal of alkyl groups from DNA, the dealkylated DNA will still need to be »repaired« in order to serve as a template for the synthesis of functional DNA. Existence of such further steps in the repair of chemically damaged mammalian cell DNA came from the demonstration of non-semiconservative (»repair«) DNA synthesis in HeLa cells following alkylation with mustard gas, half mustard gas and methyl methanesulphonate (6) and in P388 cells alkylated with methyl methanesulphonate (7).

It thus appears that a mechanism analogous to the well-established »cut and patch« repair of UV irradiation-induced lesions exists for the removal of alkylation damage from the DNA of mammalian cells.

In order to establish whether these indications of repair were truly related to the recovery of cells from the effects of alkylation or constituted merely non-specific responses to damage of cells we have attempted to answer the following questions:

1. Is the amount of »repair synthesis« dependent on the initial level of DNA alkylation?

2. Are the kinetics of »repair synthesis« related to those of removal of alkyl groups from DNA, and is the latter an enzyme-mediated reaction?

3. How much »repair synthesis« is associated with the loss of each alkyl group from DNA?

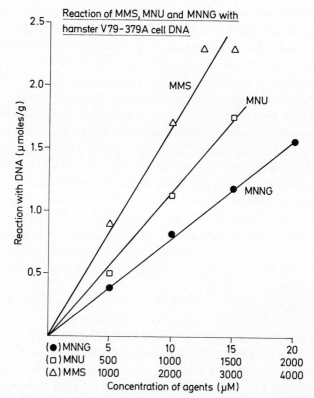

Fig. 2. Extent of methylation of DNA isolated from Chinese hamster V 79–379 A cells following treatment for 1 hour in suspension at 37° with various concentration of [³H] MNNG (●), [³H] MNU (□) and [¹⁴C] MMS (△). The concentrations of the three compounds at any one point in the abscissa were chosen to give approximately equal effects on cell survival as determined by colony-forming ability of treated cells.

4. What DNA precursors are incorporated during »repair replication«?
5. Are differences in the various manifestations of »cut and patch« repair associated with differences in the sensitivity of cell types to a particular agent (e.g. drug resistance; susceptibility to carcinogens)?
6. If not, are there other mechanisms of DNA repair?
7. Can »repair synthesis« be inhibited?

It was found that the concentrations of the methylating agents MMS, MNU and MNNG, which are equitoxic to Chinese hamster V79–379A cells, differ by nearly 200-fold (8) (Fig. 2). However, when the fraction of cells surviving treatment was plotted as a function of reaction with DNA, essentially the same plot was obtained for all three compounds (Fig. 3).

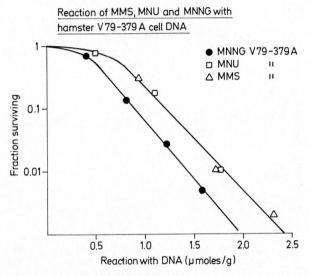

Fig. 3. Relationship between the survival of Chinese hamster V79–379A cells and the extents of methylation of their DNA by [³H] MNNG (●), [³H] MNU (□), [¹⁴C] MMS (△).

Repair replication was then determined in hamster cells following treatment with these same compounds by following the incorporation of [³H]BUdR (or a mixture of BUdR and [³H]TdR which was shown to be equivalent to [³H]BUdR) into light single-stranded DNA (9). The specific activity of this DNA gave a measurement of »repair replication« and was plotted against dose to give a linear relationship, although this did not hold at higher concentrations when the repair mechanism was either inhibited by other cellular reactions or became saturated. Again it was found that for the three methylating agents, at equitoxic concentrations, resulting in an equal extent of DNA binding, there was an equal amount of repair replication (Fig. 4). This approach was extended to other cell lines and to other cytotoxic compounds and it was apparent that in every case examined the extent of repair replication was broadly speaking directly proportional to the amount of reaction occurring with DNA. This was so despite the fact that in these situations equal extents of DNA reaction did not always elicit the same cytotoxic effect (see later).

Repair replication was shown to occur for many hours following alkylation of hamster cells with MNNG or of HeLa cells with mustard gas (9). Loss of

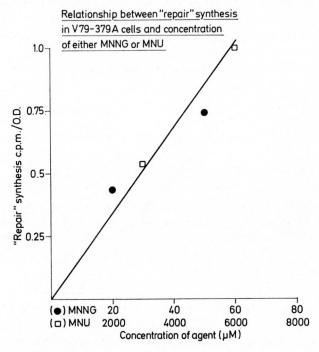

Fig. 4. Relationship between amount of »repair synthesis« in Chinese hamster V 79–379 A cells and the concentration of MNNG or MNU.

labelled methyl groups from DNA of hamster cells alkylated with [³H]MNNG was also followed over this period, and it was found that both events proceeded at comparable rates, suggesting that one was a consequence of the other. This is consistent with the biochemical evidence which indicated that recovery of cells from low concentrations of drugs which permitted high survival occurred during a period of several hours (Fig. 1).

From a knowledge of the actual number of methyl groups lost from DNA in a given time and of the number of thymidine molecules incorporated into DNA by repair replication during the same period and under the same conditions it was possible to arrive at a rough estimate for the number of nucleotides inserted into DNA per methyl group lost. The calculation which assumes that the DNA polymerase(s) used for normal and repair DNA synthesis does not discriminate differently as between BUdR and [³H]TdR, suggests that 100 nucleotides are inserted into DNA for every methyl group lost.

The method used for measuring repair replication permits us to examine the fourth question posed, namely, what precursors can be used for DNA repair? We have reported that [³H]TdR or [³H]CdR and BUdR are equivalent to [³H]BUdR for the detection of »repair synthesis«. Initially we failed to detect »repair synthesis« with [³H]deoxyguanosine or [³H]deoxyadenosine and BUdR (9). More recently by use of highly labelled purine nucleosides and with frequent rebanding to remove radioactive label associated with normal DNA and RNA synthesis it is clear that these DNA precursors can, like the pyrimidines, be used during »repair replication«.

These quantitative and kinetic aspects of »repair replication« clearly indicate that it is related to the level of DNA alkylation produced by these various agents. Furthermore it would seem that it is involved in the recovery of cells containing damaged DNA by a process related to the »cut and patch« repair of UV-induced thymine dimers (10). It would not appear to be a non-specific response to cell death possibly involving end-addition of nucleotides (7). This latter view was fostered by the apparent need for supralethal doses of agents in order to detect repair replication as was the case following treatment of HeLa cells with X-rays (11) or mustard gas (6). With the relatively non-toxic monofunctional compounds such as MMS and »resistant« cells like P388 lymphoma or Chinese hamster V79-379A and improved methods for detecting »repair synthesis«, this can now be observed at concentrations resulting in nearly 100% survival.

If we accept that repair replication is involved in the recovery of cells from alkylation we may now ask the question, why do cells differ in their response to a particular agent? Do sensitive cells lack excision enzymes or the ability to undergo repair replication? Comparison of these two manifestations of repair in sensitive and resistant Yoshida sarcoma cells showed that this was not the case. Despite a nearly 20-fold difference in the level of alkylation at equitoxic doses both cell types exhibited the same rate of excision of mustard gas and the same extent of »repair replication« (12).

HeLa cells and hamster cells differ markedly in their response to MNNG and MNU, less so to MMS while mustard gas and half mustard gas affect both cell lines to the same extent (8). We have therefore considered whether hamster cells can repair lesions introduced by MNNG or MNU more readily than can

HeLa cells. Again it was found that at equal levels of DNA reaction both cell types exhibited the same amount of »repair synthesis« (9) suggesting that the greater sensitivity of HeLa cells to MNNG or MNU did not reside in their inability to repair lesions introduced by these compounds by a »cut and patch« mechanism. This prompted us to consider that a difference in the efficiency of some other mechanism for repairing DNA lesions existed as between the two cell lines. Some evidence for this was obtained from a comparison of the

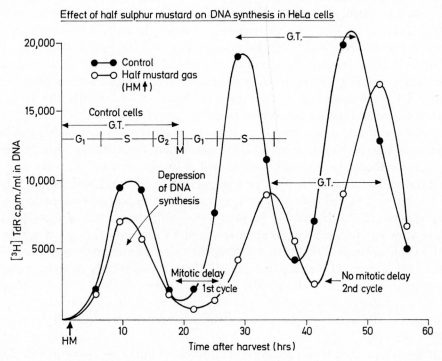

Fig. 5. The effect of treatment with half mustard gas during the G_1 phase of the cell cycle (arrowed HM) on subsequent DNA synthesis in a synchronous population of HeLa cells. DNA synthesis was determined as in Fig. 1. ●—● Control; ○—○ 1.5 μg/ml.

effects of mustard gas, half mustard gas and MNU on DNA synthesis in synchronous populations of either HeLa or hamster cells at equitoxic concentrations of these agents. Treatment of HeLa cells with low concentrations of MNU led to effects on DNA synthesis and progression through the cell cycle quite different from those previously observed after treatment with mustard gas (Fig. 1) or half mustard gas (Fig. 5). Both these agents caused an immediate dose-dependent depression of DNA synthesis in the S phase of the cycle in which treatment occurred and a subsequent mitotic delay. MNU however failed to produce any immediate effect on the rate of DNA synthesis. Treated cells divided without delay but in the following cell cycle showed a clear dose-dependent depression in the rate of DNA synthesis (Fig. 6) and commensurate mitotic delay. It thus appears that DNA alkylated by MNU is required to undergo replication before a lesion is produced which constitutes a block to DNA synthesis (13) and subsequent cell division. Substantiation of this view came from a study of the fate of G_2-treated cells. These cells divided twice before

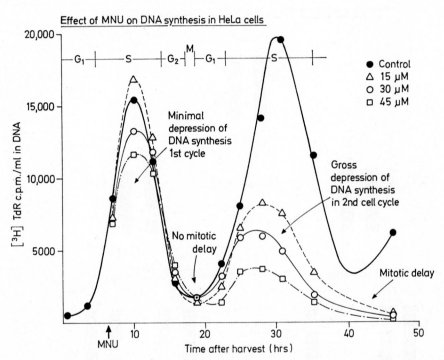

Fig. 6. The effect of treatment with MNU during the G_1 phase of the cell cycle on DNA synthesis in synchronous populations of HeLa cells. Replicate cultures were treated with MNU 6 hours after mitosis (arrowed MNU). ● Control; △ 15 μM; ○ 30 μM; □ 45 μM.

exhibiting a like depression in the rate of DNA synthesis. Fig. 7a depicts this alkylation of DNA schematically and Fig. 7b shows its consequences for cells treated during the G_1 or G_2 phases of the cell cycle. The newly introduced lesion could be a gap in the DNA. Such gaps could be repaired subsequently either by the insertion of bases or by a mechanism akin to recombination.

Synchronous populations of hamster cells were similarly treated with either mustard gas, half mustard gas or MNU. As was found for HeLa cells mustard gas and half mustard gas introduced lesions into hamster cell DNA which constituted an immediate block to DNA synthesis (Fig. 8). Both cell lines were equally affected by these two agents and therefore it must be presumed that they possess similar repair potential towards lesions introduced by these agents. Repair probably requires elimination of a cross-link in the case of mustard gas or a »pseudo« cross-link in the case of half mustard gas (by virtue

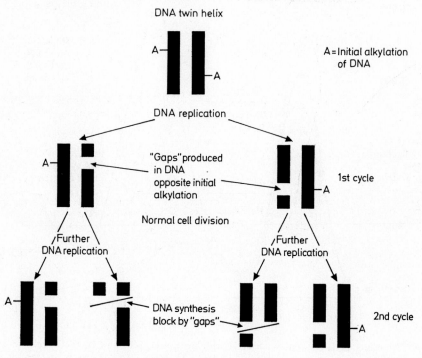

Fig. 7a. Scheme showing possible mechanism of inhibition of DNA synthesis in HeLa cells by MNU.

of its additional –OH group which could be involved in hydrogen bonding) by a »cut and patch« mechanism.

In contrast to these agents MNU is far less toxic towards hamster cells than towards HeLa cells (Fig. 9). At equitoxic doses hamster DNA is alkylated 20 times that of HeLa DNA. Cell death following treatment of hamster cells with MNU also probably results from lesions in DNA introduced during DNA

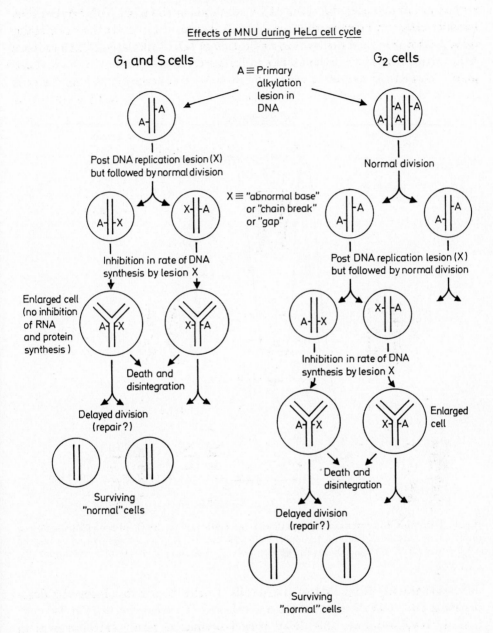

Fig. 7b. Sheme showing the effect of alkylation of HeLa cells with MNU during different phases of the cell cycle.

replication in one cycle blocking DNA synthesis in the next. This implies that
hamster cells can more readily repair DNA damaged by MNU than can HeLa
cells. As it was argued earlier that replication of MNU-alkylated DNA produces
gaps then it follows that the ability to bridge these gaps differs in the two cell
lines. There is one aspect in which the response to alkylation of hamster cells

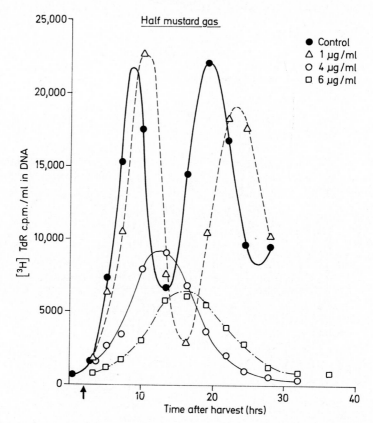

Fig. 8. The effect of treatment with half mustard gas during the G_1 phase of the cell cycle
on DNA synthesis in Chinese hamster V 79–379 A cells. Replicate cultures were treated
2 hours after mitosis (arrowed). ● Control; △ 1 μg/ml; ○ 4 μg/ml; □ 6 μg/ml.

differed markedly from that of HeLa cells. In the former we observed a dose-
dependent delay in the onset of DNA synthesis of G_1-treated cells (Fig. 10) (14).
Conceivably, therefore, this delay period permitted repair of these gaps in
DNA before their effects were manifest in the following cell cycle.

Support for the existence of an additional repair mechanism other than
»cut and patch« repair has come from an examination of the effects of caffeine

on the survival of MNU-treated HeLa and hamster cells and its effect on repair replication. While the sensitivity of hamster cells towards MNU was increased by caffeine there was no comparable increase in the toxic effect of MNU towards HeLa cells (15). This suggests that a repair mechanism present in hamster cells but not HeLa cells is inhibited by caffeine. Furthermore, since caffeine does not inhibit repair replication it follows that this alternative repair pathway does not elicit this phenomenon.

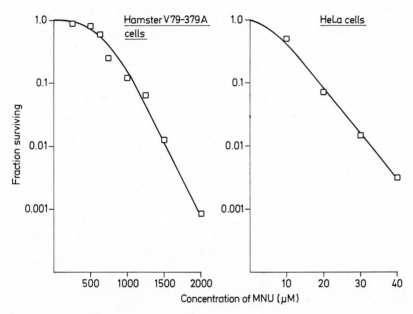

Fig. 9. The effect of MNU on survival of hamster V 79–379 A and HeLa cells.

In summary, therefore, there is evidence that mammalian cells in culture recover from the otherwise lethal effects of alkylation by at least two mechanisms. In the one, alkyl groups are eliminated from DNA and the »breaks« so produced are probably repaired by a mechanism requiring non-semicon-servative or »repair« synthesis. However, since the sensitivity of cells to various agents cannot be explained in terms of differences in this mechanism of repair another mechanism probably exists in mammalian cells for re-pairing DNA. This is possibly analogous to that postulated for the repair of UV-induced thymine dimers which involves the by-passing of DNA lesions during DNA synthesis and the subsequent filling of the gaps so produced. In

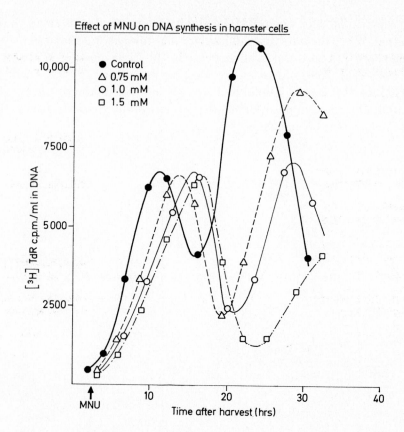

Fig. 10. The effect of treatment with MNU during the G_1 phase of the cell cycle on DNA synthesis in synchronous populations of Chinese hamster V 79–379 A cells. Replicate cultures were treated 2 hours after mitosis (arrowed). ● Control; △ 0.75 mM; ○ 1.0 mM; □ 1.5 mM.

bacteria it has been suggested that this involves a mechanism akin to recombination (16). Experiments with microorganisms have shown that this recombination repair is error prone and results in a high mutation yield. It is perhaps significant that the compounds which cause DNA lesions in mammalian cells, which, we are postulating, are repaired by a similar mechanism, increase the spontaneous mutation rate in Chinese hamster cells and are potent carcinogens. A scheme depicting these various forms of repair is shown in Fig. 11.

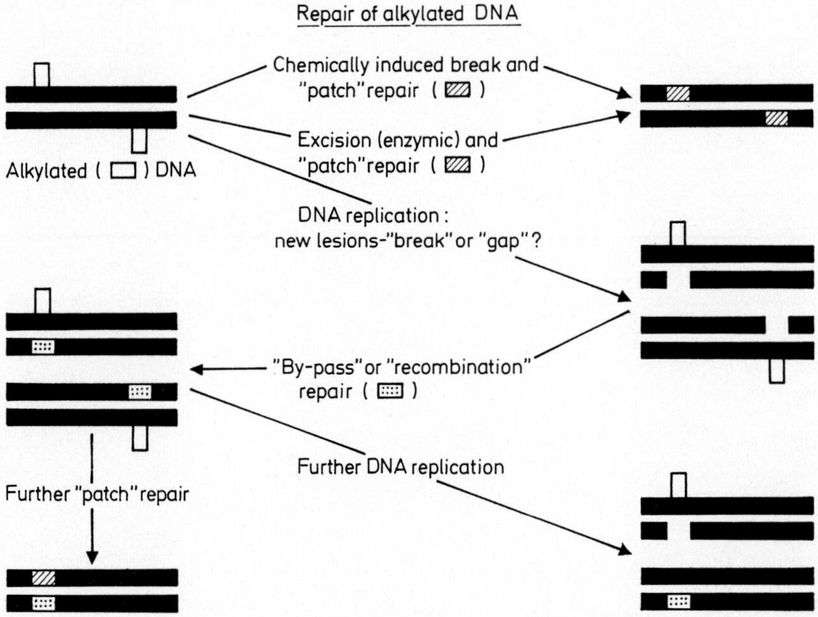

Fig. 11. Scheme showing the various possible forms of repair of DNA alkylations in mammalian cells.

References

(1) CRATHORN, A. R., J. J. ROBERTS: Nature *211:* 150 (1966).
(2) ROBERTS, J. J., T. P. BRENT, A. R. CRATHORN: Europ. J. Cancer *7;* 515 (1971).
(3) REID, B. D., I. G. WALKER: Biochim. biophys. Acta (Amst.) *179:* 179 (1969).
(4) BALL, C. R., J. J. ROBERTS: Chem. Biol. Interactions *4:* 297 (1971/2).
(5) LAWLEY, P. D.: Progr. nucl. Acid Res. molec. Biol. *5:* 89 (1968).
(6) ROBERTS, J. J., A. R. CRATHORN, T. P. BRENT: Nature *218:* 970 (1968).
(7) AYAD, S. R., M. Fox, B. W. Fox: Mutation Res. *8:* 639 (1969).
(8) ROBERTS, J. J., J. M. PASCOE, J. E. PLANT, J. E. STURROCK, A. R. CRATHORN: Chem. Biol. Interactions *3:* 29 (1971).
(9) ROBERTS, J. J., J. M. PASCOE, B. SMITH, A. R. CRATHORN: Chem. Biol. Interactions *3:* 49 (1971).
(10) HOWARD-FLANDERS, P.: Ann. Rev. Biochem. *37:* 175 (1968).
(11) PAINTER, R. B., J. E. CLEAVER: Nature *216:* 369 (1967).
(12) BALL, C. R., J. J. ROBERTS: Chem Biol. Interactions *2:* 321 (1970).
(13) PLANT, J. E., J. J. ROBERTS: Chem. Biol. Interactions *3:* 337 (1971).
(14) PLANT, J. E., J. J. ROBERTS: Chem. Biol. Interactions *3:* 343 (1971).
(15) ROBERTS, J. J., K. WARD: (Unpublished results).
(16) RUPP, W. D., P. HOWARD-FLANDERS: J. molec. Biol. *31:* 291 (1968).

This work was supported by grants to the Chester Beatty Research Institute (Institute of Cancer Research: Royal Cancer Hospital) from the Medical Research and the Cancer Research Campaign.

Discussion

ORMEROD: I would like to describe some experiments performed in our laboratory by P. KARRAN.

We wanted to know whether the repair capacity of a cell is, in some way, related to the ability of the cell to replicate its DNA. We took cells from different tissues of an animal and looked at the ability to rejoin X-ray-induced strand breaks.

Since we were interested in cells that did not divide, we could not label the DNA radioactively. We, therefore, used a fluorescent method [KISSANE, J. and E. ROBINS, J. Biol. Chem. *233*: 184 (1958)] by which we could detect 0.1 μg of DNA in a fraction from a sucrose gradient. We used a 30 ml gradient of 5–20% sucrose on a shelf of 60% CsCl. The cells (5 $\times$ 10^5 containing about 5 μg of DNA) were pipetted into a layer of 2% SDS solution on the top of gradients which were then centrifuged for 70 min at 25,000 r.p.m.

Using a murine lymphoma cell (L5178Y) grown in tissue culture, it could be shown that the DNA from unirradiated cells sediments rapidly through the gradient onto the shelf. This DNA is in a complex, and has a molecular weight greater than 10^9 daltons. A radiation dose of 3 krads introduced single-strand breaks into the DNA, lowered the molecular weight and released the DNA from the complex. Immediately after irradiation the DNA was found on the top of the gradient. If the cells were incubated for half an hour at 37° C after irradiation, the strand breaks rejoined and the DNA is again found on the shelf. We chose this method of observing the repair of strand breaks in cells, since it is easier to follow the accumulation of DNA in a single fraction on the shelf rather than trying to measure the position of a profile on the gradient.

We have prepared cell suspensions from the following tissues: thymus, spleen and bone-marrow from a rat and peripheral blood lymphocytes from a chicken. In all cases, these cells contained high molecular weight DNA (> 10^9 daltons) and could rejoin single-strand breaks in tissue culture after a radiation dose of 3 krads. Although less than 10% of the cells from these tissues are in S phase at a time, most of the cells in the population are capable of undergoing division.

As an example of a post-mitotic cell, we chose the chicken erythrocyte. Unlike mammalian cells, avian erythrocytes retain their nuclei. When these cells were layered on the sucrose gradients, we found that only about 7% of the DNA sedimented onto the shelf of CsCl. The rest of the DNA was of comparatively low molecular weight (about 10^8 daltons). Furthermore, the cells were not able to rejoin X-ray-induced strand breaks.

If the bird was bled extensively, three days later the percentage of high molecular DNA had increased to about 25%. Over a two-week period, the percentage of the DNA sedimenting onto the shelf dropped to the normal value. It appears that the nucleus of the newly created erythrocyte contains high molecular weight DNA but that single-strand breaks are accumulated over a period of time.

To summarize, lymphocytes, which are capable of cell division, contain DNA of high molecular weight and enzymes which can rejoin strand breaks; the chicken erythrocyte, a terminal cell, has no »rejoining« enzymes and its DNA is of low molecular weight.

PAINTER: How do you measure repair in DNA on the top of the gradient?

ORMEROD: We centrifuged the gradients for longer periods of time in order to bring the DNA to the middle of the gradient, and then measured the position of the peak fraction in the usual way.

STRAUSS: I would like to comment on the design of experiments intended to show repair in peripheral blood lymphocytes. Dr. NORMAN pointed out correctly that one could demonstrate increased repair in lymphocytes that were stimulated by phytohemagglutinin. I would like to discuss a recent finding in our laboratory which shows that the progeny of stimulated lymphocytes themselves require stimulation to divide. Let me first describe our experiment and then indicate how it relates to the problem of studying repair in peripheral lymphocytes. Peripheral human blood lymphocytes were stimulated with concanavalin A (conA) and then, after 24 hours, the mitogen was washed out with methyl-alpha-mannoside, a competitor which makes it possible to remove the mitogen completely. The cells were then incubated with ^{14}C-labelled thymidine which was present in the culture from 42–48 hours after the initial addition of conA. The labelled thymidine was removed and the cells were divided into two portions; the first portion was stimulated by a second addition of conA, the second was incubated without additional mitogen. Both sets of lymphocytes were then incubated in medium with bromodeoxyuridine. If the lymphocytes have gone through two generations, or two DNA replications, the DNA will be both radioactive and hybrid in density. If the lymphocytes have gone through only one division, the DNA will be radioactive but light. As one can see (Fig. 1), cultures which were not restimulated with conA (sets e and f) did not replicate labelled DNA. Cultures which were restimulated with conA did replicate labelled DNA over a period of 48–96 hours in these experiments by N. MUNAKATA (sets a–d). In more recent experiments in which deoxycytidine was added to the medium, transfer to hybrid density has been observed

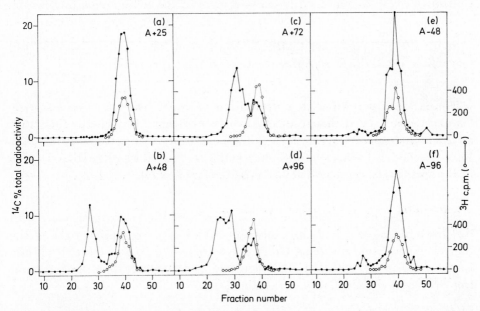

Fig. 1. Density analysis of DNA from cells restimulated with conA. Cultures were treated as described in the comment. The DNA synthesized during the period 42-48 hours from the start of incubation was labelled with ^{14}C-TdR. The cells were washed and resuspended in fresh medium; conA was added to half of the tubes. After 8 hours incubation in non-radioactive medium, BUdR (10^{-5}M) and FUdR (5×10^{-7}M) were added. Sets (a–d) represent CsCl gradients from cultures taken 25, 48, 72 and 96 hours after the second conA stimulation. Sets (e) and (f) represent gradients from non-restimulated cultures at 48 and 96 hours after the removal of conA with methyl alpha mannoside. The lighter lines represent ^{3}H-TdR-labelled light DNA from phytohemagglutinin-stimulated lymphocytes, added as a density marker.

within 24 hours. We conclude that the progeny of cells which have been stimulated with mitogen themselves require stimulation if they are to replicate.

In most experiments in which the behaviour of activated lymphocytes is studied, mitogen is added to cells and the mixture is allowed to remain together throughout the course of the experiment. One therefore has a culture that is active in replication and that has the membrane properties characteristic of stimulated cells. However, if one removes the mitogen, an »active« culture will be converted to one which is inactive after the first division, that is within about 48–52 hours; i.e. the cells will revert to a population whose properties probably resemble the original, unstimulated lymphocyte population. It would seem therefore that repair experiments with mitogen-stimulated cells may require a more careful control of the »proliferative state« of the cells. Such control can only be obtained by close control of the cell-mitogen interaction.

SLOR: I have a question to Dr. NORMAN about the repair in sperms. Did you follow DNA repair at different stages during spermatogenesis?

NORMAN: As you know it is very difficult to get males to give a testicle for experiments even though most have two of them. Our results show that all the human spermatogenic cells, with the exception of mature sperm cells, show unscheduled DNA synthesis. It remains to be seen whether DNA damage in the sperm cells can be repaired in the fertilized ovum.

SLOR: I also have a question to Dr. ROBERTS. In your experiment with the mustard gas you had three division cycles. The generation time in the control experiment was remarkably short compared to the treated culture. In the experiment with the MNU you had normal generation time in control and treated cells. Can you explain this?

ROBERTS: In point of fact the generation time of the control cells is fairly constant during the course of these synchronous experiments. In the particular figure (Fig. 1, p. 42), showing the effect of mustard gas on DNA synthises, the curve as drawn does appear to show some small difference between the length of the first and second cell cycles of the control cells but this is due to the paucity of readings at later times during this experiment which did not permit determination of the precise time of the peak of the third DNA synthetic period in control cells. This difference, however, is small compared to the much longer mustard gas-induced delay of the first mitosis. The more complete curves shown in the experiment using half mustard gas (Fig. 5, p. 48) emphasize that the time between the three S phases of control cells is remarkably constant. However, the point I wished to make was that there was a marked dose-dependent extension of the first cell cycle following the treatment with mustard gas or half mustard gas. This was not followed by a similar extension of the second cell cycle. The time between second and third DNA synthetic phases of the treated cells being essentially the same as that for the control cells.

RÉVÉSZ: I now wish to invite comments on the differences in the action of UV, X-rays and alkylating agents on DNA repair. Would POHLIT start the discussion?

POHLIT: I think, one difference between UV and X-rays is that the point of absorption of UV and the point of reaction is more or less the same, but with X-rays the point of radical production and the point of reaction is not the same. During the diffusion of the radicals towards the DNA, several reactions may occur which influence the final reaction at the DNA. For example, a primary radical can react with an organic molecule and is able to produce two or more organic radicals. These organic radicals may either react with the DNA, or recombine. In the first case we observe a sensitization and, in the second case, a protective effect. These effects are dependent on absorbed dose rate (due to the fact that recombination of organic radicals depends on the concentration of these radicals) and on absorbed dose (since the number of organic molecules able to react with primary radicals decreases with absorbed dose). The reduction of protecting reactions with increasing absorbed dose will result in an increase of radiation sensitivity and this could be one of the reasons for the »shoulder« in cell survival curves. The reversed reaction, that means the decrease of radiation sensitivity, can be called »recovery« in the cell. If by a radical reaction, for example, a single-strand break is produced in the DNA as a lethal reaction, this radiation effect can be reversed by the cell and only such a reversed reaction at the essential molecule itself I would like to call »repair« in the living cell. Very often, both effects occur simultaneously in the cells as can be seen, for example, in experiments with yeast cells.

FOX: How do you define recovery: as biological recovery of survival or as some other repair mechanism?

POHLIT: In the cited experiments with yeast cells, we have determined the recovery by observing the survival of the cells in a split dose experiment. The slope of the dose effect curve of the second irradiation can be used as a quantitative measure of the »radiation sensitivity«. This radiation sensitivity is increased due to the first irradiation and is decreased with time until the second irradiation starts. To explain the difference between »recovery« and »repair« I would like to give an intuitive example from human life: By hard working over a period of time, the probability for a heart attack in human beings increases. To reduce this »sensitivity« for heart attacks one goes on vacation, for example, to the Alps for climbing or skiing. This reversed change of sensitivity usually is called »recovery«. If, however, one has got really a heart attack one has to go into a hospital for »repair«. Repair in this definition is the reduction in number of the lesions of interest, and recovery is the reduction of sensitivity for this reaction. In more mathematical terms: Repair is a change of the quantity itself and recovery is a change of the derivative of this quantity with respect to the dose.

This, I think, is also a difference between the reactions of UV and X-rays that the sensitivity of the object of interest remains constant in the case of UV and may change in the case of X-rays from different reasons.

ORMEROD: What cell is this?

POHLIT: The experiments shown in Fig. 1 have been done with yeast cells because it is possible to work with high accuracy and precision. All cells are diploid and are in a certain part of the G1-phase, so that one is dealing with a homogeneous population. The cells are irradiated up to an absorbed dose of $D_1 = 60$ krad and then after a certain time interval the irradiation is continued with increasing absorbed doses. As can be seen, the shoulder of the dose

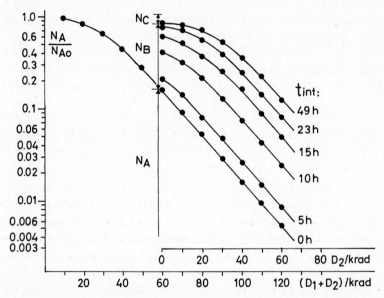

Fig. 1. Dose effect curves for diploid yeast cells in G1-phase. N_A is the number of vital cells, N_B the number of cells with repairable damage and N_C the number of cells with unrepairable damage. Dose effect curves are shown for an irradiation with $D_1 = 60$ krad and different absorbed doses D_2 with an time interval t_{int} between D_1 and D_2.

effect curve is reproduced as a function of time t_{int}. This means that the radiation sensitivity for a subsequent irradiation is decreased (recovery). But at the same time the number of surviving cells is increased for $D_2 = 0$ (repair).

RÉVÉSZ: Dr. POHLIT may wish to comment also on the effect of heavily ionizing radiations in addition to that of UV and X-rays.

POHLIT: I think we should not discuss here in this symposium the reactions of densely ionizing particles, such as alpha particles or heavy recoil nuclei in living cells. The situation there is more complicated again. The reactions due to secondary delta electrons produced by the heavy particles would also result in a very low number of unrepairable DNA damage as with X-rays. But the heavy particle itself is assumed to produce in particular double-strand breakage in the DNA. In this case, quite different biological reactions would be necessary for repair, if it occurs at all. On the other hand, the radiation reactions of such heavy particles may play an important role in radiation therapy in future, especially because of the differences in repair capacity in the cell.

NORMAN: The relationship of survival curves and DNA breakage and repair is quite obscure. As long as it remains obscure I think any such efforts to correlate them remain questionable.

POHLIT: Of course, you are right that we are observing today two different things, called »repair«: the reactions at the isolated DNA and the biological effects in a living cell. But there are many experiments in our and in other laboratories which show that these both endpoints could be related, as long as other influencing parameters are excluded or are taken into consideration in a more complicated model of the living cell.

RÉVÉSZ: In his excellent review in »Current Topics in Radiation Research« [7: 45 (1970)] PAINTER a couple of years ago discussed the problem of DNA breakage and its biological significance especially in regard to cellular survival after irradiation. He concluded that no certain correlation exists. A similar conclusion was made subsequently also at a meeting in Manchester devoted to this problem. A report of this meeting was published in Internat. J. Radiat. Biol. in 1971 and I particularly liked the summary in the last sentence: it clearly stated that this problem was discussed extensively but no certain associations were found.

PAINTER: I would like to comment on several things. Certainly there are a number of reasons that you cannot correlate, for instance, the repair of single-strand breaks with, let us say, split dose recovery. But I think the problem is that we emphasize repair replication because that is what we observe. We are looking at the lesions that are repaired and we don't know much about those which are unrepaired. If you have one unrepaired lesion in the presence of a hundred repaired, the former is very difficult to demonstrate. At this stage of the game we only talk about the repair mechanism. We cannot see these few unrepaired lesions which are probably very important to the cell. Secondly I want to comment very briefly on the last two discussions about the difference between UV and X irradiation. It turns out that mammalian cells are capable of repairing much more UV damage then they can X-ray damage. If you look at survival curves and then try to calculate the number of damaged areas in DNA there are about 1500 times as many damaged sites per surviving cell after UV as they are after X-rays.

The X-ray damage is much more effective in killing a cell than is the UV. Repair mechanisms therefore must not be as effective after X irradiation. I would like to ask about the fact that Dr. POHLIT says there is a difference between the survival curves after UV and X-rays. In mammalian cells I know of no difference. Most UV-survival curves (there is an exception) have a shoulder.

FOX: I think Dr. PAINTER is saying what I meant to say but more clearly. Within the biological dose range of the survival curve, one is obviously getting either more UV lesions repaired, which means you see more repair, or you are getting more nucleotides incorporated/lesion, which means you see it more easily. It is easier in fact to irradiate cells with a 300 kv X-ray machine than it is to irradiate with UV, but that is irrelevant. It is just that working within the biological range of the survival curve, UV repair replication is easier to demonstrate than X-ray-induced repair replication.

ORMEROD: I would like to make two points. First, one ought always to state what meaning is being given to the word »repair«. If one looks at the shoulder on a survival curve, the criterion of repair is cell survival without knowledge of the biochemistry involved. If one measures the removal of pyrimidine dimer, one is looking at a specific lesion. If one looks at the rejoining of strand breaks, one is observing the repair of one specific lesion in a cell that has suffered many different lesions. When you observe repair replication, quite frankly, a lot of the time you do not know what you are looking at; but you hope that it is some form of repair.

The other point relates to the comparison of repair processes after UV or high energy radiation. Our ignorance of the radiation chemistry of DNA within a cell is abysmal. We can measure the number of single-strand breaks and there have been a few reliable measurements of double-strand breaks; but we do not know what end-groups result.

We have very little knowledge about what changes occur in the bases. We do not even know the importance of indirect as compared to direct action. Until we have more detailed knowledge of this chemistry, to seek a correlation between ill-defined repair processes and cell survival is likely to be fruitless.

Révész: Dr. Ormerod, do you think, by what you have said, that the difference between what we understand with the words »repair« and »recovery« is a matter of semantics?

Ormerod: I think that when you mention repair you should carefully define either which lesion you are studying, or which manifestation of repair you are observing.

Fox: I would also put in an appeal in agreement with Dr. Ormerod that we define the difference between recovery and repair very clearly. To a radiobiologist recovery really means recovery of survival between split doses and nothing else. There are other recovery systems but in radiobiological terms which have to be used also by people who are working with drugs; this is what is most commonly meant by the term »recovery«.

Révész: Dr. Fox, do you now consider Elkind type of recovery from sublethal damage or recovery from, what is termed, potentially lethal damage?

Fox: Well, sublethal recovery was really the first system to be described, i.e. recovery from the sublethal damage. I think if we again use the word recovery we have to define recovery from what; recovery from sublethal damage or recovery from potentially lethal damage which have probably different mechanisms. We cannot just say recovery.

Pohlit: It was my intention to demonstrate that »recovery« is often taking place simultaneously with »repair« in a living cell. Therefore, one should not only determine the increase of survival of cells in a split dose experiment as a measure of repair and try to correlate this with measurements at the DNA itself. If it is necessary to add some explaining words to »recovery« I would like to use »recovery from sublethal damage« since the reactions involved here seem to be not lethal for the living cell.

Fox: We do not know what sublethal damage is. We know that the cell can recover from it.

Pohlit: Therefore, I have tried to define the »recovery« independent of a certain mechanism in the cell only as a »change of sensitivity« or more precisely as a change of the slope of the survival curve. Dr. Painter raised

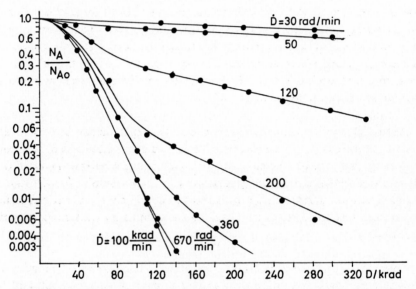

Fig. 2. Dose effect curves for diploid yeast cells in G1-phase for different absorbed dose rates.

the question how much of the radiation reactions in the living cell can be repaired, and how much cannot. This can be seen from dose effect curves obtained again with diploid yeast cells in G1-phase with different absorbed dose rates as shown in Fig. 2. If the absorbed dose rate is extremely low then repair can occur during irradiation and only the unrepairable reactions contribute to the slope of the dose effect curve. As can be determined quantitatively from Fig. 2 only about 2% of the original lethal lesions are irrepairable in this cell if irradiated with X-rays or high energy electrons.

The number of irrepairable lesions in the cell should be much higher if the cells are irradiated with densely ionizing particles. But for such cases I have only some calculated dose effect curves with me.

KIEFER: I would just like to comment very shortly about these last calculated curves. We have done experiments with alpha-rays on yeast cells and got the same amount of »repair« what we call liquid holding recovery. It is essentially equal after alpha-rays as compared with 100 kv roentgen-rays.

RÉVÉSZ: Dr. POHLIT showed us that energy is necessary for repair. Does any of the participants know the energy metabolism in the lymphocyte, i.e. the cell which is actually the subject of our present discussion? The energy metabolism in yeast cells is well understood, thanks to the contributions made by Drs. KIEFER, POHLIT, KOROGODIN [KOROGODIN, V. J.: Radiation Research (G. Silini, Ed.), p. 538. North Holland Publishing Company (1967)] and others. In view of the energy requirement of the repair process, it is conceivable that the great radiosensitivity of the lymphocyte is associated in some way to its particular energy metabolism. Could Drs. KIEFER and POHLIT think that the differences in the sensitivity of different cell types is due to differences in their energy reserves?

KIEFER: I think we have shown with our experiments in yeast cells that energy metabolism and functioning of the energy metabolism are certainly important. But I think, it has to be checked in all these experiments how much important it is in the actual experiment. I don't think we can say energy metabolism is *the* limiting step in the metabolic pathway. It can turn out to be the limiting step but I think this depends very much on the kind of experiments you are doing.

NORMAN: When we talk about cell death in radiation biology generally reproductive death is the criterion that we use; that is, the ability of the cell to reproduce continuously. This is not possible with lymphocyte cultures. We have a survival curve which usually is based on something quite different – the reactions of vital stains for example. I suspect more and more that in lymphocytes cell killing may have little to do with DNA damage and repair.

STRAUSS: May I return to the question of the number of lesions and the possible differences between the repair of ultraviolet and of alkylation and X-ray-induced damage. In procaryotes, or at any rate in bacteria, it is clear that there is a big difference in the repairability and perhaps in the type of repair of different lesions. It takes about 3700 pyrimidine dimers to introduce one lethal hit into *Escherichia coli* strain K 12. It takes only 10 to 25 ionizing events resulting from X-ray treatment and less than 100 lesions induced by sulfur mustard to result in one lethal hit. Furthermore, it is quite impossible to demonstrate appreciable repair synthesis in bacteria after any reasonable dose of either X-rays or monofunctional alkylating agents. Dan BILLEN and some of his students have reported their inability to demonstrate repair synthesis in bacteria after X-rays [J. Bacteriol. *94:* 1538 (1967)] and monofunctional alkylating agents [ACHEY, P. and V. WHITFIELD: Biophys. Soc. Abstracts, TPM-03 (1970)]. Some years ago, we [REITER and STRAUSS: J. molec. Biol. *14:* 179 (1965)] demonstrated a small amount of repair synthesis after MMS treatment of *B. subtilis* but the survival of our treated cells was only 3×10^{-6}. It would therefore seem to me that the repair systems, or the way they deal with pyrimidine dimers, are very different from the repair systems, or the way they deal with whatever the lethal lesions are, after treatment with X-rays or monofunctional alkylating agents.

LUCAS: It was reported by the group of CRADDOCK [J. Lab. clin. Med. *74:* 109 (1969)] that long-living lymphocytes should repair UV damage as demonstrated by »unscheduled DNA synthesis« better than do short-living lymphocytes. I would like to ask Dr. NORMAN whether he has been able to confirm these findings, and if he thinks that the capacity to perform repair replication has some relation to the state of differentiation of a cell.

NORMAN: Both short-lived and long-lived lymphocytes show unscheduled DNA synthesis. The granulocytes also show repair; but the rate limiting enzyme is probably down by a factor of ten in comparison to the amount in lymphocytes. These granulocytes are terminal cells with very short life expectancy. Unfortunately, there is no simple unambiguous method presently available to distinguish the two major lymphocyte populations in human peripheral blood.

JUNG: I can refer to these experiments. Lymphocytes which are able to be stimulated by phytohemagglutinin show a better incorporation than those which are not able to be stimulated.

STRAUSS: The question I have is: how can you distinguish between lymphocytes that can be stimulated by phytohemagglutinin and those that are unresponsive before doing the experiment? Once phytohemagglutinin has been added it is clear that those cells which are stimulated by this mitogen will be metabolically active. I think that Dr. NORMAN is saying that it would be helpful if one could separate the potentially responsive cells from those which cannot be stimulated by mitogen before starting the experiment, because we would then be able to distinguish what is happening. Unfortunately, in spite of some attempts, it does seem to be difficult to separate the T(hymus) lymphocytes which are proably the ones stimulated by mitogen from the B(one marrow) lymphocytes which respond to antigen.

ROBERTS: I would like to extend Dr. ORMEROD's cautionary comments on the nature of the lesion(s) which are repaired following irradiation-induced DNA damage to consideration of repair of chemically induced damage to DNA. When we consider »repair« following treatment of cells with a cytotoxic difunctional alkylating agent it can reasonably be supposed that this relates to removal or circumvention of the cross-links between guanine moieties in DNA. In the case of monofunctional agents such as N-methyl-N-nitrosourea or methyl methanesulphonate, however, it is by no means clear which, if any, of the many possible chemical reactions with DNA is responsible for a particular biological effect, be it cytotoxicity, carcinogenicity or mutagenicity. Furthermore it will not always be apparent which of the various biochemicaf manifestations of repair, such as loss of labelled alkyl groups from DNAl unscheduled DNA synthesis or repair replication of DNA, relate to repair o, which particular chemical group.

I would like to ask Dr. NORMAN if he can elaborate on his studies on repair in lymphocytes following treatment with MMS particularly with regard to the levels of alkylation at which this can be detected.

NORMAN: We have been dealing only with the kinetics of unscheduled DNA synthesis. I would like to pretend that we know exactly what is going on after both X-ray and UV irradiations. X-rays either produce free radicals which abstract a hydrogen atom from the sugar or ionize the sugar directly. The sugar moiety then spontaneously disintegrates to endproducts which we now can identify. As you heard we also know exactly what is going on after UV. And the only real mystery that remains is, what is going on after exposure to alkylating agents? What is the evidence for the existence of repair processes following exposure to alkylating agents that are not of the cut and patch system?

ROBERTS: I will try to avoid giving my entire talk again. There are essentially three pieces of evidence for postulating repair mechanism(s) in mammalian cells other than »cut and patch repair«. Firstly, it is not possible to correlate differences in the sensitivity of various cell types to a particular alkylating agent with differences in manifestations of »cut and patch repair«. Secondly, we have evidence for damage to DNA being introduced during replication of methylated DNA (i.e. possible introduction of breaks). Since hamster cells can withstand much higher levels of DNA alkylation than can HeLa cells following treatment with N-methyl-N-nitrosourea it would seem that hamster cells can repair damaged DNA before or after it is replicated more efficiently than can HeLa cells. Thirdly, alkylation damage (as evidenced by effects on colony-forming ability) to the resistant hamster cells but not the sensitive HeLa cells is increased when cells are incubated, following alkylation, in the presence of caffeine. Presumably this sensitization results from inhibition of a DNA repair mechanism(s). Since caffeine does not decrease alkylation-induced »repair replication«, it is possibly inhibiting some form of repair, other than cut and patch repair, which presumably does not require »repair synthesis«. This could be a form of repair akin to »recombinational repair«.

Fox: May I come back to the question Dr. ROBERTS is asking, if we are to look at this data on the losses of alkylating groups from the DNA. Thymidine is taken up by the cells in unscheduled synthesis, which occurs in response to the loss of the alkyl groups. In comparing this data with that people have got for the time course of repair after UV and X-rays, then the whole time scale of the process is different. I should like to ask Dr. NORMAN whether he found a different time kinetics with an alkylating agent and X-rays for example.

NORMAN: The kinetics experiments that we have done suggest that the repair process is quite different following UV and X-rays; our studies with alkylating agents are not extensive enough to make positive statements about the kinetics.

CHANDRA: A few years back I carried out some studies on MNNG action with Professor LINGEN's group at Hohenheim. The problem was to study the mechanism of mutagenesis by MNNG in bacteria. We found a very interesting correlation between DNA methylation, survival rate and the rate of mutation (see Table 1).

I mentioned this work, because some data presented by you on MNNG action in animal cells are very interesting in this connection. In one of your slides you showed that the lethal action of MNNG on hamster as well as HeLa cells is much stronger (almost a factor of 100) than MNU and MMS. On the other hand, you observed that the kinetics of MNNG reaction with cellular DNA is much slower than that observed with MMS and MNU. Do you think that these differences are due to histone guanidination, or that some other mechanisms are involved.

Could you please, give an estimation of how many nucleotides are involved for the removal of one methyl group from DNA?

Table 1. Action of 3-nitro-1-nitroso-1-methyl-guanidine (MNNG) on various cellular processes in E. coli B.

System	Survival (%)	Mutation rate (%)	MNNG-uptake (%)	Nucleic acid methylation (%)	
				RNA	DNA
Sensitive	2.0	11.7	100	100	100
Resistant (I)*	26.2	5.2	83	74	81
Resistant (II)*	53.7	3.7	50	58	57

Conditions: * Resistant (I) cells were obtained by a pretreatment of the sensitive strain with MNNG for 32 hours; further treatment of resistant (I) cells with MNNG for another 32 hours gave resistant (II) cells. Incorporration and methylation experiments were done with ^{3}H-methyl-MNNG. 100% in controls were fixed arbitrarily.

ROBERTS: Yes, we have considered the possibility that guanidination could be responsible for some of the effects of MNNG. However, we favor methylation of DNA as the important cytotoxic reaction since the levels of methylation of DNA following treatment of hamster cells with labelled MNNG, MNU and MMS were the same at doses of these agents which produced the same cytotoxic effects. This was not so for the alkylation of other macromolecules such as proteins or RNA. These findings support the concept of DNA as the target for all three methylating agents. Moreover MNNG like MNU produced inhibition of DNA synthesis in the cell cycle following that in which treatment occurred. This, we argued, was a consequence of an initial reaction with DNA which led to a further lesion when the alkylated DNA replicated.

Hamster cells are more sensitive to MNU and MNNG than are HeLa cells but only the latter compound is thought to be thiol activated. Hence we do not think these differences in sensitivity are the result of differences in cellular thiol levels which lead to different sites of DNA methylation in hamster and HeLa cells.

In answer to your third question we feel that the levels of reaction with proteins at toxic doses of methylating agents are too low to cause an inhibition of protein enzymes such as a polymerase used in repair. No inhibition of thymidine kinase was in fact found with toxic doses of these agents.

In answer to your fourth question we have estimated that approximately 100 nucleotides are inserted into DNA for each labelled methyl group eliminated from DNA.

CHANDRA: The studies involving hydroxyurea are not clear to me. We know, that hydroxyurea (HU) inhibits the DNA synthesis by blocking the conversion of uridine to deoxyuridine. As a result the precursor of DNA synthesis, thymidine, is no more available. In experiments reported by Dr. PAINTER and others, the precursor used was labelled thymidine. Could Dr. PAINTER kindly comment, as to what is the mechanism of hydroxyurea inhibition in his experiments.

PAINTER: I don't know the mechanism of action of hydroxyurea. First of all the enzymatic studies had shown that hydroxyurea acts by blocking nucleotide reduction to the deoxynucleotides. However at concentrations of hydroxyurea that we and most other people use to inhibit normal DNA synthesis the addition of high amounts of deoxynucleosides does not reverse the block. Thus this is only one of the actions of hydroxyurea; there are certainly others. Now ROSENKRANZ also says that there is a direct effect on a DNA molecule; I don't know what that is. So there isn't any doubt that if one uses hydroxyurea he is not completely sure what it is doing and this is certainly something everyone has to recognize. The point in all the studies we have done on irradiation-induced repair replication is that the residual repair replication after irradiation is not affected by hydroxyurea.

CHANDRA: The reason for my asking this question has some therapeutical implications on the use of hydroxyurea (HU) in clinical studies. This compound has been used with a great success to treat Psoriasis [LEAVELL et al.: Arch. Derm. *102:* 144 (1970)], an almost non-curable disease. It has been indicated that HU may cause chromosomal breaks. So, the question is whether you observed any DNA breaks after HU treatment?, and secondly, will it not be useful to clear these doubts before using it in replication studies?

PAINTER: I don't know about strand breaks but people who have done strand breaks say hydroxyurea does not cause breaks and hydroxyurea does not block single-strand break reunion.

RÉVÉSZ: So far, this general discussion was concerned with substances which *inhibit* repair or recovery. Could the experts who are present here comment also upon substances which *enhance* these processes? I refer, e. g., to the work of a Yougoslavian group [PETROVIC et al.: Curr. Top. Radiat. Res. *4:* 251 (1968)] who showed that nucleosides enhance repair. There may be many other substances of a practical importance.

BOYLE: There seems to be some confusion over whether some effects seen with hydroxyurea are caused by hydroxyurea itself or an impurity in commercial preparations.

PAINTER: Dr. KENDRIC SMITH [KAPP, D. S. and K. SMITH: Technical inhibition of the repair of single-strand breaks in DNA: post-irradiation sensitization to X-rays. Int. J. Radiat. Biol. *19:* 255 (1971)] used with bacteria concentrations of hydroxyurea 40 times as great as used for mammalian cells. A contaminant seems to be responsible for the effect he observed.

AVERBECK: During the congress in Yugoslavia H. S. KAPLAN was talking about chemical inhibitors of the repair of X-ray-induced single-strand breaks in cellular DNA. He reported that contaminated hydroxyurea can act as an inhibitor of postreplication repair after X irradiation. This was already published by D. S. KAPP and K. SMITH, 1971.

SLOR: Hydroxyurea is used to inhibit DNA replication but not DNA repair. We feel that this may be due at least in part to competitive inhibition with the purines pool. Has anybody used labelled purines instead of thymidine in DNA repair studies? Can one notice different effects of hydroxyurea on DNA repair and DNA replication using adenine and guanine instead of labelled thymidine?

STRAUSS: I would like to comment again about hydroxyurea. There is a paper published by Ben-Hur and Ben-Ishai in »Photochemistry and Photobiology« [*13:* 337 (1971)] which reports essentially the same findings. They demonstrated the formation of breaks in HeLa cells incubated after UV irradiation in the presence of hydroxyurea. Hydroxyurea is a peculiar compound which has been reported by YU and SINCLAIR to cause chromosome fragmentation [J. Cell Physiol. *72:* 39 (1968)]. In the presence of hydroxyurea DNA is synthesized in relatively small fragments relative to the size of the DNA made in its absence [COYLE, M. and B. STRAUSS: Cancer Res. *30:* 2314 (1970)]. Although it has been demonstrated that repair synthesis is not inhibited by hydroxyurea, this does not mean that the integrated repair process is not inhibited by this compound, since repair synthesis is only one of the steps in the complete repair sequence. It is not inconceivable that hydroxyurea might inhibit the rejoining of breaks and still not inhibit repair replication.

ROBERTS: In answer to Dr. SLOR's earlier question I can report that we have found that pyrimidines and purines can be utilized for repair replication following methylation of mammalian cells in culture.

PAINTER: I have a comment on the use of purines after ultraviolet light damage. SMETS has reported that there is absolutely no repair measurable

using purine precursors. I have looked at this with labelled adenine. You have
to be very careful with the gradients and the rebands. What you get after
UV is a low level similar to non-induced repair replication, but I don't think
we get UV-induced repair replication using adenine. Adenine yields very good
counts when used as a precursor for normal DNA synthesis.

KALTHOFF: I would like to raise a further question to the experts in this
field. Is there anything known about repair systems acting on extranuclear
DNA, let's say on mitochondrial DNA? Photoreversion (or photoreactivation)
has been demonstrated to occur after UV effects to cytoplasmic targets, for
instance in microbian experiments on Amoeba and after UV induction of
cytoplasmatically determined petite mutants in yeast. But as far as I remember these experiments show only the biological effect, and what I want to
know is whether there is any work done on the molecular level, let's say to
separate the mitochondrial DNA and see if it can be repaired.

ANTONI: From the point of view of the cytologist it is admissible to speak
of DNA in general. On the basis of latest biochemical investigations distinction
[Progress in Nucleic Acid Research and Molecular Biology *10* (1970), *11* (1971)]
is made between DNAs according to their localization and function as well.
Thus, we distinguish between chromosomal DNA, satellite DNA, membrane
DNA and mitochrondrial DNA. As regards the repair and damage of DNA
it is essential to indicate the fraction of DNA which has been studied. In
the morning lecture Dr. Fox reported on the light and heavy DNA. Would
you be so kind as to let us know the procedure of isolation, and whether you
have used synchronized or mixed culture.

FOX: We used asynchronous cultures of the cell lines and we prepared the
DNA in a number of different ways. One method was to lyse the cells with
SDS and extract the DNA with phenol or to lyse cells with PAS and extract
with phenol. The other method we use is to lyse with SDS, then to extract
the proteins using chloroform-isoamylalcohol and then RNase and then more
deproteinisation with chloroform-isoamylalcohol. With the first two methods,
we got very high yields of DNA from the cell, and we always got, using these
methods, high amounts of this complex material which banded lighter than
the light density DNA. With the Marmur procedure we get rather less of this
»complex« material. The amount of DNA you obtain from this latter procedure
is lower than with the other two methods, ten times less in some cases. So
you are obviously being much more brutal to the DNA with the last procedure than with the other two.

KALTHOFF: Why I asked is that I found photoreversion of a UV effect in an insect egg which is due to a merely cytoplasmic irradiation.

KIEFER: I do not know about any studies on the molecular level of mitochondrial DNA but I heard of some mutation work going on in yeast. Dr. MOUSTACCHI of Paris showed at the Baden Meeting that there is obviously some kind of repair going on in the mitochondria. These activities can be coded for either in the nuclear genes or in mitochondrial genes. She has several mutants for this second type of »repair«. But as far as I know she doesn't have any evidence on the molecular level.

NORMAN: Under what circumstances would you find DNA in cells which was not exposed to the same enzymatic system as the DNA in the nucleus?

KALTHOFF: But the nuclear envelope has pores while mitochondria are surrounded by closed membranes. So enzymes made in the cytoplasm will have to travel through these membranes.

PAINTER: At least in mammalian cells it is a very difficult experiment to do because the total mitochondrial DNA is very small.

STRAUSS: Not if you have circular DNA as you do in some mitochondria.

ROBERTS: Perhaps it is relevant that liver mitochondrial DNA has been shown to be alkylated more extensively than nuclear DNA, following injection of N-nitroso [14C]-dimethylamine into rats or hamsters. It is also of interest that neither repair synthesis nor mitochondrial DNA synthesis are inhibited by hydroxyurea.

Repair Replication in Mammalian Cells*

R. B. Painter

The importance of repair replication after UV-induced damage to DNA in human cells has, I believe, been amply demonstrated by Cleaver who has shown that human cells defective in excision repair are more sensitive (by at least a factor of three) to UV light than are normal human cells (1).

The role of repair replication in the repair of damage to DNA induced by ionizing radiation is much more poorly understood. No good data for its action in bacteria have been forthcoming, although Billen et al. (2), at least, have searched rather diligently for it. The great amount of DNA degradation that occurs after X-irradiation of bacteria probably obscures repair replication which, as I will show, almost certainly must occur.

Three groups have recently investigated the chemical nature of DNA single-strand breaks. Their data agree extremely well. The proposal of Krushinskaya and Shal'nov (3) that the $3'$-$4'$ group in deoxyribose was the main point of attack was confirmed by Kapp and Smith (4). Although Kapp and Smith (4) and Bopp and Hagen (5) both showed that the $5'$phosphate was by far the most frequent chain terminus formed, the failure of a polynucleotide ligase to rejoin the break showed that the single-strand break cannot consist of a simple rupture of the $3'OH$-$5'PO_4$ position (6). Previously, Hems (7) had shown that base elimination occurred with a G value of 0.228, very close to the value of 0.24 for sugar damage (production of malonic aldehyde) determined by Kapp and Smith (4). These data all suggest that single-strand breakage is usually accompanied by base loss from the DNA. It follows that single-strand rejoining must be accompanied by base insertion, which is synonymous with repair replication.

We reported (8) that repair replication occurred in HeLa cells after 100,000 R; this observation was received without much enthusiasm since this dose of radiation is, to put it mildly, supralethal. In the intervening four years, I have attempted to detect repair replication at lower doses of X-radiation. This effort has met with a certain measure of success, because it no longer is a problem

---

* Work performed under the auspices of the U.S. Atomic Energy Commission.

to detect repair replication at zero dose. The problem has become that I cannot detect an increase in extent of repair replication over that occurring in unirradiated cultures until the dose administered to the cells exceeds 1000 R. I hope to convince you that this is really not surprising and that repair replication after X-irradiation is a real and necessary process in mammalian cells.

We obtained almost identical results with several mammalian cell lines, including human (HeLa, an aneuploid line, and WI-38, a diploid), Chinese hamster (Don and B14FAF), mouse L, and another mouse line, P388F. Our results with the latter line differ from those reported by AYAD and Fox (9) and Fox et al. (10) but are entirely consistent with the results from other cells we have investigated. I will present the data from mouse L cells because our experience with repair replication after X-irradiation is most extensive with this line.

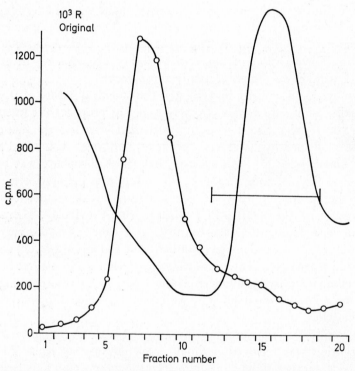

Fig. 1. Original equilibrium density gradient profile of DNA from cells irradiated with 1000 R and incubated for three hours in the presence of ³HBUdR, ●—● ³H c.p.m. The line without data points is a reproduction of trace of transmittance at 260 nm automatically monitored during sample collection; the lower the transmittance, the higher the line. Normal density DNA lies between fractions 12 and 18. These fractions were combined and run in a second gradient (first reband, see Fig. 2).

The cells were grown in Eagle's medium supplemented with 15% calf serum plus streptomycin (50 μg/ml) and penicillin (50 units/ml). Irradiations were performed at about 2000 R/min, using 300 kVp, 20 ma, 2.0 mm Cu. Repair replication was demonstrated as described previously (8) with multiple re-bandings when necessary (11). In this method, one seeks to show uptake of ^{3}H-bromouracil deoxyriboside (^{3}HBrUdR) into single strands of DNA at normal density regions of CsCl equilibrium density gradients. This is taken as evidence for repair replication because, under the conditions used for these experiments (in which incubation with unlabelled BrUdR is used before and after the ^{3}HBrUdR incubation), the incorporation of ^{3}HBrUdR by semiconservative replication causes exclusively the formation of heavy tritium-labelled DNA strands, which are found at or near the bottom of the density gradients. Tritium is found at normal density regions only when ^{3}HBrUdR is present in segments of DNA which are so short, compared to the fragments isolated for gradient analysis, that they do not appreciably alter the density of those fragments.

Mouse L cells were irradiated with 0, 250, 1000, or 10,000 R. After the first centrifugation the equilibrium density gradient patterns from cells irradiated with 0, 250, or 1000 R were indistinguishable from one another and are typified by the results from the 10^3 R sample shown in Fig. 1. No indication of a peak of radioactivity was seen in the normal density regions of three gradients. In the pattern from the cells irradiated with 10^4R (not shown) a small peak of radioactivity was found in the normal density region. The normal density region of each gradient (shown by the enclosed bar in each figure) was rebanded into a second gradient. Fig. 2 shows the results from the 0, 10^3, and 10^4R gradients. Note that there are peaks of radioactivity of similar heights at densities slightly greater than normal in both the 0 and 10^3R gradients. The results from the 250 R gradient are not shown but were similar. The 10^4R gradient, however, has a peak of radioactivity at normal density, and this peak contains more radioactivity than the peaks from the other gradients. The DNA at normal density regions of each of these gradients was collected again, converted to single strands by heating, and rebanded; the results are shown in Fig. 3. Again the 0 and 10^3R gradients are very similar with the greatest amount of radioactivity appearing near the bottom, at high density, of each gradient. The amount of radioactivity decreases through the normal density regions. The pattern from the 10^4R gradient, while showing similar amounts of radioactivity at high density positions, also has a well-defined peak containing more radioactivity at a density slightly greater than that of normal DNA. The normal density region of each gradient was rebanded once more. This time (Fig. 4) the patterns are very similar, but the 10^4R gradient

R. B. Painter

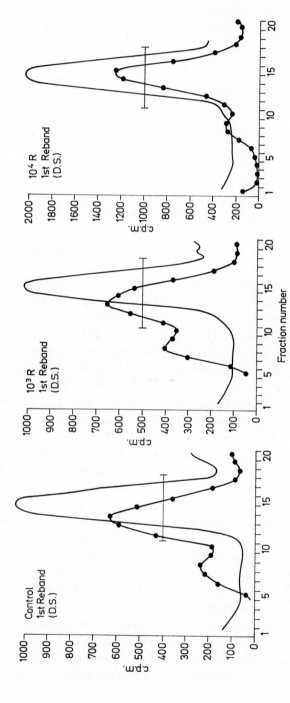

Fig. 2. Profiles of first rebands from normal density regions or original equilibrium density gradients. Note change of scale for 10^4 R gradient. Fractions encompassed by the indicated bars were combined, dialyzed, heated to 90° C, treated with formaldehyde, and run in a third (second reband) gradient (see Fig. 3). Symbols as in Fig. 1.

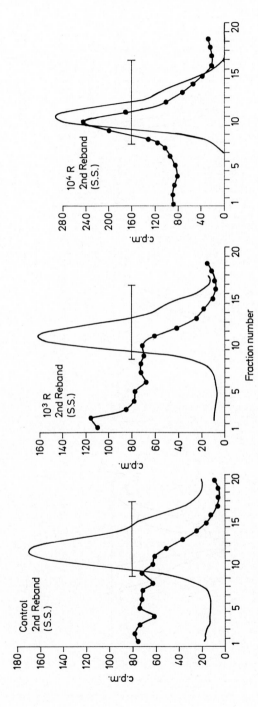

Fig. 3. Profiles of second rebands, this time as single-stranded DNA. Note change of scale for 10^4R gradient. Symbols as in Fig. 1.

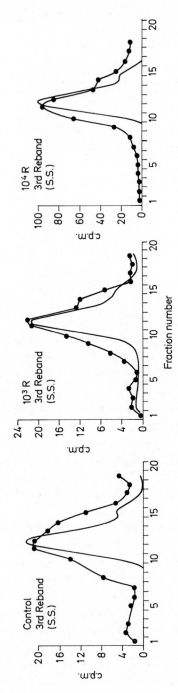

Fig. 4. Profiles of third rebands (single-stranded DNA). Note change of scale for 10⁴R gradient. Symbols as in Fig. 1.

shows much more total radioactivity. The peaks of radioactivity in each case are very close to the density of normal DNA.

To quantify the results the specific activities of repaired DNA were determined. All fractions showing significant amounts of radioactivity or optical density at 260 nm were combined and dialysed. The A_{260} of 1 equals 50 μg DNA. An aliquot of the solution was counted, the count corrected to cpm/ml, and this value divided by DNA concentration to give final specific activity in cpm/μg. The results, after the first reband (double-stranded DNA) and third reband (single-stranded DNA) are shown in Table 1. In the single-stranded

Table 1. Specific activity of L cell repaired DNA (cpm/μg).

Dose to culture	After first reband (double-stranded)	After third reband (single-stranded)
0 (control)	163	15
250	150	19
1000	209	19
10 000	249	51

state DNA from cultures irradiated with 10^4R has a significantly higher specific activity than the unirradiated control. Thus, irradiation with doses of 1000 R or less does not induce any more repair replication than that occurring (for whatever reason) in unirradiated cells.

The data from cultures irradiated with 10^4R can be used to estimate the extent of base insertion that has occurred in these cells. The counting efficiency under the conditions used here (DNA on Whatmann 3 MM paper in PPO, POPOP, toluene) is about 10 percent, so that the specific activity of the DNA was about 500 dpm/μg. The decay constant (in minutes) for tritium is 10^{-7}, so that there were $5 \times 10^2/10^{-7} \simeq 5 \times 10^9$ tritium-labelled BrUdR molecules per μg of this DNA. The specific activity of ^{3}HBrUdR (100 μCi/ml were used in this experiment) was 11 Ci/mmole, which is 0.38 of the specific activity of ^{3}HBrUdR in which each molecule has exactly one tritium atom. Therefore, 1.3×10^{10} BrUdR molecules existed in each μg of this DNA. Because FUdR was used in this experiment no endogenous DNA thymine was made. If base elimination is random, then 4.3×10^{10} bases were inserted per μg, since thymines make up about 0.3 of the total bases in mammalian DNA. The unirradiated cells, however, incorporated about 40 percent as much BrUdR as did the 10^4R cells so that the amount induced by irradiation was about 2.6×10^{10} bases per μg DNA.

A dose of 10^4R is roughly equivalent to 6×10^{11} ev/μg. The efficiency of single-strand production is about 60 ev/break (12, 13) so 10^4R produces about 10^{10} single-strand breaks per μg DNA. Therefore, about $2.6 \times 10^{10}/$ $10^{10} = 2.5$ bases are inserted by repair replication for each radiation-induced single-strand break that occurs in mammalian cell DNA. Since base damage probably exceeds break production (14), part of this repair may be associated with events other than single-strand breaks. It seems almost certain that fewer than three bases are inserted per radiation-induced break. These observations suggest that X-irradiation of mammalian cells causes single-strand DNA breaks which, although the majority are gaps due to the loss of one or more bases, are repaired without extensive widening of the gaps. This form of repair, therefore, does not involve the large-scale degradation of DNA that has been observed in X-irradiated bacteria (15, 16) and explains the inability of previous investigators (17–19) to detect X-ray induced DNA degradation in mammalian cells.

These data also indicate why the extent of repair replication does not increase significantly above control values until the dose of radiation exceeds 1000 R. About 1.7×10^{10} bases per μg were inserted into control cell DNA. A dose of 1000 R induces 10^9 single-strand breaks/μg DNA and increases the total insertion only by about 3×10^9 bases, or 0.9×10^9 molecules of BrUdR, or 3.5×10^8 ³HBrUdR molecules, or 35 dpm, or 3.5 cpm/μg which is within the range of the uncertainty of the method.

I would now like to compare the DNA damage induced by ionizing and ultraviolet (UV) radiations. The rad is the absorption by tissue of 100 ergs/ gram, or 6×10^{13} ev/gram of ionizing radiation. The yield of ion pairs in tissue is somewhere between 30 to 60 ev/ion pair; we will use the former value to be safe. Thus, one rad will yield about 2×10^{12} ($6 \times 10^{13}/3 \times 10^1$) ion pairs/ gram. Because ionization is the only important means of energy release by this kind of radiation, the maximum number of primary lesions will not appreciably exceed the number of ion pairs.

For UV at 260 nm, the yield of thymine dimers in DNA in mammalian cells has been measured; about 0.05 percent of DNA thymines are converted to dimers per 100 ergs/mm² incident radiation (20, 21). Therefore, 5×10^{-6} of DNA thymines are converted to dimers per ergs/mm². (This value probably includes mixed dimers but not cytosine-cytosine dimers). Thymines make up about 30 percent of the bases in mammalian DNA, so there are about 6×10^{20} thymines per gram; thus one erg produces 3×10^{15} ($6 \times 10^{20} \times 5 \times 10^{-6}$) dimers per gram of DNA in mammalian cells. One erg/mm² of incident light at 260 nm, therefore, induces at least 1500 times as much damage to mammalian DNA as does one rad of ionizing radiation (damages other than thymine-containing dimers are not used for this estimate). Thus, the dose, 10,000 R, after which we can always demonstrate repair replication induced by ionizing radiation, is equivalent in terms of DNA damage to only about 7 ergs/mm² UV. It is not surprising, to me at least, that it is difficult to demonstrate repair replication in mammalian cells after ionizing radiation. First, the amount of DNA damage really is small, and second, there is in unirradiated cells a nonconservative replication that is phenomenologically identical to that induced by radiation.

The role of repair replication in unirradiated cells is unknown. We have hypothesized before (22) that this may result from DNA damage caused by »normal wear and tear«, including thermal damage simply by existing at 310° Kelvin. I do not now believe, however, that this is correct. The specific activities of repaired DNA given in this paper are those measured in DNA from cells incubated with hydroxyurea. Recently, we have been looking at repair replication in unirradiated cells incubated with ³HBrUdR in the absence of hydroxyurea. To our great surprise, we found that the extent of repair replication, again measured as tritium activity in normal density single-stranded DNA, is much greater in these cells. In fact, the effect of hydroxyurea is to suppress repair replication in these unirradiated cells to the same extent that it suppresses normal semiconservative replication. This result is both embarrassing and revealing. It is embarrassing because we have not observed it earlier – our work has concentrated on hydroxyurea-treated cells in which *radiation-induced repair replication* is much easier to observe. It is revealing because it implies that repair replication observed in unirradiated cells is primarily if not exclusively a consequence or a component of normal semiconservative replication. This phenomenon is not correlated with unscheduled DNA synthesis. Unscheduled DNA synthesis induced by 200 ergs/mm² can be demonstrated easily either in the presence or absence of hydroxyurea. The extent of repair replication observed in unirradiated L cells is roughly equivalent to that induced by about 200 ergs/mm² but is not demonstrable autoradiographically. This nonconservative DNA synthesis seems to be a manifestation of a very important process and much of the work in our laboratory is now devoted to its study.

References

(1) CLEAVER, J. E.: Int. J. Rad. Biol. *18:* 557 (1970).
(2) BILLEN, D., R. R. HEWITT, T. LAPTHISOPHAN, P. M. ACHEY: J. Bacteriol. *94* (1967).
(3) KRUSHINSKAYA, N. P., M. I. SHAL'NOV: Radiobiology *7:* 36 (1967).
(4) KAPP, D. S., K. C. SMITH: Radiation Res. *12:* 340 (1970).
(5) BOPP, A., V. HAGEN: Biochim. biophys. Acta (Amst.) *209:* 320 (1970).
(6) KAPP, D. S., K. C. SMITH: Int. J. Rad. Biol. *14:* 467 (1968).
(7) HEMS, G.: Nature *186:* 710 (1960).
(8) PAINTER, R. B., J. E. CLEAVER: Nature *216:* 369 (1967).

 (9) AYAD, S. R., M. FOX: Int. J. Rad. Biol. *15:* 556 (1969).
(10) FOX, M., S. R. AYAD, B. W. FOX: Int. J. Rad. Biol. *18:* 101 (1970).
(11) PAINTER, R. B., J. S. UMBER, B. R. YOUNG: Radiat. Res. *44:* 133 (1970).
(12) LETT, J. T., I. CALDWELL, C. J. DEAN, P. ALEXANDER: Nature *214:* 790 (1967).
(13) ELKIND, M. M., C. KAMPER: Biophys. J. *10:* 237 (1970).
(14) JUNG, H., U. HAGEN, M. ULLRICH, E. E. PETERSEN: Naturforschung *24:* 1565 (1969).
(15) STUY, J. H.: J. Bacteriol. *79:* 707 (1960).
(16) POLLARD, E. C., P. M. ACHEY: Science *146:* 71 (1964).
(17) PAINTER, R. B.: In: Effects of Radiation on Cellular Proliferation and Differentiation; p. 91. I.A.E.A., Vienna 1968.
(18) LOONEY, W. B., L. O. CHANG: Radiat. Res. *37:* 525 (1969).
(19) HILL, M.: Int. J. Rad. Biol. *15:* 483 (1969).
(20) TROSKO, J. E., E. H. Y. CHU, W. L. CARRIER: Radiat. Res. *24:* 667 (1965).
(21) REGAN, J. D., J. E. TROSKO, W. L. CARRIER: Biophys. J. *8:* 319 (1968).
(22) RASMUSSEN, R. E., B. L. REISNER, R. B. PAINTER: Int. J. Rad. Biol. *17:* 285 (1970).

Genetic Studies on Repair in Xeroderma Pigmentosum Cells

D. Bootsma*, E. A. De Weerd-Kastelein*, G. Veldhuisen**, W. Keÿzer*.

Xeroderma pigmentosum (XP) is an autosomal recessive disease in which the skin is extremely sensitive to sunlight. In cultivated fibroblasts of XP patients DNA-repair replication after ultraviolet irradiation is absent or markedly reduced (1, 2). Using the dark-repair mechanism in microorganisms as a model, evidence has been presented that XP cells are defective in the incision step of DNA repair (3, 4, 5). However, the possibility of different mutations leading to comparable clinical defects in XP patients cannot be excluded. In cells from patients of different families with XP different rates of DNA-repair replication have been observed (2, 6, 7, 8) indicating genetic heterogeneity in the basic defect of XP. Moreover, two different forms of XP have been described. In the classic form of XP the patients show skin lesions only, whereas in the de Sanctis-Cacchione syndrome, a rare variant of XP, there are severe neurological abnormalities in addition.

In the present report experiments are described using cells from different patients with XP in which we studied DNA repair. Genetic heterogeneity of XP was demonstrated by somatic cell hybridization techniques.

Different rates of DNA-repair replication in XP Cells

Fibroblast cultures originating from skin biopsies of patients with XP were grown in thymidine free F12 medium supplemented with 15% foetal calf serum. Repair DNA synthesis was studied by exposing 2 to 4-days-old cover-slip cultures to ultraviolet irradiation (a 15W Philips TUV low pressure mercury tube, dose rate 9 ergs/mm²/sec, predominantly 254 nm). Immediately after irradiation the cultures were incubated for 3 hours in ³H-thymidine-containing medium (10 μCi ³H-TdR per ml medium, spec. act. 2.0 Ci/mmole). In later experiments the cultures were labelled for 1 hour with ³H-TdR, exposed to ultraviolet light and subsequently incubated again in ³H-TdR-containing medium for 2 hours. After labelling the cells were fixed and processed for auto-

* Dept. of Cell Biology and Genetics, Rotterdam Medical Faculty, Netherlands.
** Med. Biol. Lab. TNO, Rijswijk, Netherlands.

radiography. Repair DNA synthesis after UV irradiation was measured by grain countings over weakly labelled cells in the G1- or G2-phase of the cell cycle. The results obtained with cells from a mild case of XP (XP1) and from a moderate case of XP (XP2) are given in Fig. 1. A decreased level of unscheduled DNA synthesis is found in cells from both patients (70 and 50% of the control at the 100 ergs/mm² dose). In cells of a second cousin of patient XP2,

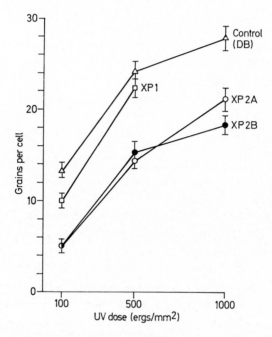

Fig. 1. Repair DNA synthesis in normal human fibroblasts (DB), cells from a mild case of XP (XP 1) and from a moderately severe case of XP (two different strains, XP2A and XP2B). Repair DNA synthesis is measured as the average number of grains over weakly labelled cells in G_1- and G_2-phase after UV exposure. Autoradiographic exposure time: 3 days.

also suffering from xeroderma, the same decreased level of repair activity was present (2).

These levels of repair replication clearly differ from those observed in cells from a severe case of XP (XP4), representing the classic form of the disease (severe skin lesions, normal mentality). This is seen in Fig. 2 representing ³H-TdR labelling after an autoradiographic exposure time of 3 days. An exposure time of one month yielded a grain number that was 10–20% of that in control cells.

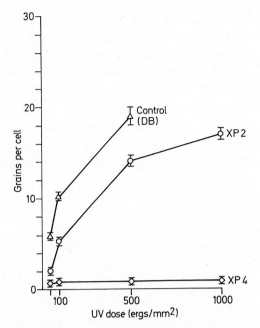

Fig. 2. Repair DNA synthesis after UV exposure of normal human fibroblasts (DB), cells from patient XP2 (moderately severe case of XP) and patient XP4 (classic form of XP). Exposure time: 3 days.

At the present time we have extended our studies to 14 different patients with XP and 5 presumed heterozygotes. The heterozygotes for the classic form of XP could not be distinguished from control cells under our experimental conditions.

Repair DNA synthesis in cells of a patient with the de Sanctis-Cacchione syndrome

A skin biopsy of a patient with the de Sanctis-Cacchione form of XP (XP12) was obtained from Dr. V. DER KALOUSTIAN at Beiruth. The pedigree, constructed by Dr. DER KALOUSTIAN, is presented in Fig. 3. The 8 daughters in this family are normal whereas the 3 sons show the symptoms of the disease.

XP12 cells did not perform repair DNA synthesis, even after long exposure times of the autoradiographs. Skin cultures from the mother (XP14) showed repair DNA synthesis in all the cells in G1- and G2-phase indicating an autosomal inheritance of the mutation. However, the level of repair DNA synthesis was significantly lower than in control cells after high doses of ultraviolet irradiation (Fig. 4). The same decrease in repair activity was found in skin cultures of the father (Fig. 4: XP15). These results might indicate that in these cells of heterozygotes for the de Sanctis-Cacchione mutation the repair DNA synthesis has a slower rate, leading to incomplete repair after relatively high doses of UV irradiation during the 2–3 hours of ³H-TdR labelling.

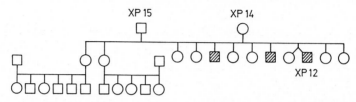

Fig. 3. The de Sanctis-Cacchione syndrome in a family from the Libanon (Courtesy Dr. V. der Kaloustian). Cell strains have been made from skin biopsies of patient XP12 and the parents XP14 and XP15.

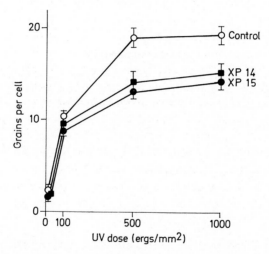

Fig. 4. Repair DNA synthesis in cells of the two parents (XP14 and XP15, see Fig. 3) of a patient with the de Sanctis-Cacchione syndrome. Exposure time: 3 days.

Repair of UV-irradiated virus in normal human and XP cells

Similar to the work of RABSON et al. (9) the survival of herpes simplex virus, irradiated with ultraviolet light, was determined by plaque titration on fibroblasts from patients with XP and compared with the survival on normal fibroblasts. The survival on XP cells was lower than on normal fibroblasts, which points to a repair of UV damage in the herpes DNA by the host (host cell reactivation, HCR). The results obtained in the first series of experiments indicate that the degree of HCR observed in the different xeroderma strains (e.g. XP2, XP4, XP9, XP12) is related with the degree of repair DNA synthesis in the host cell as measured with autoradiography.

Repair DNA synthesis in binuclear cells after fusion of cells from different XP patients

A new approach in the study of genetic heterogeneity is introduced by the application of cell fusion techniques. These techniques have been successfully used in the demonstration of complementation between different genes (intergenic complementation) in human – human hybrid cells by SINISCALCO et al. (10) and SILAGI et al. (11). Recently genetic heterogeneity in galactosemia has been described by NADLER et al. (12), who found interallelic complementation after fusion of fibroblasts from different patients and subsequent determination of galactose-1-phosphate uridyl transferase in the various hybrid combinations.

To avoid the rather complicated isolation of a pure mononuclear hybrid cell line, we have studied complementation between different XP strains using the binuclear cells which can easily be identified after cell fusion.

In the first series of experiments cells of the XP4 strain (classic form of XP) were fused with those of the XP12 strain (de Sanctis-Cacchione syndrome). After trypsinization the parental cells were mixed in a ratio of 1:1 and fusion was induced with UV-inactivated Sendai virus according to HARRIS et al. (13). Subsequently the cell suspension was seeded in Petri dishes on coverslips. At 1, 2 or 3 days after fusion the cultures were labelled with 10 μCi ^{3}H-TdR per ml medium (spec. act. 2 Ci/mmol) for 1 hour and exposed to 100 ergs/mm^2 ultraviolet irradiation. After irradiation cells were incubated again in ^{3}H-TdR-containing medium for 2 hours. XP4/XP4 and XP12/XP12 fusions served as controls, the autoradiographic preparations were exposed for 1 week.

The frequency distribution of grain counts in the two parental XP strains and in one normal strain is given in Fig. 5. Repair DNA synthesis is very slow or absent in the two XP cell strains. On the basis of the distribution in normal cells we adopted the grain numbers of 8 and 50 as the limits of unscheduled DNA synthesis.

The grain numbers found over the binuclear cells in the preparations obtained after fusion are presented in Fig. 6. Only in the fused and irradiated population of XP4/XP12, binuclear cells were observed showing a weakly labelling indicative of repair DNA synthesis (8–50 grains over each of both nuclei, Fig. 6f and 7b). This labelling was found in 25–35% of the binuclear cells (Table 1).

D. Bootsma et al.

Comparable fusion experiments were performed using four different XP cell strains (XP4, XP9, XP12 and XP16) in order to study the specificity of the occurrence of labelling in binuclear cells. In Table 2, the results of six different fusions are presented, showing the percentages of binuclear cells with 8–50 grains over each of both nuclei. It may be seen that a high percentage (30 to 40%) of weakly labelled binuclear cells is found only in those combinations where XP12 cells (de Sanctis-Cacchione syndrome) are involved. Binuclear cells obtained after fusions of cells from different patients, each with the classic

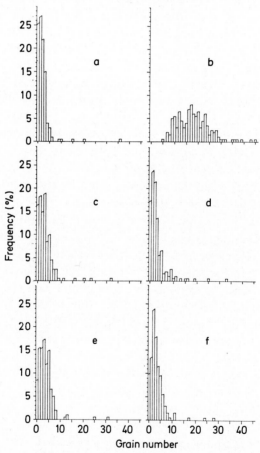

Fig. 5. Repair DNA synthesis in fibroblast cultures of normal individuals and patients with XP. The frequency distributions of grain numbers over nuclei in autoradiographic preparations after UV exposure and ^{3}H-TdR labelling are presented. Only cells with 50 or less grains per nucleus were counted. a, c, and e: unirradiated cells of the control (C2), the XP4 and the XP12 cell strain respectively. b, d, and f: C2, XP4 and XP12 cells after exposure to 100 ergs/mm^2 of UV irradiation.

form of XP, did not show any increase in labelling upon irradiation. The 8 percent labelled binuclear cells observed after fusion of XP4 with XP9 cells might be the result of a relatively high residual activity of the repair process in XP9 cells.

Characterization of binuclear cells showing repair DNA synthesis

In the fused XP4/XP12 cell population one might expect three types of binuclear cells: XP4/XP4, XP12/XP12 and XP4/XP12. To determine which class of binuclear cells shows the labelling pattern indicative for repair re-

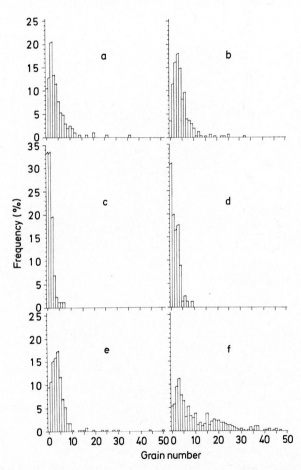

Fig. 6. Frequency distributions of grain numbers over nuclei in binuclear cells in unirradiated cultures (a, c, and e) and UV-exposed cultures (100 ergs/mm², b, d, and f) after XP4/XP4 (a and b), XP12/XP12 (c and d) and XP4/XP12 (e and f) fusion.

plication, the technique of identification of sex chromosomes in interphase
nuclei with the aid of fluorescent atebrin staining has been used.

Fusion between XP4 and XP12 cells was carried out as described before.
However, after UV exposure and ^{3}H-TdR incorporation the preparations were
not immediately processed for autoradiography, but instead fixed in ethanol-
ether (1:1) for 2.5 hours, air-dried and stained for 5 min in 0.5% aqueous atebrin
(G. T. GURR). After rinsing and mounting in buffer the preparations were
studied with a fluorescence microscope. With the atebrin staining the Y chromosome in male interphase nuclei (14) and the Barr body in female nuclei (15)
are visible as fluorescent spots. Four classes of binuclear cells in the female
XP4/male XP12 fusion were observed, characterized by

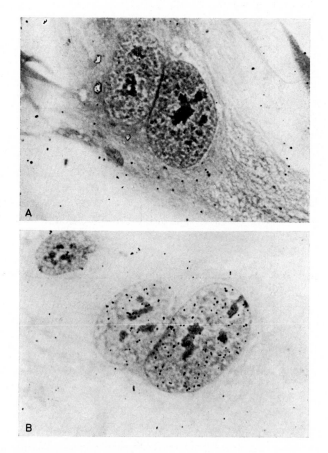

Fig. 7. Two binuclear cells in a XP4/XP12 fused cell population after UV exposure followed by ^{3}H-TdR labelling. Repair DNA synthesis is absent in A and present in B.

1. two nuclei each with a Barr body (Fig. 8a),
2. two nuclei each with Y chromatin (Fig. 8b),
3. one nucleus with a Barr body and one with Y chromatin (Fig. 8c), and
4. one or two unidentifiable nuclei.

The positions in the preparations of about 100 binuclear cells of each of the first three classes were recorded. Subsequently the preparations were subjected to the autoradiographic procedure. After autoradiography the labelling pattern was studied in the very same cells (Fig. 8).

Table 1. Tritiated thymidine labelling following UV exposure of fused cell populations.

Fusion	Time after fusion (days) $\varnothing$	Percentage of labelled binuclear cells* after		Number of binuclear cells counted	
		0 ergs/mm²	100 ergs/mm²	0 ergs/mm²	100 ergs/mm²
XP4/XP4	1	0	3	101	118
	2	3	4	104	150
	3	0	5	150	150
XP12/XP12	1	0	0	101	100
	2	< 2	< 2	43	45
	3	< 2	0	59	100
XP4/XP12	1	1	25	300	334
	2	1	36	200	200
	3	0	31	219	219

* Only cells with 0–50 grains over each of both nuclei were counted, cells with 8–50 grains over each of both nuclei were counted as labelled.

Table 2. Tritiated thymidine labelling following UV exposure of fused cell populations using different XP cell strains.

Fusion	Percentage of labelled binuclear cells*		Number of binuclear cells counted	
	0 ergs/mm²	100 ergs/mm²	0 ergs/mm²	100 ergs/mm²
XP4/XP9	<1	8	50	50
XP4//XP12	1	36	200	200
XP4/XP16	<1	2	50	50
XP9/XP12	<1	30	50	50
XP9/XP16	<1	4	50	50
XP12/XP16	<1	36	50	50

* See footnote Table 1.

In the UV-irradiated cultures 87% of the binuclear cells having one nucleus with Y chromatin and a second with a Barr body (XX/XY) showed 8–50 grains over each nucleus (Table 3). In the XP4/XP12 combination weakly labelled cells were only found in 8% of the XX/XX and in 2% of the XY/XY binuclear cells. The frequency distributions of grain counts presented in Fig. 9 clearly

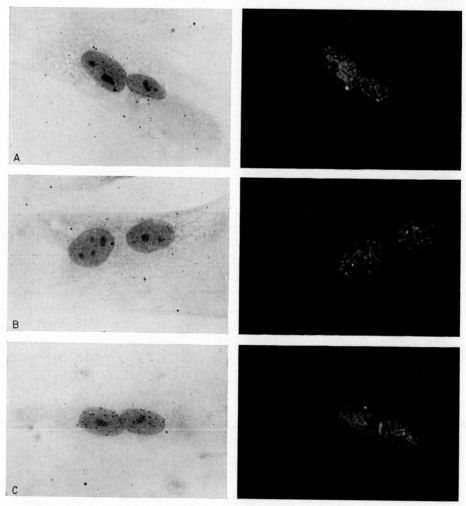

Fig. 8. Repair DNA synthesis in binuclear cells after fusion of XP4 (classic form of XP) and XP12 (de Sanctis-Cacchione) cells. Autoradiograms (on the left) and fluorescence after atebrin staining (on the right) are shown. A Binuclear cell, two nuclei with a Barr body (XP4/XP4). B Binuclear cell showing Y chromatin in both nuclei (XP12/XP12). C Binuclear cell having one nucleus with a Barr body and another nucleus with Y chromatin (XP4/XP12). Only the XP4/XP12 binuclear cell shows repair DNA synthesis.

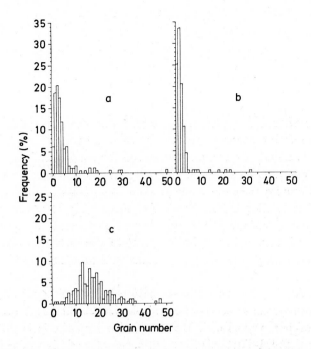

Fig. 9. Frequency distribution of grain numbers over the three types of binuclear cells after UV exposure that can be identified by atebrin staining of XP4/XP12 fusions. a) Binuclear cells having two nuclei with a Barr body (XP4/XP4). b) Binuclear cells having two nuclei with Y chromatin (XP12/XP12). c) Binuclear cells having one nucleus with a Barr body and the other nucleus with Y chromatin (XP4/XP12).

Table 3. Tritiated thymidine labelling of binuclear cells that have been identified by atebrin staining following exposure to 100 ergs/mm² UV light.

Fusion	Atebrin diagnosis of sex chromosomes in binuclear cells	Grain count*	Number of nuclei counted	Percentage of labelled bi-nuclear cells**
XP4/XP4	XX/XX	4,4 ± 0,2	186	<1
XP12/XP12	XY/XY	1,8 ± 0,2	180	<1
XP4/XP12	XX/XX	4,2 ± 0,4	174	8
	XY/XY	2,0 ± 0,3	178	2
	XX/XY	17,5 ± 0,5	196	87

* The average number of grains per nucleus in binuclear cells and the standard error of the mean. 100 binuclear cells were counted in each group. Only nuclei with 50 grains or less were included.
** See footnote Table 1.

indicate that based on atebrin characterization of the binuclear cells two different classes can be distinguished:

1. XX/XX (Fig. 9a) and XY/XY (Fig. 9b) binuclear cells showing grain count distributions comparable with those found in the parental cell strains (see Fig. 5d and 5f),
2. XX/XY binuclear cells (Fig. 9c) showing the same labelling pattern as normal cells after UV exposure (see Fig. 5b).

The average number of grains per nucleus found over the XX/XY binuclear cells (Table 3) is about the same as observed for control cells showing repair DNA synthesis after UV exposure.

The present results strongly suggest that the ^{3}H-TdR labelling in the binuclear hybrid cells after UV irradiation represents repair DNA synthesis as a result of complementation. The most simple interpretation is that two different genes are involved in the basic defect of the de Sanctis-Cacchione and the classic xeroderma pigmentosum syndromes. As a consequence in binuclear cells of hybrid nature normal gene product will be present (intergenic complementation). Analogous to complementation in heterokaryons of fungi (16), in binuclear human cells interallelic complementation might occur in some combinations of parental nuclei. However, this hypothesis is not supported by our finding that ^{3}H-TdR labelling is absent after fusion of cells from different patients with the classic form of XP, even if parental cells perform different levels of repair replication.

To distinguish between intergenic and interallelic complementation further studies are required on the properties of the enzyme involved in this repair process in the binuclear cells compared to normal cells.

References

(1) CLEAVER, J. E.: Nature *218:* 652 (1968).
(2) BOOTSMA, D., M. P. MULDER, F. POT, J. A. COHEN: Mutation Res. *9:* 507 (1970).
(3) CLEAVER, J. E.: Proc. Nat. Acad. Sci. (Wash.) *63:* 428 (1969).
(4) SETLOW, R. B., J. D. REGAN, J. GERMAN, W. L. CARRIER: Proc. Nat. Acad. Sci. (Wash.) *64:* 1035 (1969).
(5) KLEIJER, W. J., P. H. M. LOHMAN, M. P. MULDER, D. BOOTSMA: Mutation Res. *9:* 517 (1970).
(6) JUNG, E. G.: Nature *228:* 361 (1970).
(7) BURK, P. G., M. A. LUTZNER, D. D. CLARK, J. H. ROBBINS: J. Lab. clin. Med. *77:* 759 (1971).
(8) JUNG, E. G.: Arch. Derm. Forsch. *241:* 33 (1971).
(9) RABSON, A. S., S. A. TYRRELL, F. Y. LEGALLAIS: Proc. Soc. exp. Biol. Med. *132:* 802 (1969).
(10) SINISCALCO, M., H. P. KLINGER, H. EAGLE, H. KOPROWSKI, W. J. FUJIMOTO, J. E. SEEGMILLER: Proc. Nat. Acad. Sci. (Wash.) *62:* 793 (1969).

(11) SILAGI, S., G. DARLINGTON, S. A. BRUCE: Proc. Nat. Acad. Sci. (Wash.) *62:* 1085 (1969).
(12) NADLER, H. L., C. M. CHACKO, M. RACHMELER: Proc. Nat. Acad. Sci. (Wash.) *67:* 976 (1970).
(13) HARRIS, H., J. F. WATKINS: Nature *205:* 640 (1965).
(14) PEARSON, P. L., M. BOBROW, C. G. VOSA: Nature *226:* 78 (1970).
(15) MUKHERJEE, A. B., P. J. BLATNER, H. M. NITOWSKY: Lancet *I:* 709 (1971).
(16) FINCHAM, J. R. S.: J. gen. Microbiol. *21:* 600 (1959).

Repair Mechanism in Xeroderma Pigmentosum and Related Traits*

ERNST G. JUNG

Since CLEAVER's (5) observation of a defective excision repair mechanism in fibroblasts of xeroderma pigmentosum (x.p.) photobiological studies in light-sensitive skin diseases have gained importance. We have tried to combine the traditional dermatological experience with modern biochemical methods to investigate the light-sensitive skin diseases. Since a major part of actinic damage, including skin carcinomas, in light-exposed areas are predominantly of epidermal and not of dermal origin, we have adapted the autoradiographic method (11, 14) for use in short-term dermo-epidermal tissue cultures. The second reason for employing this procedure was to avoid damage due to incorporated radioactive thymidine in living human beings (9).

Method

Skin grafts of 0.2–0.3 mm thickness were cut with a dermatome from unaffected skin of the gluteal region and divided into small pieces (2 × 2 mm). These pieces were irradiated with an unfiltered xenon arc lamp (11) at various energies (total output: 2.1×10^6 erg cm^{-2} sec^{-1}, measured by a compensated thermopile CAl (Kipp & Zonen). Immediately after irradiation the specimens were incubated in TC medium 199 (Difco) for 4 hours at 37° C with 1 μCi/ml ^{3}H-methyl-thymidine (5 Ci/mM). They were then fixed in formalin, sectioned (5 μ), stained with acid hemalum and autoradiographed (exposure 7 days, Kodak AR 10 film).

Excision (dark) repair activity was expressed by the number of lightly marked epidermal cells per 200 cells investigated in each section. Replication activity was expressed by the number of heavily marked cells (S-phases) per 1000 basal cells investigated in each section.

---

* This work was supported by a grant from the Deutsche Forschungsgemeinschaft DFG (Ju 80/1).

Excision repair and semiconservative replication in human skin diseases

The only light-sensitive skin disease with a constant lack of excision repair activity is xeroderma pigmentosum. The results obtained in fibroblasts by various research groups are similar. The defective enzyme-mediated step seems to be an initial one (15) at the endonuclease level (incision).

Our own results in epidermal cells, as shown in Table 1, are in accordance with the investigations in fibroblasts (3, 5, 10, 15) and those in epidermal cells (8, 9). A regular decrease of lightly marked cells in xeroderma pigmento-

Table 1. Values obtained in epidermal cells.

Diagnosis	Excision repair	UV depression of semiconservative replication
Xeroderma pigmentosum (6 cases)	−	+
Pigmented xerodermoid (2)	+	+++
Bloom syndrome (1)	+	+
Poikiloderma congenitale (1)	+	+
Oculocutaneous albinism (1)	+	+
Progeria adultorum (1)	+	+
Porphyria cutanea tarda (2)	+	+
Basal-cell-nevus syndrome (2)	+	+
Photoallergies (3)	+	+
Persistent light reactor (1)	+	+
Normal (control group of 10 cases)	+	+

sum was observed. However, it was not possible to establish individual levels of the repairing defect by our method, as reported by Bootsma et al. (3) in cultured fibroblasts of x.p. patients. The repairing defect in x.p. can be demonstrated not only in fibroblasts but also in epidermal cells and lymphocytes (4, 14).

On the other hand, the semiconservative replication as expressed by the number of heavily marked S-phases per 1,000 basal cells was unaltered in all skin diseases investigated (Table 1). Normal epidermis shows a dose-dependent UV-induced depression of S-phases (after 4 hours) that can be found in skin diseases, too (12). Further studies on two female cases of a clinical variety of xeroderma pigmentosum exhibited a different biochemical behavior at the cellular level. The repair activity seems to be normal while the UV-induced S-phase depression is almost total after a relatively low dose of UV light (13). We call this trait »pigmented xerodermoid« (pig. xoid.).

Further characterization of pigmented xerodermoid (pig. xoid.)

Pigmented xerodermoid is a skin disease similar to xeroderma pigmentosum. Both solitary female cases with normal brown pigmentation showed on extensive exposure to sunlight an alteration of the exposed skin resembling x.p. with atrophy, poikiloderma and multiple malignancies (Fig. 1). The manifesta-

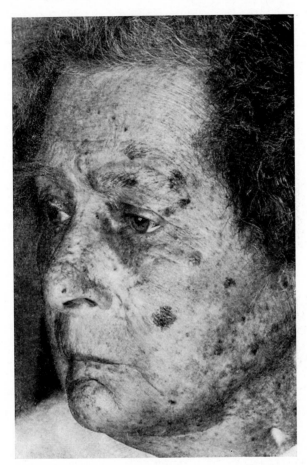

Fig. 1. Pigmented xerodermoid, actinic skin changes with atrophy and multiple malignancies.

tion of these actinic skin changes occurred between 35 and 40 years of age. Nevertheless epidermal cells show normal repair activity (Table 1). In spite of good pigmentary protection and the extensive lesions of sun-exposed skin with multiple keratomata and malignancies the early manifestation led us to separate this phenomenon from what is usually well known as actinic or solar damage.

In these two cases of pig. xoid. one has to suggest, therefore, an increased light sensitivity of the semiconservative DNA replication which could give a clue for the extensive damage of light-exposed skin.

GOLDSTEIN (10) demonstrated that cultured fibroblasts from x.p. have a decreased survival rate. He correlates the deficiency in repair replication to the sensitivity against UV light. Our experiments with irradiation of lymphocytes from normal, from x.p. and from pigmented xerodermoid subjects give another evidence for such a correlation (13, 14) (Fig. 2). In lymphocytes from

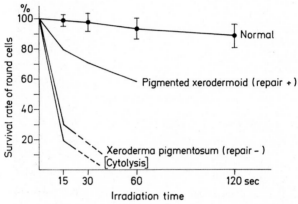

Fig. 2. Survival rate of human lymphocytes, 3 hours after UV irradiation in vitro.

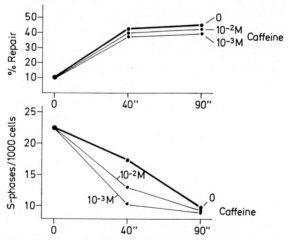

Fig. 3. Influence of caffeine (10^{-2} and 10^{-3}M) on repair replication and S-phase activity in normal human epidermis (in vitro).

pig. xoid. one can demonstrate repairing activity expressed by sparse labelling of the surviving cells. The reduction of the UV resistance of these cells supports the idea that in pigmented xerodermoid a repairing process other than excision repair could be defective. One has to consider the recombinational repair occurring during the semiconservative replication (1, 6, 7). Since there is evidence that the recombinational form of repair, but not the excision repair, can be inhibited by caffeine, we tried to imitate the UV-induced depression of S-phase observed in pigmented xerodermoid by adding caffeine (10^{-2} and 10^{-3}M) to the culture medium of UV-irradiated normal skin. As shown in Fig. 3, caffeine has no effect on excision repair in normal epidermis but inhibits the post-irradiation semiconservative replication.

All these facts give evidence of a defect in the recombinational form of repair in these two patients with pigmented xerodermoid. An analogy to the mutant of Escherichia coli rec$^-$ A, B, C and lex$^-$ is evident.

Excision repair and semiconservative replication in actinic-damaged skin

Actinic epidermal damage of old (more than 50 years old) and sun-exposed skin imitates the clinical picture of atrophy, keratoses and malignancies occurring in x.p. in the first 2 decades. To prove whether this is the result of an acquired lack of recovery due to exhausted repair mechanisms, or an expression of cumulative short-term overcharge of these mechanisms by extensive sun exposure, we investigated both, excision repair and semiconservative replication in the epidermis of the following three groups:

a) 20–35 year old male volunteers (gluteal region and forearm) as a control group (n = 5).
b) 65–80 year old males with extensive sun exposure in their case history and marked actinic changes on the forearms. Specimens were taken from the atinic-damaged skin of the forearm. (Patient group with old and solar-damaged skin, n = 6).
c) From the patients of group b) we simultaneously took specimens from the non-irradiated skin of the gluteal region as a control, without sun-exposure (patient group, age alone, n = 6).

As seen in Fig. 4 the excision repair activity in all three groups, a, b and c, is about the same and shows the same saturation effect. There is no sign of a decrease of excision repair either in epidermal cells of old skin or in epidermal cells of old skin with marked actinic damage in comparison to normal young skin. Regarding the semiconservative replication and the S-phase depression after UV irradiation, there is no significant difference between the three groups. Replication activity of the old skin is, as expected, lower than that of young skin (Fig. 5). The most surprising fact is the increased S-phase activity in the skin with actinic damage (group b) in comparison to that in undamaged skin of the same patients (c). This may be an evidence for a sort of premalignant state of epidermal areas with marked actinic damage (2).

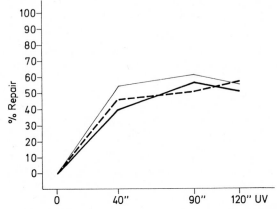

Fig. 4. Repair replication in human skin. —— group a (young skin); – – – group b (old skin with solar damages, forearm); —— group c (old non-irradiated skin, gluteal region).

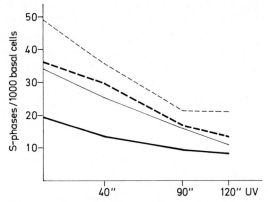

Fig. 5. S-phase activity (semiconservative replication) in human skin. —— group a (gluteal region); – – – group a (forearm); – – – group b (see Fig. 4); —— group c (see Fig. 4).

Differential diagnostic criteria of xeroderma pigmentosum and related syndromes

To summarize, in Table 2 a synoptic attempt is made to classify xeroderma pigmentosum, de Sanctis-Cacchione syndrome (x. p. with microcephaly, mental deficiency, dwarfism and gonadal hypoplasia), pigmented xerodermoid and actinic solar damages.

Table 2.

	Xeroderma pigmentosum	De Sanctis-Cacchione-syndrome	Pigmented xerodermoid	Actinic solar damages
Heredity	autosomal-recessive		?	none
Occurrence of first symptoms	Early childhood		30–40 years	late
Expectation of life	reduced	strongly reduced	normal	normal
Neurol. sympt.	±	+++	–	–
Excision repair	strongly reduced		normal	normal
UV-induced S-phase depression	normal	?	increased	normal

References

(1) ARLETT, C. F.: The influence of metabolic inhibitors on the response of Chinese hamster cells to ultraviolet. Ann. Ist. Super. Sanità *5:* 367 (1969).
(2) BOHNERT, E., W. ASBACH, E. G. JUNG: Replikation und Reparatur epidermaler DNS; Einfluß von Lichtexposition und Alter. Arch. derm. Forsch. (im Druck).
(3) BOOTSMA, D., M. P. MULDER, F. POT, J. A. COHEN: Different inherited levels of DNA repair replication in xeroderma pigmentosum cell strains after exposure to UV irradiation. Mutation Res. *9:* 507 (1970).
(4) BURKE, P. G., W. R. LEVIS, M. A. LUTZNER, J. H. ROBBINS: Thymidine incorporation into DNA of lymphocytes and monocytes after UV irradiation in vitro. Fed. Proc. *28:* 295 (1969).
(5) CLEAVER, J. E.: Defective repair replication of DNA in xeroderma pigmentosum. Nature *218:* 652 (1968).
(6) CLEAVER, J. E.: Repair of mammalian cell DNA: effects of drugs and mutation. Ann. Ist. Super. Sanità *5:* 360 (1969).
(7) CLEAVER, J. E.: Repair replication of mammalian cell DNA: effects of compounds that inhibit DNA synthesis or dark repair. Radiat. Res. *37:* 334 (1969).
(8) CRIPPS, D. J., C. A. RAMSEY, D. M. RUCH: Xeroderma pigmentosum: abnormal monochromatic action spectrum and autoradiographic studies. J. invest. Derm. *56:* 281 (1971).
(9) EPSTEIN, J. H., K. FUKUYAMA, W. B. REED, W. L. EPSTEIN: Defect in DNA synthesis in skin of patients with xeroderma pigmentosum demonstrated in vivo. Science *168:* 1477 (1970).
(10) GOLDSTEIN, S.: Survival of cultured human fibroblasts from xeroderma pigmentosum and normals following UV irradiation. Ref. 6. Congr. internat. de radiobiologie & physicochimie des rayonnements. Evian (France) 1970.
(11) JUNG, E. G., F. BAY: Untersuchungen über »dark repair«-Mechanismen menschlicher Epidermis. Arch. klin. exp. Derm. *235:* 308 (1969).

(12) JUNG, E. G.: Investigations on dark repair in various light sensitive inherited disorders. Humangenetik *9:* 191 (1970).

(13) JUNG, E. G.: Das pigmentierte Xerodermoid: ein Defekt der Rekombinations-Erholung von UV-Schäden. Arch. Derm. Forsch. *241:* 33 (1971).

(14) JUNG, E. G., U. W. SCHNYDER: Xeroderma pigmentosum und pigmentiertes Xerodermoid. Schweiz. med. Wschr. *100:* 1718 (1970).

(15) SETLOW, R. B., J. D. REGAN, J. GERMAN, W. C. CARRIER: Evidence that xeroderma pigmentosum cells do not perform the first step in the repair of UV damage to their DNA. Proc. Nat. Acad. Sci. (Wash.) *64:* 1035 (1969).

Analysis of Repair in Human DNA by 5-Bromodeoxyuridine Photolysis*

JAMES D. REGAN

First a few words about how we (R. B. SETLOW and I) came to develop this method of DNA repair analysis by 5-bromodeoxyuridine (BrdUrd) photolysis.

In 1968 we first described excision repair in normal human cells (1). Thus when CLEAVER's interesting finding (2) of the low or absent unscheduled synthesis and low repair replication in xeroderma pigmentosum (XP) appeared we were, of course, anxious to examine these cells for excision of ultraviolet (UV)-induced pyrimidine dimers. We wished to determine if, in fact, XP cells

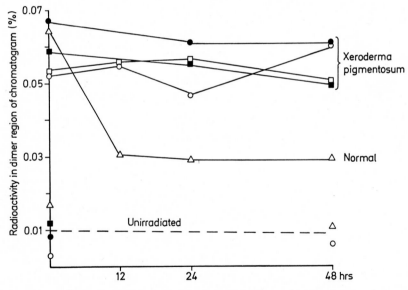

Fig. 1. Excision of pyrimidine dimers from the DNA of normal and XP cells. Male (□) and female (○) uncomplicated XP; male (■) and female (●) de Sanctis-Cacchione syndrome. [From REGAN, J. D., R. B. SETLOW, J. GERMAN, W. L. CARRIER: Proc. Symp. 4th Intern. Congr. Radiation Res., Evian (France), July 1970; in press.]

* Research sponsored by the U.S. Atomic Energy Commission under contract with Union Carbide Corporation.

were truly repair-deficient mutants at the level of excision repair and thus similar to non-excising, UV-sensitive strains of microorganisms. Fig. 1 shows the results of our excision-repair experiments with cells from patients with the uncomplicated form of XP and cells from patients with the de Sanctis-Cacchione syndrome, as well as cells from normal subjects. Clearly the XP cells excise few or no dimers compared to normal cells.

Fig. 2 shows the four presumed steps in the human cell repair system. The methods of unscheduled synthesis and repair replication are experiments which directly examine the third or DNA polymerase step in repair. The radiochromatographic method we employed (1) for examining excision of dimers really can be said to look directly at the second or exonuclease step of repair. Since, in the repair scheme, the only step that is supposed to be UV-specific is the first, or UV-endonuclease step, and, in XP, the symptoms are clearly UV-induced (the skin of the buttocks, for example, of XP patients is usually quite

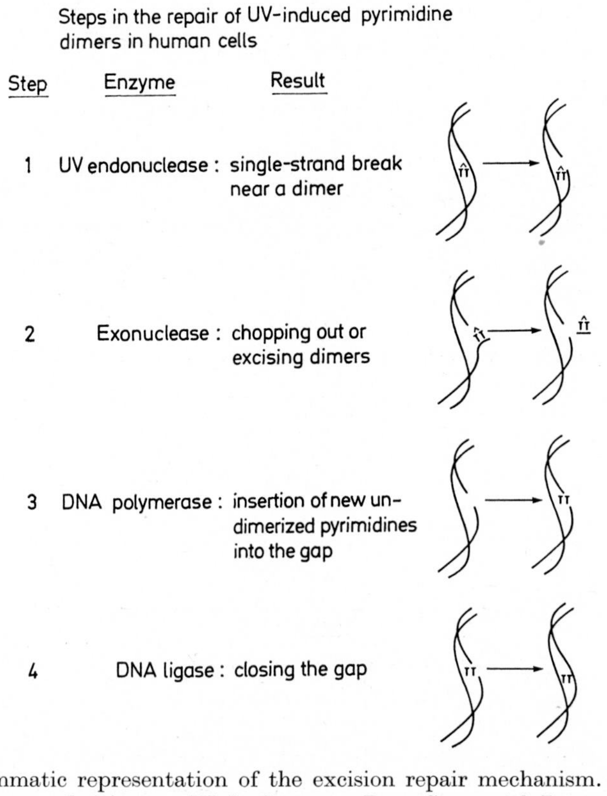

Steps in the repair of UV-induced pyrimidine dimers in human cells

Step	Enzyme	Result
1	UV endonuclease : single-strand break near a dimer	
2	Exonuclease : chopping out or excising dimers	
3	DNA polymerase : insertion of new un-dimerized pyrimidines into the gap	
4	DNA ligase : closing the gap	

Fig. 2. Diagrammatic representation of the excision repair mechanism. [From REGAN, J. D., R. B. SETLOW, J. GERMAN, W. L. CARRIER: Proc. Symp. 4th Intern. Congr. Radiation Res., Evian (France), July 1970; in press.]

normal), we wished to examine directly the first step in repair. To do this we turned to the McGrath-Williams technique of alkaline sucrose gradients (3).

Fig. 3 shows the results of typical alkaline sucrose gradients obtained after UV treatment of normal and XP cells [methods have been described in detail elsewhere (4,5)]. Whether XP cells are irradiated or not, no significant changes are seen in the weight average molecular weight of the DNA on these gradients. In the normal cells a small downward shift is seen in the irradiated cells' DNA

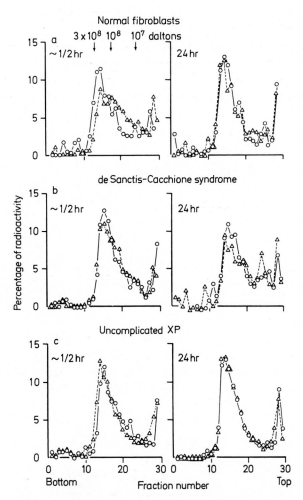

Fig. 3. Alkaline sucrose gradients of the DNA of cells from normal and XP patients. ○— ○, unirradiated; △ — △, irradiated. [From REGAN, J. D., R. B. SETLOW, J. GERMAN, W. L. CARRIER: Proc. Symp. 4th Intern. Congr. Radiation Res., Evian (France), July 1970; in press.]

after exposure to UV. This difference is admittedly rather unimpressive but we have found it consistent and reproducible. The reason this shift in normal cells is small is that, in these experiments, one measures only the number of breaks present at a particular time during repair, and since the breaks induced by the UV endonuclease and the subsequent dimer excision and rejoining of breaks are occurring continuously, the actual number of breaks observed at any instant is small. Thus we needed a method which would yield a cumulative incidence rather than an instantaneous rate for the UV-endonuclease-induced breaks. We needed a way to keep the breaks open and accumulate them.

First we turned to DNA polymerase inhibitors as a possible way to keep the breaks open. We used phleomycin and novobiocin, both antibiotics which supposedly inhibit DNA polymerase, but these compounds were totally ineffective in inhibiting DNA strand rejoining after UV-irradiation. Then we hit on what we have called ever since the »BU trick«. The method does not keep the breaks open but it does the next best thing. It enables us to mark the breaks with BrdUrd and later reopen them on the alkaline gradients after 313-nm irradiation.

The details of the method have been described elsewhere (5,6). Briefly, cellular DNA is labelled overnight with tritiated thymidine ([³H]dThd). The labelling medium is removed and replaced with regular growth medium for 4 hours. Then the cells are irradiated with 254-nm UV-radiation. The medium is immediately made 10^{-4}M with BrdUrd; control cultures receive 10^{-4}M dThd. All cultures are made 2×10^{-3}M with hydroxyurea (7) to inhibit semiconservative replication and thus avoid competition for the added nucleosides during repair synthesis. After 16 hours the cells are harvested with an ethylene diaminetetraacetic acid solution and irradiated with a high flux of 313-nm radiation from a Hilger monochromator. The cells are then lysed and sedimented in alkali in order to measure the molecular weight of the DNA. The schedule of treatments is shown in Fig. 4.

If BrdUrd is inserted into repaired regions during repair synthesis, the 313-nm radiation makes these regions alkaline labile; thus when the cells are

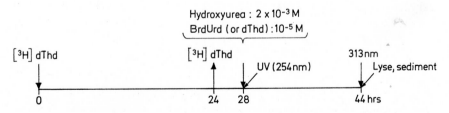

Fig. 4. Schedule of treatments for repair assay using BrdUrd photolysis. [From Regan, J. D., R. B. Setlow, R. D. Ley: Proc. Nat. Acad. Sci. (Wash.) *68:* 708 (1971).]

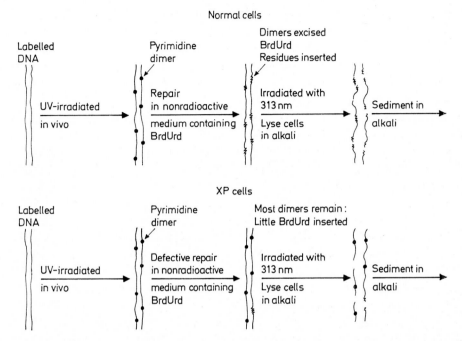

Fig. 5. Diagrammatic scheme of repair analysis in normal and XP cells by BrdUrd photolysis. [From REGAN, J. D., R. B. SETLOW, M. M. KABACK, R. R. HOWELL, E. KLEIN, G. BURGESS: Science *174:* 150 1971).]

put on the alkaline sucrose gradients, breaks appear in the DNA at the sites of BrdUrd insertion, giving an estimate of the number of repaired regions and the extent of repair.

Fig. 5 shows a diagrammatic scheme of the experiment. Since M. B. LION (8) had earlier observed that *E. coli* DNA fully substituted with BrdUrd was extraordinarily sensitive to 254-nm radiation when subsequently placed in alkali, we used 313-nm radiation to minimize damage to unsubstituted DNA while maximizing breakage in the BrdUrd-containing DNA. The first experiment we performed, therefore, was designed simply to determine the sensitivity of human DNA, unsubstituted and fully substituted with BrdUrd, to 313-nm radiation (Fig. 6). (Clearly there was a great difference in sensitivity.) Then we proceeded to apply this technique to the repair of DNA rather than to its replication.

Fig. 7 shows typical results for both normal and XP cells when this technique is used. There is a marked decrease in weight average molecular weight ($\underline{M}_w$) in the normal cells, while in XP cells there is only a minor shift in $\underline{M}_w$. This result indicates little sensitivity to 313-nm radiation in the XP cells compared

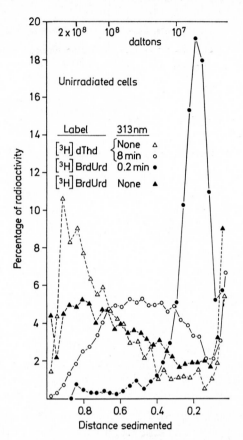

Fig. 6. Effect of 313-nm radiation on the DNA of normal human cells (as observed on alkaline sucrose gradients) which have undergone semiconservative replication in the presence of [³H] BrdUrd or [³H] dThd. [From REGAN, J. D., R. B. SETLOW, R. D. LEY: Proc. Nat. Acad. Sci. (Wash.) *68:* 708 (1971).]

to normal cells, suggesting that there was little BrdUrd substitution in their DNA after irradiation with UV.

We have also applied the BrdUrd technique to normal cells after DNA damage by gamma rays. In these experiments little 313-nm sensitivity is seen and molecular weight calculations suggest a substitution of perhaps only one or two BrdUrd residues per repaired region instead of the ~20 such residues we earlier (5) calculated to be incorporated per average repaired region after UV-irradiation. We are now applying this technique to normal cells whose DNA has been damaged by certain mutagenic and carcinogenic compounds. Results of these experiments are as yet incomplete but preliminary findings obtained with ethyl methanesulfonate, nitrosoguanidine, and propane sulfone have yielded results similar to those seen with gamma rays; that is, there is no evidence of extensive BrdUrd incorporation. With certain aromatic amines, however, our results suggest an extent of repair similar to that seen in normal cells after exposure to UV.

We have also used the BrdUrd method as a rapid, sensitive prenatal diagnostic test for XP, using cells from mid-trimester amniotic fluid obtained by amniocentesis (6). Normal amniocentetic cells employed in this assay displayed repair activities quite comparable to normal skin fibroblasts. From this we

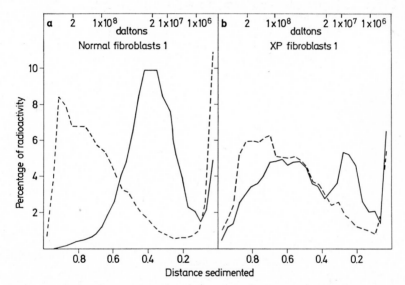

Fig. 7. Sedimentation patterns in alkaline sucrose of the radioactivity from [³H] dThd-labelled cells that have been irradiated with 200 ergs/mm⁻² of 254-nm radiation, incubated for 16–20 hours in bromodeoxyuridine (——) or thymidine (- - -), and then exposed to 4.5×10^5 ergs/mm⁻² of 313-nm radiation before being lysed on top of the gradients. [From Regan, J. D., R. B. Setlow, M. M. Kaback. R. R. Howell, E. Klein, G. Burgess: Science *174:* 150 (1971).]

assume that XP cells obtained prenatally would display the repair defect we can clearly see in the XP skin fibroblasts using this assay.

Thus, the method of assaying repair by BrdUrd photolysis has proved to be a very useful technique in the study of DNA damage induced by various types of radiation or chemical agents.

Acknowledgement

R. B. Setlow was my collaborator in all the work reviewed here. I thank him for his collaboration and for his critical reading of the manuscript.

References

(1) REGAN, J. D., J. E. TROSKO, W. L. CARRIER: Biophys. J. *8:* 319 (1968).
(2) CLEAVER, J. E.: Nature *218:* 652 (1968).
(3) McGRATH, R. A., R. W. WILLIAMS: Nature *212:* 534 (1966).
(4) SETLOW, R. B., J. D. REGAN, J. GERMAN, W. L. CARRIER: Proc. Nat. Acad. Sci. (Wash.) *64:* 1035 (1969).
(5) REGAN, J. D., R. B. SETLOW, R. D. LEY: Proc. Nat. Acad. Sci. (Wash.) *68:* 708 (1971).
(6) REGAN, J. D., R. B. SETLOW, M. M. KABACK, R. R. HOWELL, E. KLEIN, G. BURGESS: Science *174:* 150 (1971).
(7) PFEIFFER, S. E., L. J. TOLMACH: Cancer Res. *27:* 124 (1967).
(8) LION, M. B.: Biochim. biophys. Acta (Amst.) *209:* 24 (1970).

Discussion

ANTONI: The discussion is open about the afternoon lecture. Dr. LUCAS, please.

LUCAS: Let me first, briefly, introduce to you what made us, as a laboratory of immunopathology, interested in repair processes.

Our interest is the fate of damaged molecules. We asked whether it would be possible that an immune response is developed to in vivo produced molecule damage. Should this happen, cross-reactions might lead to autoimmunity.

Systemic lupus erythematosus (SLE), a well known example of an autoimmune disease, is, in addition to many other features, characterized by the occurrence of antibodies to DNA. Moreover, many of the patients with SLE are described to have a hypersensitivity to sunlight. It is tempting to combine these facts with the known damaging effect of ultraviolet light on DNA.

UV-irradiated DNA is strongly antigenic in experimental animals, while normal DNA is not. We thought that such antibodies could be of great power in the specific labelling of only the lesion in a DNA molecule. Due to the tolerance for DNA it is not very difficult to prepare specific antibodies to UV-irradiated DNA.

Fig. 1 shows a dose response curve, for which we used a radio-immunoassay. [WOLD, R. T., F. E. YOUNG and E. M. TAN: Science *161:* 806 (1968)]. Included is also the reaction with DNA which was irradiated with Black Light in the presence of acetophenone. With such a radio-immunoassay we can detect as little as 15 pg of thymine dimers.

The serum does not react at all in the indirect immunofluorescence technique (IFT) on non-irradiated rat liver cryostat sections, but shows a bright fluorescence when the IFT is performed on UV irradiated sections. Absorption studies confirmed the findings with the acetophenone-irradiated DNA. Absorption was only possible with pyrimidine dimer containing nucleic acids. This specificity was used for the study of the disappearance of dimers from nuclei of cultured UV-irradiated human amnion cells. The cells were grown on coverslips and irradiated with 300 ergs/mm². The fluorescence of cells, immediately fixed after irradiation, was compared to that of cells incubated up to 4 hours after irradiation. It was clear that 4 hours after irradiation no nuclear fluores-

cence could be seen. The sensitivity of this method does not allow us to determine the exact quantity of removed dimers, but approximately $^1/_3$ of the
dimers initially present will remain undetected. It could be seen that there
is clear fluorescence of the cytoplasm after 4 hours, which may indicate that

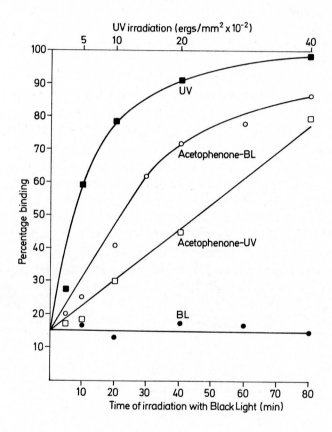

the excised dimers have moved into the cytoplasm. This would mean that
after 4 hours there are more dimers present in the cytoplasm than in the
nuclei. It is possible that they occur in the cytoplasm as large oligonucleotides,
so that by examination of whole cell extracts they should be found in the
TCA precipitable fraction.

ANTONI: Thank you, Dr. LUCAS. Please, any more comments? Dr. KRÄMER.

KRÄMER: I have not worked with xeroderma patients, we are concerned
studying physico-chemical alterations of DNA upon longwave ultra-violet

irradiation; however, Dr. BECK has worked on desoxy-ribonucleases in xeroderma patients. As far as I remember, Dr. BECK, you found four different DNases in normal persons. Would you please give us some details.

BECK: We used the modified micro-technique of BOYD and MITCHEL to separate skin DNases of healthy persons and from xeroderma patients. We used crude extracts and after electrophoretical separation, we incubated the gels at pH 5. We have seen in the skin homogenates of healthy persons 4 bands of DNases, and in those of xeroderma patients in one case 3 bands and in another case only one band with enzymatic activity. A colleague of mine, Dr. ZÖLLNER, has looked for the excretion of DNases in urine and he has seen in urine of xeroderma patients a significant decrease of two bands of DNase activity.

BOOTSMA: What type of nucleases were they?

BECK: We don't know if these nucleases are endo- or exonucleases.

KRÄMER: Dr. REGAN, in your system upon 313 nm irradiation, was the molecular weight decreased, or was it increased?

REGAN: Decreased. It apparently causes an alkaline-sensitive bond in the BUcontaining DNA.

KRÄMER: Did you find more single-strand breaks?

REGAN: Yes!

KRÄMER: We used LAMOLA's experimental conditions [LAMOLA, A. A. and T. YAMANE, Proc. Natl. Acad. Sci. (Wash.) 58: 443 (1967)] of 313 nm acetophenone-sensitized thymine dimerization at doses where all neighboured thymine residues were dimerized. Beside dimers we also found single- and double-strand breaks. The ratio of dimers to single-strand breaks was 100:1 in the sensitized reaction, and 25:1 in the unsensitized control. Dr. LINDAHL found that there are about 100 nucleotides cut out and inserted per one dimer by the repair system.

REGAN: That number is very close to what we estimate. With the BU technique we estimate about 80 nucleotides inserted per repaired region.

KRÄMER: Couldn't it be possible, that endonucleases are not necessary for the whole repair system?

REGAN: You suggest that an enzyme is not necessary to make the initial nick?

KRÄMER: Yes, maybe, because there are enough single-strand breaks there. This has been measured by us with a number of methods independent from one another, such as light scattering, sedimentation coefficient and viscosity measurements and X-ray low angle scattering.

REGAN: You know, with 100 ergs you get something like one dimer every 1.8×10^6 daltons of DNA and 50% or so of these are excised in the first 12 or 24 hours. I don't think that 100 ergs would make a strand break 3.6×10^6 daltons.

KRÄMER: DOTY and others [MOROSON, H. and P. ALEXANDER: Radiat. Res. *14:* 29 (1961); ALEXANDER, P. and H. MOROSON: Nature *185:* 678 (1960); MARMUR, J., W. F. ANDERSON, L. MATTHEWS, K. BERNS, E. GAJEWSKA, D. LANE and P. DOTY: J. Cellular Compl. Physiol. 58, Suppl. *1:* 33 (1961); MOROSON, H. and P. ALEXANDER: Proc. Third Int. Congress of Photobiology, Copenhagen 1960; p. 604] reported that it needs relatively high doses of high energy UV to put single- and double-strand breaks into DNA; however, we found that this occurs quite easily upon low energy UV irradiations.

ORMEROD: If breaks were inserted into DNA at random after UV irradiation, the cell would have to degrade its DNA extensively in order to excise an appreciable number of dimers. Dr. REGAN has estimated that only 80 bases are inserted for each dimer removed. It follows therefore, that the breaks must be introduced close to a dimer. An endonuclease which is specific for UV-irradiated DNA has been isolated from *Micrococcus luteus* [KAPLAN, J. C., S. R. KUSHNER and L. GROSSMAN, Proc. Natl. Acad. Sci. (Wash.) *58:* 240 (1967)].

KRÄMER: According to our results, which are published in »Photochemistry and Photobiology« [*14:* 515 (1971)], there is no correlation between thymine dimerization and strand-breaking reaction. We do not know if the strand breaking occurs predominantly in the close neighbourhood of dimers.

ORMEROD: There might be a few breaks put in by some other process but, if you calculate what is happening in the cell, you are forced to conclude that breaks are introduced specifically adjacent to a dimer.

CHANDRA: The system described by Dr. REGAN and the acetone-sensitized reaction are completely different, though both the systems incidentally involve the use of 313 nm. Our own studies have shown that in the acetone-sensitized reaction, doses which inactivate the survival of bacteria to more than 99%, do not cause strand breaks in DNA. However, the use of this wavelength in connection with BUdR is to me very interesting. It is known from earlier studies that the irradiation of BU-labelled DNA at 313 nm leads to debromination and formation of uracil. On the other hand, many authors have reported double-strand breaks in BU-labelled DNA on irradiation. Have you tried to look on these processes in your studies?

REGAN: No, we have not done any studies using ^{59}Br and we have not looked at double-strand breaks.

STRAUSS: I would like to return to the question of whether single-strand breaks are induced by UV. It seems to me that the enzymatic data published by GROSSMAN and his collaborators [KAPLAN, KUSHNER and GROSSMAN: Biochemistry 10: 3315 (1971)] eliminates that possibility. They prepared DNA extensively labelled with ^{32}P and heavily irradiated this DNA with UV light. They showed that the ^{32}P became sensitive to phosphomonoesterase treatment only after treatment of the irradiated DNA with a UV-endonuclease. Furthermore, they showed that exonuclease from *Micrococcus luteus* only degraded this DNA after prior endonuclease action. It therefore seems unlikely that there could be extensive phosphodiester bond breakage induced by UV even at high doses.

LUCAS: It has recently been published by BURT and BRENT [BBRC 43: 1382 (1971)] that a UV DNA specific deoxyribonuclease can be isolated from HeLa cells. Therefore we don't have to refer to the Micrococcus system, we can refer to the mammalian system.

SLOR: Can you tell us something about the UV DNA-specific DNase? We have observed that enzyme under the conditions described in the BBRC paper [BURT, D. H.: Biochem. biophys. Res. Commun. 43: 1382 (1971)] and indeed

found that it does not degrade native DNA while it degraded UV-irradiated DNA. Hoping that this is the DNase missing in xeroderma we
checked our cells and found them to have the same level of activity as in
HeLa cells. That made us think that, may be, this enzyme is not UV DNA
specific, as reported earlier. The DNA used as substrate was heavily irradiated
by UV, and it may have caused partial denaturation of DNA because of many
nonspecific breaks in the double-stranded DNA. Indeed, when we checked the
enzyme on single-stranded DNA it was about six times more active than on
the heavily irradiated UV DNA. This is contrary to the UV DNA-specific
DNase in bacteria which does not attack denatured DNA. Using DNA that
was irradiated with UV at a dose of 500 ergs/mm², the above enzyme did not
show any activity at all. We feel that the UV DNA-specific DNase described
in HeLa cells is actually a DNase specific for single-stranded DNA. The fact
that the enzyme was active on the heavily irradiated UV DNA at very
alkaline pH's can be explained. At alkaline pH's the heavily UV-irradiated
DNA is easily denatured to single-stranded DNA fragments. Using acrylamide
gel electrophoresis, we have identified several DNases from HeLa cells, one
of which resembles the above enzyme. It did not degrade native DNA or
lightly irradiated (UV) DNA, but it degraded both, denatured and heavily
UV-irradiated DNA.

KRÄMER: I again want to refer to the loops you are talking about, the
so-called loops originating from the thymine dimers. They must be very small
in fact, and so, even with our very unphysiologically highly dimerized system
we could not see them in the gross conformation. And we do not find very
much effects of them on many properties of DNA. I cannot imagine that
there are big loops. With our results we could not confirm the concept of
large denatured or melted regions in the neighbourhood of dimers [PEARSON,
M. and H. E. JOHNS: J. molec. Biol. 20: 215 (1966)]. The double helix appears
to be tremendously stable, at least, as far as its gross conformation is concerned.

KLEPPE: As far as I know the chromosomes from higher organisms contain
rather large amounts of histones, and recent results show that at least 50%
of the DNA is completely covered by these basic proteins. The question then
arises: how does the repair machinery recognize these proteins?

REGAN: In discussion this morning someone mentioned studying unscheduled synthesis in mitotic chromosomes. This would indicate that repair can
occur in highly condensed chromosomes.

ORMEROD: YASMIN and YUNIS [Exp. Cell Res. *59:* 69 (1970)] have shown that the condensed heterochromatin in mouse cells contains most of the satellite DNA. Dr. PAINTER has reported that he finds more »repair replication« in highly repetitive DNA compared with the normal DNA. A comparison of these results indicates that the condensed state of the heterochromatin does not interfere with »repair replication«.

NORMAN: There are some data which suggest a dissociation of histone from DNA in the irradiated regions.

CHANDRA: Most of the time we discussed about the pyrimidine-type of dimers but we know of many other photo-products, e. g. aminoacids and pyrimidine-bases. Is there any work regarding the nature of the repair of such products?

PAINTER: First of all I want to say that KENDRIC SMITH' [The biological importance of UV-induced DNA protein cross-linking *in vivo* and its probable chemical mechanism. Photochem. Photobiol. *7:* 651 (1968)] so-called UV-induced protein-DNA bound material is difficult to reproduce. That is you get more one time than you do another. It's a specific kind of binding which has something to do with protein release with detergents and has nothing to do with covalent bonds. Now, there is a publication by TONI HAN, that came out about a year ago, where, after high doses, he claims that there are about 50 times as many UV-induced DNA protein links as there are dimers. These are all repaired apparently.

STRAUSS: Dr. PETRUSIK working in Chicago (PETRUSIK, R., PhD thesis 1971) has some *in-vitro* results which should be mentioned. She demonstrated a dose-dependent covalent binding between ribonuclease and DNA induced by visible light in the presence of Acridine Orange. The binding was measured by a progressive reduction in the density of DNA on irradiation of a mixture of the substances. Although the *in-vivo* significance of protein-DNA binding may not be known, the possibility of its occurrence is clearly demonstrated.

FOX: In relation to what Dr. REGAN was saying: What is the current situation with regard to dimer excision in different cell types? It occurs to some extent in human cells, and less in rodent cells. Is this true?

REGAN: We have just completed survey of this. We worked with about 35 or 40 cell lines. The highest amount of excision, which ranges between 40%

to 70% is in human cells. The chinese hamster cell lines we have examined shown up to 40% excision. This excision data is in addition to the BU assays which are in close agreement with the dimer assays.

Boyle: Is this with excision measured 24 hours after irradiation?

Regan: Actually we have done various times, 12 hours, 18 hours, 24 hours.

Lucas: Dr. Regan, what exactly was the remark that only after UV irradiation at dosages less than 200 ergs/mm² excision could be found? Furthermore, I would like to ask you if anything is known about the size of the excised molecules. Does the size bear any relation to the dose of UV irradiation? Is there a possibility that you miss part of the excised molecules because they are too large?

Regan: That the dimers are in the TCA insoluble piece?

Lucas: Yes!

Regan: We have done some gradients to separate these out and showed this isn't true. We think the explanation is that you have some absolute numbers of dimers excised no matter what the dose. So if the dose is 50 ergs you get very efficient excision, and if it is 400 ergs you get a very small percent excision.

Norman: Dr. Bootsma, it's several years since Cleaver first pointed out that there is defective repair in xeroderma pigmentosum. What is the role of such defective repair in disease?

Bootsma: This is a difficult question to answer. The distance between the molecular defect and the clinical symptoms of xeroderma is broad. Many still unknown factors might have an influence. Studies of Cleaver and others [DNA repair and radiation sensitivity in human (xeroderma pigmentosum) cells. Int. J. Radiat. Biol. *18:* 554 (1970)] have shown that cultivated cells from xeroderma patients are more sensitive to ultraviolet light in terms of cell survival than cells from normal persons. This might be related to the cellular atrophy found in the skin of xeroderma patients. The relationship between defective repair and carcinogenesis is still a matter of speculation.

Slor: I would like to pose a question concerning the xeroderma pigmentosum subject. The inability to repair UV-damaged DNA explains the extreme sensitivity of xeroderma pigmentosum individuals to sunlight. But what is the relationship between the inability to repair UV-irradiated DNA and the development of various types of carcinomas? Can that be explained as a result of an increased rate of mutations including some that lead to the development of carcinomas? Could it be caused as a consequence of the thymine-dimers which are known to be mutagenic?

How can one explain the skin pigmentosum in xeroderma patients exposed to sunlight? What has that to do with a missing specific endonuclease activity? Could the pigmentation be explained as an autoimmune response of the cells to the UV-irradiated DNA? Can anyone comment on this?

JUNG: I have no explanation for your question but I would like to comment a side problem from the clinical point of view and the histological one. In xeroderma pigmentosum one can observe leukoplakia with multiple transitions into basal cell and squamous cell carcinoma. Furthermore also melanoma and one case with leucaemia were found as well as the following mesodermal tumors: fibrosarcoma, angioma, fibroma, neurofibroma, histiocytoma and hamartoma. The essential characteristics of the tumor formation in X.P. are first the occurrence of multiple tumors and second the variety of the cell types.

MOUTON: I would like to hear some comments on the recent finding reported in the literature according to which xeroderma pigmentosum cells contain RNA-dependent DNA polymerase. Does this implicate the presence of an RNA virus in these cells?

CHANDRA: I think Dr. MOUTON means the recent report of Professor ZAHN's group [Biochem. biophys. Res. Commun. 44: 433 (1971)]. They have reported that the normal human skin does not contain reverse transcriptase, whereas skin from xeroderma patients shows the reverse transcriptase activity. However, our own observations and the results of TODARO's group find this activity in normal skin. I do not know the reason for the contradictory results.

REGAN: Dr. TODARO's group [SCOLNIK, E. M., S. A. AARONSON, G. J. TODARO and W. P. PARKS: Nature 229: 318 (1971)] has reported that normal cells have the reverse transcriptase. With regard to Dr. NORMAN's remark about the nature of xeroderma pigmentosum, a paper was published by LUTZNER's group [BURK, P. G., M. A. LUTZNER, D. D. CLARKE and P. H. ROBBINS: J. Lab. clin. Med. 77: 759 (1971)] that showed normal unscheduled synthesis in a patient with xeroderma pigmentosum. CLEAVER [CLEAVER, J. E. and G. H. THOMAS: Biochem. biophys. Res. Commun. *36:* 203 (1969)], I believe, examined the cells of this patient and confirms this result and we have the culture of that patient and have done the BU assay with this patient and he is quite within the normal range. A number of pathologists examined this patient and were in complete agreement that this was a classical case of xeroderma pigmentosum at pathological level. As to Dr. SLOR's comment, there is a precedent for more than one enzyme being affected by a single recessive mutation. This is work of Dr. KROOTH [KROOTH, R. S.: Cold Spring Harbor Symp. Quant. Biol. *24:* 189] on orotic acid uria. He showed that two enzymes in pyrimidine synthesis were affected in the disease, and he postulated that this was a mutation in a regulator gene.

LUCAS: Regarding the question of Dr. NORMAN I should like to add that for a tumor to develop it is perhaps necessary that an impairment of cellular immunity occurs. What I mean is that one should not try to causally correlate the deficiency of one enzyme to the occurrence of skin tumors.

PAINTER: I only want to comment on Dr. REGAN's comment about xeroderma pigmentosum patients having normal repair. It is not only true for one patient but there are now three known patients. These are patients who have, everybody agrees, xeroderma pigmentosum. When levels of repair are measured by all the ways available they are normal and the cells have the same sensitivity to UV light as normal cells. So even the xeroderma pigmentosum thing is getting quite muddled.

SLOR: You may have a few identical phenotypic expressions that are caused by different genes. It could be that several genetic defects can lead to xeroderma pigmentosum phenotypes. As to Dr. BOOTSMA's paper, I think he has a sensational finding that those two types of xeroderma are controlled by two different genes. This is contrary to the belief of many years that both types are the same disease having different manifestations of the defective gene.

NORMAN: One of the marked properties of cancer is that the incidence is an extremely strong function of age. I think it increases with something like the seventh power of age. Perhaps the higher risk of cancer in older people is due to a failure of the lymphocytes; but to my knowledge none of the age-associated effects demonstrated in lymphocytes has shown anything like a seventh power dependence on the age of the donor. Nevertheless, I favour as a model for cancer the collapse of the surveillance system, rather than an increased mutation rate due to defective DNA repair.

Fox: Can I follow what Dr. Norman is saying about tumor cells. After all, lots of us have been working with cells in culture and looking for repair replication. I am essentially using tumor cell lines, and my own observations with the Yoshida tumor cells are on cells taken from the ascites tumor and growing in vitro. So they are essentially the same cells as those which grow as an ascites tumor in the animal. Within this system we have two cell lines which have very different UV sensitivities, but they are both tumor cells and equally will kill the animal. So I don't know that we can relate differences in repair to anything to do with the production of tumors at the moment.

Lucas: Do they only grow in the autologous system?

Fox: The Yoshida tumor is normally grown in an outbred strain of Wistar rats. There is an antigenic response to the tumor but as far as we can tell, the antigenic response to the sensitive and the resistant one is the same.

Painter: I just want to make a comment about this discussion on the relationship of repair to cancer induction. It was obvious from the very first that there is no simple relationship. The first demonstration of unscheduled DNA synthesis was in HeLa cells which are tumor cells. In xeroderma there is some correlation in most individuals – what that mechanism is between the failure to repair and the final disease state is very complex. So I think at this stage it is ridiculous to try to make correlations between repair levels and cancer induction.

Boyle: Since we have touched on some genetics, I would like to question the evidence that polynucleotide ligase is involved in repair. One would expect that if it really were, then ligase mutants should be sensitive to irradiation. The mutants of phage T4, which have been examined, show at best only a small increase in UV sensitivity. A mutant of *E. coli* isolated by E. C. Pauling is temperature sensitive for UV survival supposedly due to a defect in the ligase. But the *in-vitro* activity of the ligase extracted from this mutant is not temperature sensitive. So it seems to me that the genetic evidence for the involvement of ligase in repair is rather poor.

Painter: Is it not considered that a cell probably cannot exist without a ligase because we cannot isolate mutants with defective ligase?

Boyle: Yes, that is why they are isolated under conditionally lethal conditions, generally as ts or amber mutants, and one looks at the survival of ts mutants at temperatures which are nearly restricting. The UV sensitivity of this cell is temperature dependent, but the activity of the extracted ligase is not temperature dependent.

OKASAKI: I think some of them are sensitive but even at low temperature it has a very low specific activity.

KLEPPE: I just want to make a comment on the T 4 ligase. It has been shown that the *E. coli* host ligase can substitute for T 4 ligase when the host DNA is not attacked by the phage-induced endonuclease II [WAHNER, H. R.: J. Virol. *7:* 534 (1971)].

ROBERTS: Can I carry on with the last remark Dr. REGAN made on what he told of the mechanism of break reduction by two carcinogens. Did you say you get intercalation, or did I misunderstood you on this?

REGAN: With certain carcinogens we get quite a lot of BUdR incorporated after the damage. We get a model that is like UV repair.

AVERBECK: I would like to ask Dr. JUNG a question. Are there any indications for a recombinational type of repair system?

JUNG: We tried to copy the defect of the so-called pigmented xerodermoid in normal skin by adding caffeine (see Fig. 3, p. 104).

PAINTER: At least two groups have shown that post-replication repair does occur in the mammalian cells. There are some problems involved in the post-replication repair in Chinese hamster lines. There were indications that it might be the basis for a difference in UV-sensitivity between two Chinese hamster lines, but experiments by HUMPHREY's group indicate that it is not.

REGAN: Mr. STEVEN BUHL [Biophys. J. (In press)], a graduate student in my laboratory, has shown in human cells a kind of post-replication repair.

ANTONI: Any more comments, questions? If not I would like to appreciate very much the speakers for their presentation and the contributors for having had a very lively discussion. Thank you so much.

Session III

Chairman: J. M. BOYLE

Studies on DNA-Replication Mechanisms and Their Possible Implication in Radiation Damage and Repair of DNA

R. OKAZAKI

Our studies on the mechanism of DNA replication during the past few years have demonstrated that DNA replicates in the cell by a discontinuous mechanism, whereby DNA is first synthesized in short pieces and these pieces are subsequently joined, The studies have also suggested (a) that common functions are needed for DNA replication and repair, and (b) that the newly

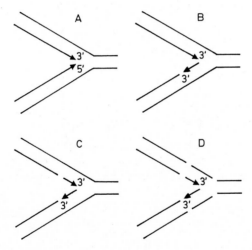

Fig. 1. Models for the possible structure and reaction in the replication region of DNA.

replicated portion of DNA may be a site which has a high sensitivity to mutagenic agents and in which chromosomal deletion takes place frequently.

It had been inferred that semiconservative replication of DNA occurs as shown in Fig. 1 (A), by continuous growth of two daughter strands in the $5' \to 3'$ direction on the one hand and the $3' \to 5'$ direction on the other. Obviously, this is not the only possibility. In 1964, we began our investigation to explore the possibility that one or both strands of DNA replicate dis-

continuously as shown in Fig. 1 (B–D). The following predictions are made
from the models of discontinuous replication: (a) The nascent portion of
daughter strands, selectively labelled by a brief radioactive pulse, will be
isolated as short DNA chains after gentle extraction and denaturation. (b)
An enzyme which joins preformed DNA chains will exist, and if one inhibits
the function of this enzyme the newly synthesized short chains which normally
exist in a small amount will accumulate in the cell. (c) The direction of synthesis
of DNA chains *in vivo* is exclusively $5' \to 3'$.

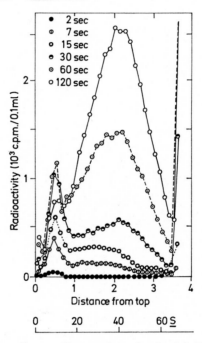

Fig. 2. Alkaline sucrose gradient sedimentation of pulse-labelled DNA from T4-infected
E. coli B.

The first prediction was confirmed by the pulse-labelling-alkaline sucrose
gradient sedimentation experiments in a number of bacterial and phage
systems, including various *E. coli* strains, *B. subtilis*, *Pseudomonas* BAL (31),
phage T4, T7, $\varphi80$, P2 and PM2 (1, 2, 3, 4). Fig. 2 shows, as an example, the
results with T4-infected *E. coli*. Cells actively synthesizing phage DNA were
exposed to ³H-thymidine for various times at 20°, and DNA was extracted
and analyzed by alkaline sucrose gradient sedimentation. After a two-second
pulse the radioactive label incorporated was recovered almost exclusively in

a DNA component with a sedimentation coefficient of 9S. After longer pulses, the radioactivity was found also in fast-sedimenting material. The radioactivity in the »9S component« increased quickly and reached a maximum in 30 seconds, while that in the fast-sedimenting component increased almost linearly. These results and pulse-chase experiments indicate that the 9S DNA is an intermediate in the formation of large DNA.

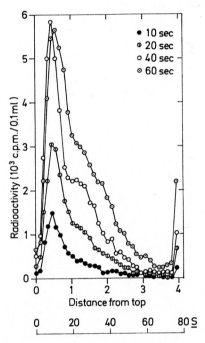

Fig. 3. Alkaline sucrose gradient sedimentation of radioactive DNA from T4 *ts* B20 (ligase-deficient mutant)-infected cells pulse-labelled at 1 min after temperature shift from 20 to 43° C.

As to the second prediction, the predicted enzyme, DNA ligase, was discovered in uninfected and phage-infected *E. coli* in 1967 (5–11), shortly after our finding of the nascent short DNA. The test if the nascent short DNA chains accumulate upon inhibition of ligase function was performed using temperature-sensitive ligase mutants of T4 (3, 12, 13). Fig. 3 shows such an experiment. Cells infected with a temperature-sensitive ligase mutant at 20° were transferred to 43° during active phage DNA synthesis and 1 minute later pulse-labelled with ³H-thymidine. The 9S DNA accumulated and its size increment was greatly inhibited. If the temperature was shifted down from

43 to 30°, joining of the accumulated short chains took place (Fig. 4). Similar observations were made with three independently isolated DNA ligase mutants of *E. coli* by PAULING, GELLERT and HIROSE and their coworkers (14, 15, 16).

The T4 nascent short DNA chains found under steady-state conditions and those accumulated during ligase inhibition anneal equally with the separated complementary strands of phage DNA, indicating that these chains consist of complementary components (17).

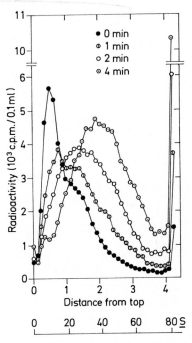

Fig. 4. Effect of incubation at 30° C subsequent to pulse-labelling at 43° C on the sedimentation pattern of radioactive DNA from T4 *ts* B20-infected cells.

The results presented up to this point indicate that in the T4 system the discontinuities exist in the nascent portion of both daughter strands and that joining of the short segments is carried out by DNA ligase. However, it can still be argued that DNA strands may be synthesized continuously and selective nicks introduced in the newly synthesized portions by some specific nuclease. This possibility would be eliminated, at least for one of the strands, if one could definitively verify the third prediction, that is the exclusive $5' \rightarrow 3'$ synthesis of DNA.

This was achieved by labelling the growing ends of the short chains and determining the location of the label in the molecules. T4 nascent short DNA labelled at the growing ends with ^{3}H and those labelled wholly with ^{14}C were prepared as shown in Fig. 5. One culture was pulse-labelled for 6 seconds with ^{3}H-thymidine at 8° and another culture for 2.5 minutes with ^{14}C-thymidine. Case A shows the situation expected when the short chains of both strands are produced by discontinuous synthesis in the $5' \rightarrow 3'$ direction. Case B is the situation one should expect when the short chains are produced by continuous

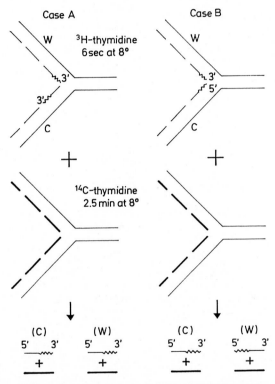

Fig. 5. Preparation of T4 nascent short chains labelled with ^{3}H and those labelled uniformly with ^{14}C.

synthesis followed by nicking. After DNA extraction, the ^{3}H- and ^{14}C-labelled preparations were mixed and the short chains were isolated by sedimentation. They are then separated into complementary components, C and W 9$\underline{S}$ short chains, by annealing with the W or C strand of phage DNA.

To determine the location of the ^{3}H-label in the molecule the mixture of ^{3}H- and ^{14}C-labelled C or W short chains was degraded by *E. coli* exonuclease I in the $3' \rightarrow 5'$ direction, or by *B. subtilis* nuclease in the $5' \rightarrow 3'$ direction,

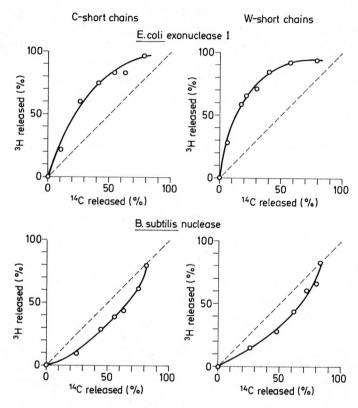

Fig. 6. Degradation of ^3H- and ^{14}C-labelled C and W nascent $9\underline{S}$ chains of T4 by *E. coli* exonuclease I and *B. subtilis* nuclease.

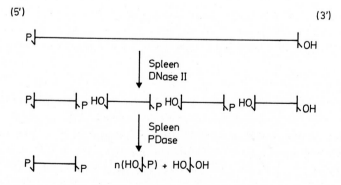

Fig. 7. Degradation of DNA by successive treatment with spleen DNase II and spleen phosphodiesterase.

and the extent of release of ^{3}H was compared with that of ^{14}C at various times during digestion. The results presented in Fig. 6 show that with both C and W short chains, the release of ^{3}H preceded the release of ^{14}C when the DNA was degraded by *E. coli* exonuclease I, whereas the release of ^{14}C preceded the release of ^{3}H when *B. subtilis* nuclease was used (18). Thus ^{3}H label was at the 3' ends of both the C and W short chains, indicating that both short chains are synthesized in the 5' → 3' direction in accordance with Case A.

For further critical test of this crucial point, we examined if the ^{3}H label is present at the 5' ends of the 9S short chain (19). For this purpose a method was developed for selective isolation of the 5'-terminal region of a DNA chain. As illustrated in Fig. 7, spleen DNase II produces three kinds of oligonucleotides from DNA terminated with 5'-P and 3'-OH: Oligonucleotides with 5'-OH and 3'-P ends from the internal portion, those with 3'- and 5'-P ends from the 5' terminus, and those with 3'- and 5'-OH ends from the 3' terminus. Spleen phosphodiesterase degrades oligonucleotide with 5'-OH end but does not attack oligonucleotide with 5'-P end. Therefore the oligonucleotide produced by DNase II from the 5'-P terminus of DNA will survive subsequent treatment with spleen PDase, while those from the other portion will be degraded, permitting selective isolation of the 5'-phosphoryl terminal region of DNA as oligonucleotide fragments.

In the experiment presented in Fig. 8, the C and W 9S short chains labelled at the growing ends with ^{3}H thymidine by 12 sec pulse at 8° and those labelled wholly with ^{14}C-thymidine by 2.5 min pulse were prepared, treated successively with spleen DNase II and phosphodiesterase and subjected to gel filtration on Sephadex G25. With both C and W short chains, about 10% of ^{14}C but virtually no ^{3}H was found in oligonucleotide, which was excluded from the column. Thus the 5' termini of both C and W short chains are not the growing ends.

It is expected that by increasing the time of ^{3}H-thymidine pulse the ^{3}H label begins to appear in the 5' end of the 9S chains at a certain time, and this corresponds roughly to the time required for the formation of the individual short chains. As shown in Fig. 9, the ^{3}H label began to appear in the 5' oligonucleotides about 1 minute after the addition of ^{3}H-thymidine. Since the 9S DNA is about 1000 nucleotides long, this suggests that the average chain growth rate at 8° is about 20 nucleotides per second. Fig. 10 shows the results of similar experiments at 14°, which support the conclusion that the direction of chain growth is 5' → 3' and that the time required for formation of individual 9S short chains at 14° is about 10 seconds, suggesting a chain growth rate of about 100 nucleotides per second. The elongation rate of the short DNA chains revealed by these experiments is 100 times faster than the *in-vivo* chain growth

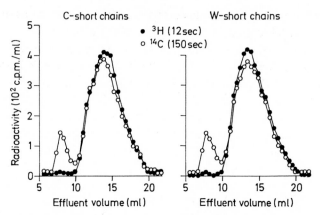

Fig. 8. Sephadex G25 gel filtration after spleen DNase II and phosphodiesterase treatment of ^{3}H- and ^{14}C-labelled C and W short chains of T4. Pulse-labelling at 8° C.

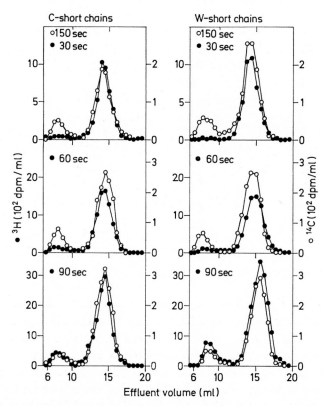

Fig. 9. Sephadex G25 gel filtration after spleen DNase II and phosphodiesterase treatment of the 9$\underline{S}$ DNA chains labelled by »long« ^{3}H-thymidine pulses at 8° C.

rate of mRNA and rRNA as well as that of DNA polymerization *in vitro* by isolated DNA polymerase.

The fact that all of the three predictions have been confirmed leaves little doubt that DNA replicates in the cell by a discontinuous mechanism. Recently, however, WERNER (20) argued that the nascent short pieces might be an

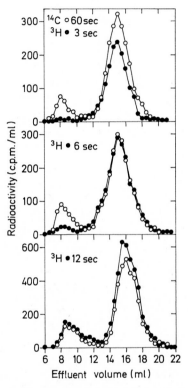

Fig. 10. Sephadex G25 gel filtration after spleen DNase II and phosphodiesterase treatment of T4 9$\underline{S}$ short pieces labelled with pulse of ^{3}H- and ^{14}C-thymidine at 14° C.

artefact of the thymidine pulse, which would produce a disturbance of deoxynucleotide metabolism and be preferentially utilized for DNA repair. His argument is mainly based on his results that with a ^{3}H-thymine pulse little nascent pieces were found, and the amount of radioactivity found in small DNA increases with time in the beginning. Since his results are completely different from those we had obtained with ^{3}H-thymine pulse some time ago, we reinvestigated this point. In WERNER's experiments, *E. coli* 15TAMT incubated in the presence of thymine at a density of 2×10^{10} cells/ml was exposed to ^{3}H-thymine at 14°. In our experiments, cultures (5×10^8 to 10^9 cells/ml) of *E. coli* 15TAMT and P3478 (*polA⁻*) or T4 td8-infected *E. coli* JG116 (*thy⁻*) in medium containing 11 to 160 μM (1.4 to 20 μg/ml) thymine were pulse-labelled by the addition of 1 μM ³H-thymine under physiological steady-state conditions. ³H-thymine was purified before use to remove impurities which obscure the implication of the results. As shown in Figs. 11–15, essentially the same patterns of alkaline

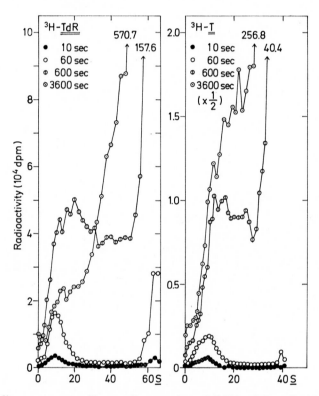

Fig. 11. Alkaline sucrose gradient sedimentation of DNA of *E. coli* 15TAMT growing on 14 μM thymine and pulse-labelled with 0.2 μM ³H-thymidine or 1 μM ³H-thymine at 8° C.

sucrose gradient sedimentation of radioactive DNA were obtained with the ³H-thymidine and ³H-thymine pulses. More than 75% of the label was found in slowly sedimenting DNA after a brief ³H-thymine pulse, and the portion of the radioactivity found in this fraction decreased with an increase of pulse time.

Another basis of WERNER's argument is his finding that when *E. coli* B/r grown in heavy medium is transferred to light medium and then pulse-labelled with ³H-thymidine, labelled short and long DNA chains exhibit an intermediate density. We performed similar experiments with *E. coli* B/r, JG 116, and P 3478. Cells were grown in heavy ($^{15}N, D_2O$) medium and pulse-labelled with ^3H-thymidine at a physiological cell density. The results were again totally different from those of WERNER. Figs. 16 and 17 show the experiments with B/r. There was little DNA synthesis immediately after density shift so that in the experiment of Fig. 16 the amount of DNA synthesized in the light medium

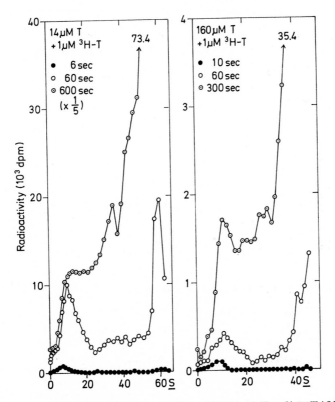

Fig. 12. Alkaline sucrose gradient sedimentation of DNA of *E. coli* 15 TAMT growing on thymine and pulse-labelled with ^3H-thymine at 14° C.

before the pulse-labelling corresponded to only a few per cent of the amount of heavy DNA. In the experiment of Fig. 17, the amount of DNA doubled in the light medium so that the heavy label was only in the parental strands at the time of pulse-labelling. It is evidently shown by CsCl density gradient analysis of the labelled short and long DNA chains that the ^3H-thymidine pulse under our standard conditions labels the replicating portion of the daughter strands. Essentially the same results were obtained with ^3H-thymine pulses.

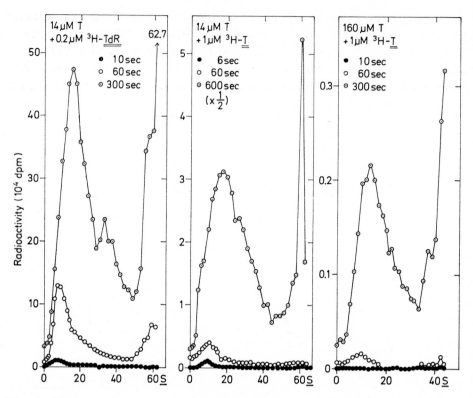

Fig. 13. Alkaline sucrose gradient sedimentation of *E. coli* P3478 (*pol Al*) DNA pulse-labelled at 14° C.

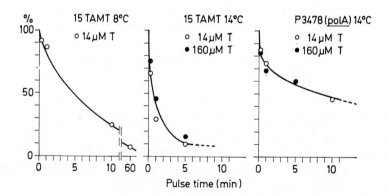

Fig. 14. Percentage of ³H-thymine label in short chains at various times of pulse-labelling of *E. coli* 15TAMT and P3478.

The results presented up to this point support strongly that both strands of *E. coli* and T4 DNA are replicated discontinuously. The same appears to be true of λ and T7 DNA (21, 22, 23). There is, however, suggestive evidence that one of the two DNA strands of P2 phage as well as *B. subtilis* might be synthesized discontinuously (23). As shown in Figs. 18 and 19 after brief ³H-thymi-

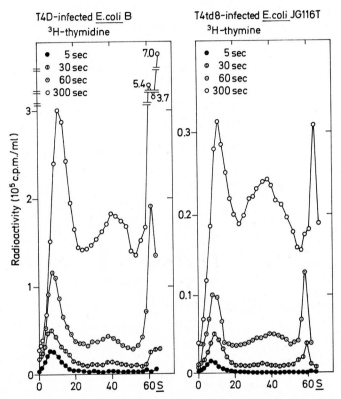

Fig. 15. Alkaline sucrose gradient sedimentation of replicative T4 pulse-labelled with ³H-thymidine (0.5 μM) or ³H-thymine (13 μM thymine + 1 μM ³H-thymine) at 8° C.

dine pulse of P2-infected cells only about a half of the labelled DNA sedimented slowly (9S) in alkali, and the rest was found in a fast sedimenting fraction (34S). As shown in Table 1, the 9S and 34S DNA annealed predominantly with the isolated »L« and »H« strand of phage DNA, respectively, indicating that the discontinuity in the replicating P2 DNA exists predominantly (or exclusively) in the »H« strand.

It would be worth noting that the movement of the replicating fork appears to be bidirectional in *E. coli*, λ T4 and T7 (24, 25, 26, 27) while it is unidirectional in *B. subtilis* and P2 (28, 29). It is possible that bidirectional replication somehow requires a two-strand discontinuous mechamism or a certain degree of symmetry of discontinuous synthesis.

Assuming that DNA in fact replicates by a discontinuous mechanism *in vivo*, one of the important questions to ask is how the discontinuity of the

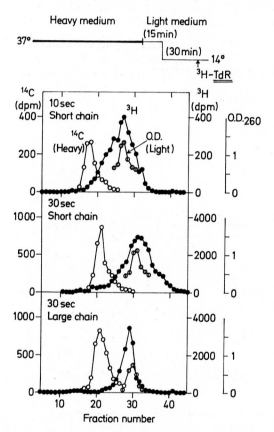

Fig. 16. CsCl equilibrium density gradient centrifugation of DNA of *E. coli* B/r pulse-labelled with ³H-thymidine shortly after transfer from heavy (¹⁵N–D₂O) medium to light medium.

Table 1. Asymmetry of discontinuous replication of P2 DNA.

Pulse-labelling	Unfractionated H : L	Short chains H : L	Long chains H : L
10 sec at 8°	1 : 1	17 : 1	1 : 13
5 sec at 20°	1 : 1	17 : 1	1 : 11
15 sec at 20°	1 : 1	23 : 1	1 : 9

chain growth is controlled, that is, what is the mechanism of initiation and termination of synthesis of the »replication unit«. An intriguing possibility is that there are initiation and/or termination signals on the template strands. The signals could be special base sequences, unusual bases, interruption of phosphodiester linkages or unusual secondary structure. The mean size of the unit of discontinuous synthesis appears to correspond to the estimated average size of the cistron. This suggests that the replication unit might be the cistron and that the ends of the cistron might be the initiation and termination points in the discontinuous synthesis. Alternatively, the size of the segment synthesized by one continuous act of polymerase might be determined primarily by the intrinsic nature of the replication apparatus.

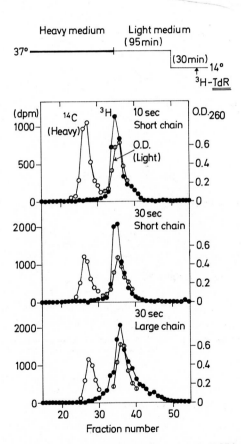

Fig. 17. CsCl density gradient centrifugation of *E. coli* B/r DNA pulse-labelled with ^{3}H-thymidine following a long incubation in light medium after transfer from heavy to light medium.

Some insight into such problems would be obtained by experiments with
E. coli mutants deficient in Kornberg DNA polymerase isolated by CAIRNS (30)
and others. *E. coli* P 3478, the first mutant of this kind, produces short DNA
pieces as do the wild-type cells. However, as shown in Fig. 20, the joining of
the short pieces is about 10 times slower in the mutant than in the parental
and revertant strains (32). Fig. 21 shows that the same is true of *E. coli* R15,
a mutant which was isolated by KATO and KONDO (33) originally as an X-ray-
sensitive strain and later found to be deficient in DNA polymerase. As shown
in Table 2, while DNA polymerase activity of extracts of P 3478 and R15 was
extremely low, these strains had a normal level of DNA ligase activity. It was

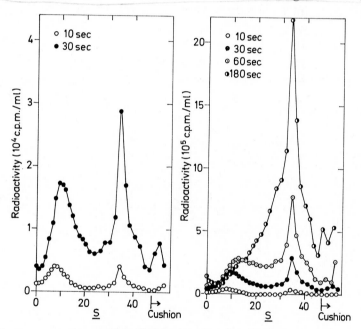

Fig. 18. Alkaline sucrose gradient sedimentation of P2 *viri*-infected cells pulse-labelled
with ³H-thymidine at 20° C.

Table 2. DNA polymerase and ligase activity in extracts of various *E. coli* strains.

Strain	Polymerase	Ligase
	(units/mg of protein)	
W3110	1.6	8.5
P3478	0.04	10.5
P3478R	2.6	6.4
B/r30R	1.6	6.1
R15	0.04	7.5

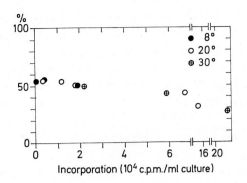

Fig. 19. Percentage of the label found in P2 short chains after ³H-thymidine pulses under various conditions.

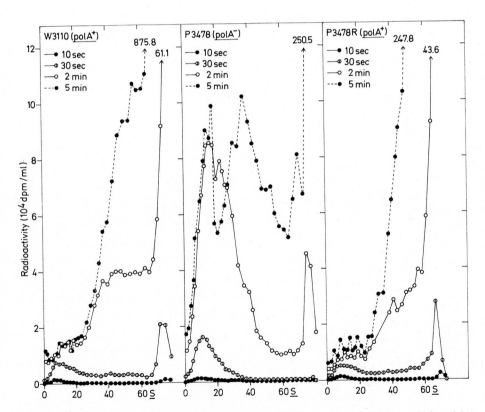

Fig. 20. Alkaline sucrose gradient sedimentation of DNA of *E. coli* W 3110 *(thy⁻, polA⁺)*, P 3478 *(thy⁻, polA⁺)*, and P 3478R *(thy⁻, polA⁺)* pulse-labelled with ³H-thymidine at 30° C.

also ascertained by density shift experiments that the short DNA pieces of these mutants are newly synthesized chains in the nascent portion of daughter strands. These results suggest that DNA polymerase I normally functions in joining the short segments synthesized by the replication complex, possibly by filling gaps that may exist between the segments. The function of this polymerase (DNA polymerase I) for »gap filling« may be dispensable for rep-

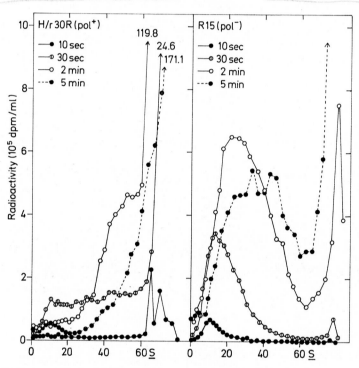

Fig. 21. Alkaline sucrose gradient sedimentation of DNA of *E. coli* H/r30R (*pol*+) and R15 (*pol*-) pulse-labelled at 30° C.

lication of *E. coli* chromosomes, because it could be partially replaced by some other enzyme, possible candidates being DNA polymerase II and III, recently isolated by several investigators (34–36), and a product of *rec*A gene. In any event, in the DNA polymerase I-deficient mutants the discontinuity appears to persist in a large portion of the daughter strands corresponding to as much as a few per cent of the entire chromosome, as shown in Fig. 22.

Although the polymerase I-deficient mutants grow, they exhibit several abnormal properties (30, 33, 37–45). These abnormalities may be attributed to this »amplification of the newly replicated state«. Single-stranded DNA is

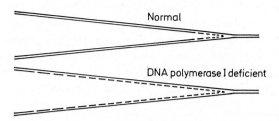

Fig. 22. Possible structure of the newly replicated region of normal and DNA polymerase I-deficient cells.

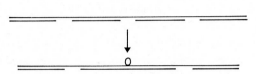

Fig. 23. A possible mechanism of chromosomal deletion in the newly replicated portion, which would occur at a high frequency in *pol⁻* cells.

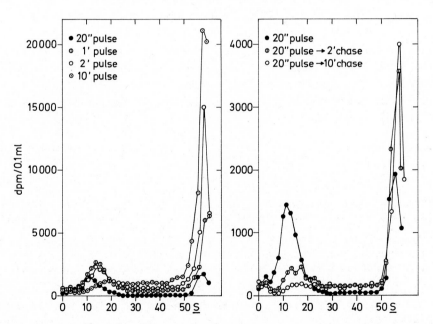

Fig. 24. *In-vitro* synthesis and joining of short DNA chains in the membrane fraction prepared by lysozyme-Brij-EDTA treatment from *E. coli* B/r30R.

more sensitive to X-ray, ultraviolet light and other mutagenic agents than is double-stranded DNA. Thus, the high sensitivity of the mutants to these agents could partly be due to the increased single-stranded sections in the parental strands, although the high sensitivity may largely be due to the decreased ability to repair the lesion in DNA produced by these agents. It is noteworthy in this connection that the replicating region is the site most sensitive to the action of a mutagenic agent (46).

The increase in the frequency of deletion mutations could also be due to the persistence of gaps in the daughter strands and the single-stranded sections in the parental strands. One possible mechanism for chromosomal deletion involves the formation of a loop in a single-stranded section in the parental strands that results in joining of the daughter strand segments without filling the gaps (Fig. 23).

The discontinuity of the daughter strands will have a lethal effect if the gaps are not filled and the daughter segments are not connected before that portion of the DNA becomes the template in the next cycle of replication. The replication of certain small plasmid or phage DNA may become abortive in the absence of DNA polymerase I, because of the incomplete joining of the daughter segments before the subsequent cycle of replication. Whatever the detailed mechanism is, the participation of DNA polymerase I as well as ligase in joining of the newly replicated DNA segments encourages the idea that common mechanisms are involved in DNA replication and repair.

Analysis of the detailed mechanism of discontinuous replication will be facilitated by the development of *in-vitro* systems which carry out this reaction (31, 47, 48). Fig. 24 shows the *in-vitro* synthesis and joining of DNA pieces in the membrane fraction of *E. coli* B/r30R prepared by lysozyme-EDTA-Brij treatment.

References

(1) SAKABE, K., R. OKAZAKI: Biochim. biophys. Acta (Amst.) *129:* 651 (1966).

(2) OKAZAKI, R., T. OKAZAKI, K. SAKABE, K. SUGIMOTO, A. SUGINO: Proc. Nat. Acad. Sci. (Wash.) *59:* 598 (1968).

(3) OKAZAKI, R., T. OKAZAKI, K. SAKABE, K. SUGIMOTO, R. KAINUMA, A. SUGINO, N. IWATSUKI: Cold Spring Harbor Symp. *33:* 129 (1968).

(4) SUGINO, A., KAINUMA-KURODA, Y. IMAE, R. OKAZAKI: Unplublished observations.

(5) GELLERT, M.: Proc. Nat. Acad. Sci. (Wash.) *57:* 147 (1967).

(6) OLIVERA, B. M., I. R. LEHMAN: Proc. Nat. Acad. Sci. (Wash.) *57:* 1426 (1967).

(7) GEFTER, M. L., A. BECKER, J. HURWITZ: Proc. Nat. Acad. Sci. (Wash.) *58:* 241 (1967).

(8) WEISS, B., C. C. RICHARDSON: Proc. Nat. Acad. Sci. (Wash.) *57:* 1021 (1967).

(9) BECKER, A., G. LYN, M. GEFTER, J. HURWITZ: Proc. Nat. Acad. Sci. (Wash.) *58:* 1996 (1967).

(10) COZZARELLI, N. R., N. E. MELECHEN, T. M. JOVIN, A. KORNBERG: Biochem. biophys. Res. Commun. *28:* 578 (1967).

(11) FAREED, G. C., C. C. RICHARDSON: Proc. Nat. Acad. Sci. (Wash.) *58:* 665 (1967).
(12) SUGIMOTO, K., T. OKAZAKI, R. OKAZAKI: Proc. Nat. Acad. Sci. (Wash.) *60:* 1356 (1968).
(13) IWATSUKI, N., R. OKAZAKI: J. mol. Biol. *52:* 37 (1970).
(14) PAULING, C., L. HAMM: Proc. Nat. Acad. Sci. (Wash.) *64:* 1195 (1969).
(15) GELLERT, M.: Personal communication.
(16) HIROSE, S.: Personal communication.
(17) SUGIMOTO, K., T. OKAZAKI, Y. IMAE, R. OKAZAKI: Proc. Nat. Acad. Sci. (Wash.) *63:* 1343 (1969).
(18) OKAZAKI, T., R. OKAZAKI: Proc. Nat. Acad. Sci. (Wash.) *64:* 1242 (1969).
(19) SUGINO, A., R. OKAZAKI: J. mol. Biol. *64:* 61 (1972).
(20) WERNER, R.: Nature *230:* 570 (1971).
(21) TOMIZAWA, J.-I., T. OGAWA: Cold Spring Harbor Symp. *33:* 533 (1968).
(22) GINSBURG, B., J. HURWITZ: J. mol. Biol. *52:* 265 (1970).
(23) KAINUMA-KURODA, R., R. OKAZAKI: In preparation.
(24) MASTERS, M., P. BRODA: Nature New Biology *232:* 137 (1971).
(25) SCHNÖS, M., R. B. INMAN: J. mol. Biol. *51:* 61 (1970).
(26) DLIUS, H., C. HOWE, A. W. KOZINSKI: Proc. Nat. Acad. Sci. (Wash.): *68;* 3094 (1971).
(27) WOLFSON, F., M. MAGAZIN, D. DRESSLER: Proc. Nat. Acad. Sci. (Wash.) *69;* 499 (1972).
(28) SUEOKA, N., H. YOSHIKAWA: Cold Spring Harbor Symp. *28:* 47 (1963).
(29) SCHNÖS, M., R. B. INMAN: J. mol. Biol. *55:* 31 (1971).
(30) DE LUCIA, P., J. CAIRNS: Nature *224:* 1164 (1969).
(31) OKAZAKI, R., K. SUGIMOTO, T. OKAZAKI, Y. IMAE, A. SUGINO: Nature *228:* 223 (1970).
(32) OKAZAKI, R., M. ARISAWA, A. SUGINO: Proc. Nat. Acad. Sci. (Wash.) *68:* 2954 (1971).
(33) KATO, T., S. KONDO: J. Bacteriol. *104:* 871 (1970).
(34) KORNBERG, T., M. L. GEFTER: Proc. Nat. Acad. Sci. (Wash.) *68:* 761 (1971).
(35) MOSES, R. E., C. C. RICHARDSON: Biochem. biophys. Res. Commun. *41:* 1557 (1970).
(36) KNIPPERS, R.: Nature *228:* 1050 (1970).
(37) GROSS, J., M. GROSS: Nature *224:* 1166 (1969).
(38) KANNER, L., P. HANAWALT: Biochem. biophys. Res. Commun. *39:* 149 (1970).
(39) BOYLE, J. M., M. C. PATERSON, R. B. SETLOW: Nature *226:* 708 (1970).
(40) TOWN, C. D., K. C. SMITH, H. S. KAPLAN: Science *172:* 851 (1971).
(41) MONK, M., M. PEACEY, J. D. GROSS: J. mol. Biol. *58:* 623 (1971).
(42) SLATER, E. E., M. D. ANDERSON, H. S. ROSENKRANZ: Cancer Res. *31:* 970 (1971).
(43) GROSS, J. D., J. GRUNSTEIN, E. M. WITKIN: J. mol. Biol. *58:* 631 (1971).
(44) COUKELL, M. B., C. YANOFSKY: Nature *228:* 633 (1970).
(45) KINGSBURY, D. T., D. R. HELINSKI: Biochem. biophys. Res. Commun. *41:* 1538 (1970).
(46) CERDÁ-OLMEDO, E., P. C. HANAWALT, N. GUEROLA: J. mol. Biol. *33:* 705 (1968).
(47) OGAWA, T., R. OKAZAKI: In preparation.
(48) SCHALLER, H., B. OTTO, V. NÜSSLEIN, J. HUF, R. HERRMANN, F. BONHOEFFER: J. mol. Biol. *63;* 183 (1972).

The Relationship of Repair Mechanisms to the Induction of Chromosome Aberrations in Eucaryotic Cells*

Bernard S. Strauss

If a population of HEp.2 cells is allowed to attach to a plate and is then treated with methyl methanesulfonate (MMS), the progeny cells observed after several days have an extremely heterogeneous morphology as compared to populations of untreated cells. Particularly striking are the colonies containing only a few cells, many of them of peculiar shapes (Fig. 1; Myers and Strauss, 1971). Such observations are common enough and similar cellular abnormalities are observed after treatment of cells with ionizing radiation (Todd, 1968).

In measurements of cell survival, clones are counted only if they contain some minimal number of cells. Giant cells, and colonies containing only a few cells, are not counted since we ordinarily define »viability« as the capacity for indefinite proliferation at the normal rate. However, the existence of micro-colonies made up of cells which divide for a time and then stop, shows that »cell death« does not mean cessation of metabolic activity or even the loss of the ability to divide. Furthermore, as Belli (1971) has shown, repair of X-ray-induced damage may occur in one or several of the cells in a microcolony after the first division has taken place. The initial damage is therefore only »potentially lethal«.

Therefore, to understand the nature of the damage induced in cells by the alkylating compounds we must study events that occur well after the treatment. Furthermore, replication of the nuclear DNA does not demonstrate that the cell will continue to divide indefinitely. Cells must be studied for several generations after the original treatment to find out the molecular basis for any eventual failure to replicate. In this paper I will describe some experiments done in my laboratory by Dr. M. Coyle and myself on DNA replication and repair. I will then outline some speculations about the relationship between

* These studies were supported in part by grants from the National Science Foundation (GB 8514), the National Institutes of Health (GM 07816) and the Atomic Energy Commission (AT [11-1] 2040).

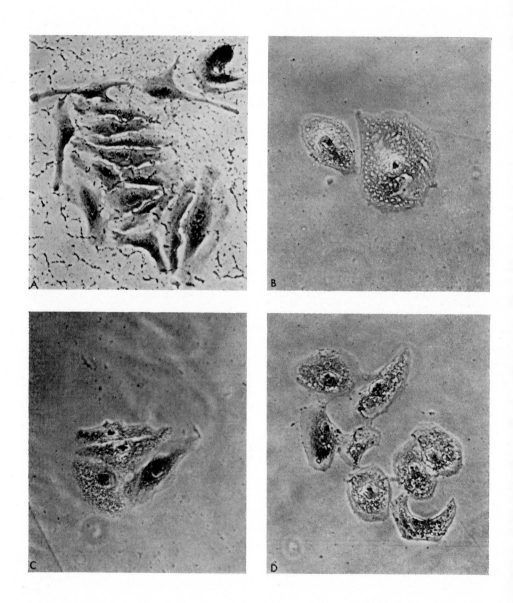

Fig. 1. Morphology of HEp. 2 cells 4 days after treatment with MMS. Cultures on Petri dishes were fixed overnight with Carnoy's fixative and stained for 20 min with toluidine blue. Photomicrographs were taken at $\times$ 50. All photographs are reproduced at the same magnification. A: clone of sixteen cells from control culture; B: doublet from a culture treated with 4×10^{-3} M MMS; C: clone of four cells from a culture treated with 2×10^{-3} M MMS; D: clone of eight cells from a culture treated with 2×10^{-3} M MMS.

abnormal replication and the production of chromosome aberrations. Finally, I will discuss the question: »What kills cells after treatment with alkylating agents?«

We use methyl methanesulfonate as a paradigm of a monofunctional alkylating agent. Recently we have also used propiolactone because of the report by FUKUDA and YAMAMOTO (1970) that β-propiolactone inactivated hcr^- strains of *Salmonella typhimurium* more rapidly than the wild-type. This observation implies that, in some organisms at least, alkylation damage might be recognized by the excision repair system for UV-induced damage. However, our experiments with *Bacillus subtilis* (Fig. 2) indicate that although a UV-sensitive mutant is slightly more sensitive to propiolactone than is its normal allele, the difference is small and not comparable to the difference in response to propiolactone of MMS-sensitive and resistant strains. Our data with *B. subtilis* agree with those of FUKUDA and YAMAMOTO (1970) in indicating that most propiolactone-induced damage is recognized by those systems which detect MMS-induced damage. Since the MMS-induced damage recognized by cells is primarily the induction of single-strand DNA breaks (PRAKASH and STRAUSS, 1970), propiolactone treatment must also result in the induction of breaks in the DNA of *B. subtilis*. However, although I use the term »alkylate« in this paper interchangeably with »methylate«, it should be understood that different monofunctional alkylating agents might induce different responses in the target organism.

We have recently published our observations on the failure to replicate of DNA made by HEp.2 cells immediately after treatment with MMS (COYLE, McMAHON and STRAUSS, 1971) and I will merely summarize our results. We used the following protocol: HEp.2 cells were treated with MMS and then incubated for one hour with tritiated thymidine. The isotope was removed and fresh medium substituted. After 22 hours, medium containing BUdR was added and incubation was allowed to proceed for an additional 48 hours. DNA was isolated from these cells and subjected to density gradient centrifugation through CsCl. This experimental design resulted in the labelling of DNA made after alkylation. Replication of this newly made DNA was indicated by its transfer to the hybrid region of the gradient. We distinguished between repair and semiconservative replication by experiments based on the protocol of PETTIJOHN and HANAWALT (1964). Cells were alkylated and then incubated with ^{3}H. BUdR. Repair synthesis is indicated in such an experiment by incorporation of isotope into DNA which centrifuges in the light density region of a CsCl gradient. Repair synthesis was also measured as the hydroxyurea-resistant incorporation of thymidine into DNA because of the reports that this inhibitor (HU) does not interfere with repair synthesis (CLEAVER, 1969). (There is,

B. S. Strauss

however, recent evidence that HU may inhibit the joining of breaks produced
in the course of excision repair (BEN-HUR and BEN-ISHAI, 1971). Finally, we
measured the degradation of DNA into fragments of about 20S by the method
of HIRT (1967) which depends on the precipitation by 1 M NaCl of large DNA
molecules attached to cellular constituents. All our experiments have been
carried out with cells attached to the surface of Petri plates. This methodology
removes cells which are immediately killed by treatment since such cells round

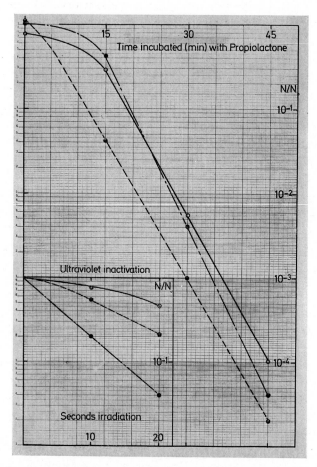

Fig. 2. Inactivation of *Bacillus subtilis* by β-propiolactone and by ultraviolet light
(insert). Overnight cultures were suspended in fresh medium and an equal volume of
0.026 M β-propiolactone in salt-solution was added. The cultures were incubated at 37° C
with shaking for the time indicated and then plated on a synthetic medium. Cultures were
irradiated as indicated with a UV-germicidal lamp for determination of ultraviolet
sensitivity. Open circles: strain 101, normal sensitivity; closed circles: strain 124, excision
defective; half-closed circles: strain 118, MMS-sensitive.

up and detach from the surface of the dish. Treatment at high MMS concentrations results in the separation of sheets of cells from the surface of culture dishes.

HEp. 2 cells treated with MMS or with propiolactone can incorporate thymidine immediately after treatment although the amount of thymidine incorporated is decreased. Most of our experiments have been carried out at doses which reduce incorporation to about 50%. DNA is synthesized by HEp. 2 cells immediately after alkylation by both semiconservative and non-semiconservative modes (Fig. 3). The exact proportion of repair synthesis depends on the dose of alkylating agent (Table 1). Only a portion of the DNA synthesized immediately after treatment goes through an additional round of replication (Fig. 4) and, as expected, this proportion is lower at higher doses of alkylating agent. A large proportion of the DNA which does not replicate is made by semiconservative synthesis as shown by the following series of experiments:

1. Much of the newly formed DNA is eventually degraded and can be found as fragments of about 20S in the Hirt supernatant (Table 2). Therefore, we were able to use the Hirt supernatant as a source of the newly formed DNA.
2. The DNA formed after alkylation and found in the Hirt supernatant did not replicate since it was not transferred to a hybrid density in a density transfer experiment (Fig. 5).
3. This DNA, found in the Hirt supernatant, was made in large part by semiconservative synthesis as demonstrated in a Pettijohn-Hanawalt type density transfer experiment (Fig. 6).

The results obtained with propiolactone were indistinguishable from those obtained with MMS in that only a portion of the DNA made immediately after alkylation replicated. This similarity is expected in view of the similarity in the response of repair-deficient bacteria to MMS and to propiolactone. We have no idea what proportion of the twice replicated DNA made after treatment with MMS or propiolactone goes through additional divisions, although the experiment of MYERS and STRAUSS (1971) suggests that much of the DNA replicated twice does not replicate a third time.

A different result is obtained when alkylated cells are incubated before addition of radioactive thymidine. Almost all of the thymidine incorporated five or twelve hours after alkylation with 2 mM MMS replicated when cultures were transferred to BUdR-labelled medium (Fig. 4, 7). However, at higher doses of MMS, newly formed DNA was not transferred to hybrid even when 12 hours intervened between alkylation and ^{3}H TdR incorporation (Fig. 8). This indicates that the failure to observe a non-replicated light density peak

Table 1. DNA synthesis in the presence of 5 mM hydroxyurea.

MMS concentration ($\times 10^3$ M)	Time of ^{3}HTdR pulse after MMS (hr)	Acid precipitable (c.p.m.)	Fraction of uninhibited incorporation
0	0–1	158	0.024
2		416	0.23
3		568	0.56
0	2.5–3.5	187	0.026
2		209	0.062
3		317	0.15
0	5–6	237	0.024
2		245	0.058
3		294	0.13

Table 2. Degradation of DNA as determined by the Hirt procedure.

Set Inhibitor	Time incubated (hours)	Ratio of acid-precipitable radioactivity: supernatant / pellet
1. Control	4	0.08
MMS – 2 mM	4	0.06
Control	24	0.09
MMS – 2 mM	24	0.38
2. Control	10	0.14
HU – 2.5 mM	10	0.16
Control	24	0.09
HU – 2.5 mM	24	0.17
Control	48	0.21
HU – 2.5 mM	48	0.72
3. Control	24	0.08
FUdR – 0.1 mM	24	0.46
Control	48	0.16
FUdR – 0.1 mM	48	1.52

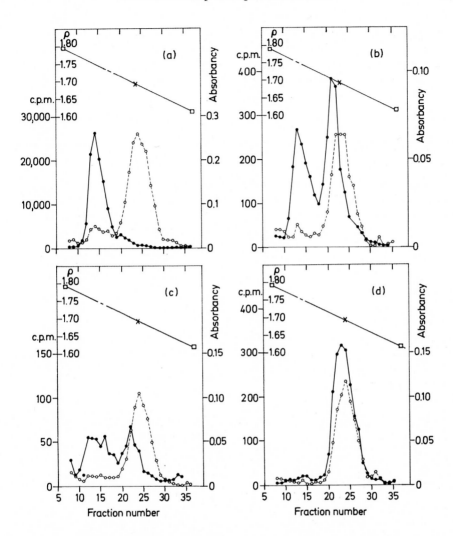

Fig. 3. Effect of hydroxyurea on ³HBUdR incorporation. HEp. 2 cells were preincubated for 2 hours in medium with 5 μg/ml BUdR in the presence of 10⁻⁶M FUdR. They were then treated for 60 min with 2.5 × 10⁻³M MMS in BUdR containing medium plus 10⁻⁶M FUdR and 5 × 10⁻³M hydroxyurea where indicated. The MMS was removed and the cells were incubated for 60 min in medium containing ³H BUdR (0.95 Ci/mM; 5 μg/ml) plus FUdR or for 120 min in medium containing ³HBUdR plus FUdR and hydroxyurea. Clortetracycline (10 μg/ml) was added at the start of incubation with BUdR and was present throughout the experiment, but the cells were grown in the absence of other antibiotics.

(a) Control, no MMS; (b) MMS-treated; (c) control plus hydroxyurea; (d) MMS-treated plus hydroxyurea. Filled circles, radioactivity; open circles, absorbancy at 260 mμ; squares, density (ϱ) as calculated from refractive index.

in the cultures treated at a lower dose was not an artefact due to failure of damaged cells to incorporate thymidine after incubation or to loss of damaged cells by detachment from the plate. We interpret these observations to mean that repair occurred in the period between treatment of cells with MMS and the addition of thymidine. According to this idea, DNA made from a damaged template is abnormal, so that cells containing such DNA cannot reproduce indefinitely. On the other hand, if DNA replication is delayed until repair is complete, the replicated DNA is normal and replicates normally. If this hypothesis is correct, a treatment which delayed DNA synthesis while permitting repair should lead to increased survival of cells. The observation of BELLI (1971), that incubation of cells in buffer (even after some cell division) led to

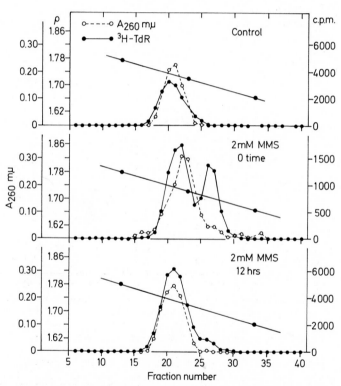

Fig. 4. Replication of the DNA synthesized by HEp. 2 cells after alkylation. Cells were treated with 2 mM MMS for 1 hour and then incubated with ³HTdR (5 μCi/ml, 3 Ci mM) for one hour either immediately (center) or twelve hours after treatment. After an additional incubation for 21 hours in unlabelled medium following incubation with ³HTdR they were incubated in medium with unlabelled BUdR (5 μg/ml) for 48 hours. DNA was isolated and subjected to centrifugation through a CsCl gradient as described in the text. Dotted line: absorbancy at 260 mμ; solid line: radioactivity in c.p.m. The slanted line indicates density (ϱ) as determined from refractive index.

increased cell survival, is in accord with our hypothesis. BELLI's observation is reminiscent of the phenomenon of »liquid holding recovery« in bacteria (HARM, 1966); bacteria maintained in buffer after treatment show increased survival over bacteria placed immediately in a medium in which growth is possible. Furthermore, my hypothesis implies that cells should be most sensitive to alkylation in late G1 or S periods since the time of repair should be minimal at these stages. These are just the periods at which Chinese hamster cells are most sensitive to N-methyl-N-nitrosoguanidine (NTG) (BARRANCO and HUM-PHREY, 1971). Since repair deficient bacterial mutants respond to NTG in the

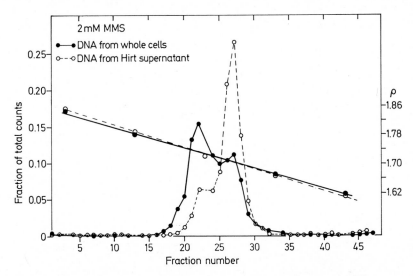

Fig. 5. Density (ϱ) distribution of DNA from whole cells and from the Hirt supernatant after incubation in BUdR. HEp.2 cells were treated with 2 mM MMS for 1 hour, labelled with ^{3}HTdR (5 μCi/ml; 3 Ci/mM) for an additional hour, incubated in unlabelled medium for 22 hours and then in BUdR (5 μg/ml) for 48 hours. The DNA was purified and centrifuged to equilibrium through a CsCl gradient. Closed circles and solid curves: DNA preparation from whole cells; open circles and broken line: DNA from Hirt supernatant. Slanted lines: density (ϱ) calculated from refractive index.

same way as to MMS (HILL, PRAKASH and STRAUSS, 1972) this observation implies that repair of alkylation-induced breaks is minimal in late G1 and S phases as predicted.

A simple explanation for the failure of DNA synthesized by alkylated cells to replicate is that such DNA contains breaks and deletions. Deletions when segregated into daughter cells are lethal when homozygous; the breaks result in DNA fragments which become lost because they are not attached to a centromere. Death then results from the genic imbalance associated with monosomy. This hypothesis depends for its explication on a discussion of the structure and mode of replication of eucaryotic chromosomes.

Despite the interest of biologists in the chromosomes, we really know very little about their structure. It is still possible to argue whether one, and only one, Watson-Crick double helix runs the length of each chromosome (WOLFF, 1969). In spite of some cytological evidence to the contrary (*loc. cit.*), the simplest way to account for the facts of genetics is to assume that a single DNA molecule is coiled so that it fits into, and extends the length of, the

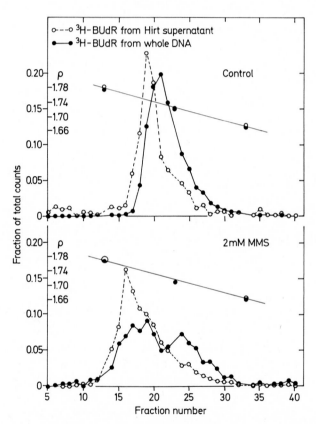

Fig. 6. Distribution of density of ³HBUdR-labelled material in the Hirt supernatant as compared to cellular DNA. HEp. 2 cells were pretreated with BUdR (5 μg/ml) for 2 hours, treated with 2 mM MMS in the presence of BUdR, labelled with ³HBUdR (5 μg/ml; 0.95 Ci/mM) for 1 hour and chased with unlabelled BUdR (5 μg/ml) for an additional 3 hours. The cells were incubated 21 hours in unlabelled medium, collected and a cellular DNA and Hirt supernatant DNA were prepared and centrifuged to equilibrium in a CsCl gradient. Solid circles: radioactivity from whole DNA; open circles: radioactivity from supernatant DNA; slanted lines: density (ϱ) as calculated from refractive index. The total radioactivity was normalized for the comparison.

chromosome. I assume that chromosomes do not contain »linkers« (non-DNA material inserted into the DNA to define sections) but it is possible that there are single-strand breaks, alkali-labile bonds, or even peculiar sequences of bases present to signal the start of special regions.

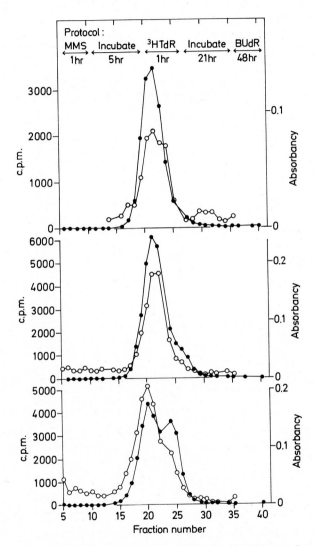

Fig. 7. Replication of the DNA synthesized by HEp. 2 cells 5 hours after treatment with MMS. Cells were treated as indicated in the protocol (top of figure). Concentrations and conditions were as in the legend to Fig. 4. Top: control; middle: treatment with 2 mM MMS; bottom: treatment with 3 mM MMS. Closed circles: radioactivity; open circles: absorbancy at 260 mμ.

Even if it is true that the eucaryotic chromosome is essentially a single long
DNA molecule, it must be different in kind from the »genophore« (RIS and
KUBIA, 1970) of the procaryotes: repetitious DNA (BRITTEN and KOHNE,
1968) is a peculiar characteristic of eucaryotes; the DNA is differentiated into
heterochromatin and euchromatin; there is the centromere which is, or contains,
DNA but which does not divide with the rest of the chromosome at the time
of the first meiotic division; and there are numerous independently replicating

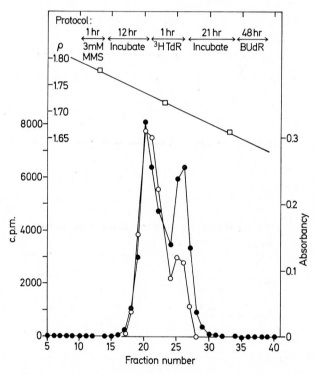

Fig. 8. Failure of DNA synthesized 12 hours after treatment with 3 mM MMS to replicate
further. Protocol as described in the legend for Fig. 4 except that treatment was with
3 mM MMS for 1 hour.

units (replicons) in each chromosome. Each bacterial chromosome or episome
normally has only one initiation point for replication. Measurement of the
duration of the S period in eucaryotes and determination of the rate of DNA
synthesis by either autoradiography or density transfer makes it clear that the
amount of DNA present in eucaryotes can only be replicated if there are many
replicating units so that synthesis can proceed simultaneously from a variety
of points in each chromosome. This multiplicity of replicating points makes

DNA replication in eucaryotic organisms different from the process in procaryotes. Replication within a molecule requires a »swivel point« often supposed to be a single-strand break at the point of origin. Multiple initiation
points require multiple »swivels«. Synthesis of most replicons must stop at
some point other than the end of the chromosome. This means that the DNA
must remain in a »Y« configuration until the adjoining replicon has completed
its replication (Fig. 9). These processes are not understood in eucaryotic cells

Replication of a section of chromosomal DNA containing two replicons

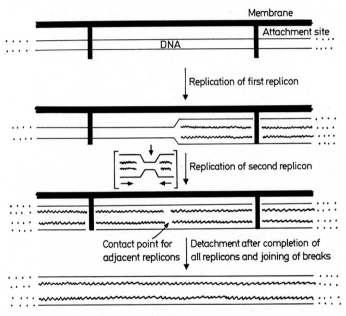

Fig. 9. A possible mode of replication of chromosomal DNA.

and this description may therefore be incorrect, but it seems inevitable that
some sort of discontinuity should exist in replicating DNA.

An unrepaired single -strand break in a procaryotic cell probably stops DNA
replication completely and leads to cell death. The great sensitivity of rec^-
and exr^- mutants to alkylating agents and to radiation indicates the lethal
effect of unrepaired breaks in procaryotes. On the other hand, breaks in DNA
do not appear to be immediately lethal to eucaryotic organisms. Cells with
aberrations, including breaks, do synthesize DNA and reach mitosis. A simple
scheme can account for this ability of eucaryotic cells to produce chromosome
aberrations. Semiconservative DNA synthesis, if it could continue in DNA

containing breaks, would convert a single-strand break into a scission, ir-
reparable by simple excision repair (Fig. 10) since replication would remove
the complementary DNA strand required to serve as a template for repair.
DNA repair after replication must require a more complex series of events in
order to restore the unbroken continuity of the DNA chain (RUPP and
HOWARD-FLANDERS, 1968).

I think that the nature of DNA replication in the eucaryotic chromosome
accounts for its ability to synthesize a relatively complete complement of DNA
from a template containing breaks. DNA replication at each replicon may

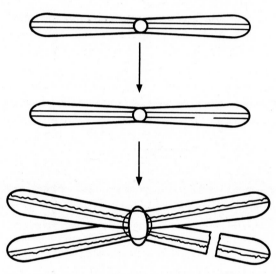

Fig. 10. Interpretation of the relationship between the formation of chromatid breaks
and the replication of broken DNA molecules.

start at a site attached to the nuclear membrane (COMINGS, 1968). Individual
replicons may be active separately and the chains may grow either in one direction or in two as proposed by HUBERMAN and RIGGS (1968). I assume that the
incomplete chromosome is held in position by the attachment sites (Fig. 9)
until the replicons are joined together. Upon completion of adjoining replicons,
i.e., at the completion of DNA synthesis, dissociation from the attachment
sites can take place and the newly replicated chromosome can condense in
preparation for mitosis.

Treatment of cells with alkylating agents results in a variety of lesions,
but I assume that the significant change for the production of chromosome
aberrations is an unrepaired single-strand break. Breaks in the DNA of alky-

lated cells will result from the depurination and chain breakage that are the inevitable consequence of alkylation. Methyl groups added to DNA by MMS are not recognized as damage by *B. subtilis* and are replicated, even though the cells do contain an enzyme which recognizes methylated DNA (PRAKASH and STRAUSS, 1970). Furthermore, alkylation damage *per se* is not excised by the UV-repair system, since UV-sensitive *B. subtilis*, unable to remove pyrimidine dimers, is hardly more sensitive than the wild-type to NTG, MMS or propiolactone (Fig. 2). It seems likely that it is the apurinic sites and single-strand breaks which are recognized as damage and repaired by bacteria. Eucaryotic cells presumably behave in the same way, except that their time scales are different. The half-life for depurination of methylated DNA is about 150 hours at 37° C (LAWLEY and BROOKES, 1963) and while this corresponds to many bacterial generations, it may correspond to only 6 eucaryotic cell generations.

I assume that the single-strand break acts as a block to replication along the strand in which the break occurs. Unless the break is repaired before the replication complex reaches the site of the break, there will be a gap in replica-

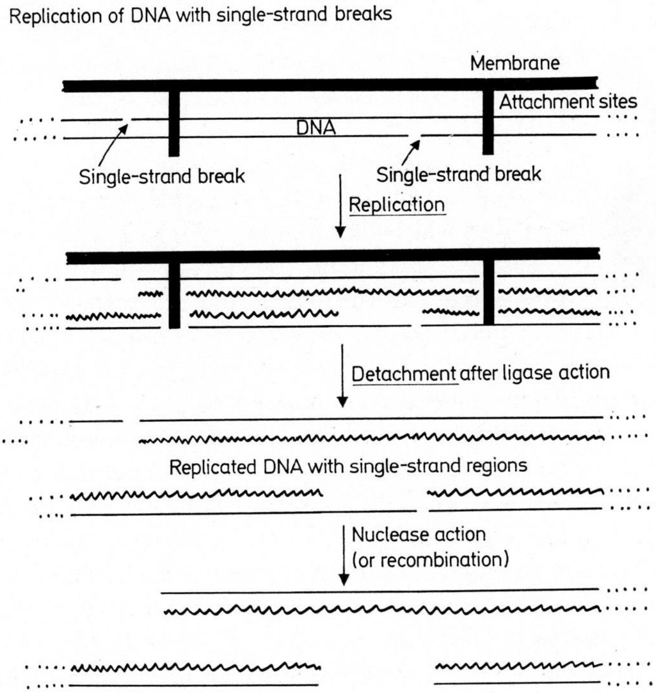

Replication of DNA with single-strand breaks

Fig. 11. An interpretation of the origin of DNA fragments as a result of the replication of DNA containing unrepaired single-strand breaks.

tion between the site of the break and the next replicon (Fig. 11). This single-strand gap will eventually result in a chromatid deletion.

An alternate hypothesis is based on the observed ability of single-strand breaks to make DNA an efficient template for DNA polymerase and on the observation of BILLEN (1969) that irradiation of *E. coli* produces new initiation sites for DNA replication. This hypothesis supposes that each break serves as a new initiation site for DNA synthesis and also predicts the production of chromatid breaks as a result of replication along a damaged template but does not predict the production of deletions. We have tested this hypothesis as follows: HEp. 2 cells were incubated for $2^1/_2$ hours in medium containing ^{3}H TdR, chased 30 min, treated with MMS in BUdR-labelled medium and then incubated 3 hours in fresh medium with BUdR. If new initiation sites were created in the newly synthesized DNA by treatment with MMS, and if these new sites were active in the S period under way, labelled hybrid DNA should have been detected. No label was detected in the hybrid, but a great deal of radioactivity was found at an intermediate density of about 1.712 in both treated and control cells. Such intermediate density DNA may indicate the elongation of growing chains. Although not decisive, this experiment suggests the use of the first hypothesis which does not require the initiation of new chains at single-strand breaks (Fig. 11). Furthermore, there is evidence that a gap along a single strand of DNA is the result of the replication complex passing a pyrimidine dimer (IVER and RUPP, 1971).

According to the hypothesis shown in Fig. 11, chromosome replication will continue in alkylated cells throughout the S period, except that the more breaks induced, the smaller will be the amount of new DNA synthesized since the number of gaps between breaks and the ends of replicons will depend on the dose of alkylating agent. At the conclusion of S, the chromosome will separate from the attachment site as indicated in Fig. 9. This particular model (Fig. 11) predicts a single-stranded, non-replicated region at the end of each fragment. Such a region might be removed by nuclease action or might serve as the basis for the pairing needed to produce more complex aberrations.

It is possible to compare some predictions of the hypothesis with data on the yield of chromosome aberrations following alkylation af cells. For example, it is clear that if there are no breaks at the time the replication complex passes the once damaged region, no aberrations can occur. The maximum yield of aberrations should therefore occur when cells are treated in S since cells at this stage will not have a chance to repair the damage. EVANS and SCOTT (1969) have made a series of relevant observations on the induction of chromosome aberrations in *Vicia faba* treated with nitrogen mustard. These investigators showed that:

1. Structural changes were produced by nitrogen mustard only when the cells carried out DNA synthesis – DNA synthesis was necessary for the production of aberrations.
2. Only chromatid type aberrations were induced by nitrogen mustard in contrast to the chromosome type aberrations characteristic of cells exposed to ionizing radiation.
3. At the first mitosis after treatment, chromatid aberrations were observed in cells exposed in G1 and S periods but not in G2.
4. Cells treated in G1 contained chromatid aberrations at the first mitosis, but the frequency observed was less than half that observed in cells treated in S, indicating the action of some »repair« process.
5. For all cells, the frequency of aberrations seen at the second mitosis after treatment was higher than at the first; cells treated in G2 gave visible aberrations at the second mitosis; cells treated in G1 or S gave a higher frequency of aberrations at the second mitosis.

Our observations on DNA replication parallel the observations of EVANS and SCOTT (*loc. cit.*) so closely that it is difficult to suppose that the same process was not being studied in different ways. DNA made immediately after alkylation fails to replicate. DNA made a period of time after alkylation does replicate and repair synthesis occurs in the interval. I assume that the DNA made immediately after alkylation can be identified with the DNA involved in chromatid breaks and that the DNA contained in a chromatid fragment does not replicate. The observation that cells treated in G2 gave visible aberrations only at the second mitosis is also understandable since a single-strand break at the time when the chromosomes have doubled will not yield a DNA scission until the next DNA replication, and such a break would show up only at the second mitosis. The observation of EVANS and SCOTT that a higher frequency of aberrations was observed in the second mitosis after treatment of cells in G1 or S may reflect the accumulation of chain breaks from alkylated sites.

This way of picturing chromosome breaks can be extended to include breaks caused by agents which inhibit DNA synthesis. If synthesis of an already active replicon continues in the presence of an inhibitor such as hydroxyurea or FUdR, and if new replicons are not initiated as the amounts of precursor diminish, growing points will remain for longer periods in the replicating DNA. If such growing points are particularly susceptible to nuclease action, scission of DNA will result from prolonged incubation with inhibitor (Fig. 12). On the chromosomal level, such nuclease action would result in the »shattering« of chromosomes, as observed during incubation with hydroxyurea (YU and SINCLAIR, 1968).

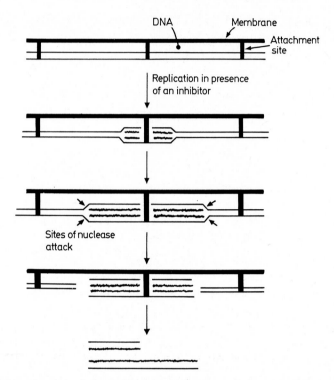

Fig. 12. An interpretation of the origin of DNA fragments as a result of incubation with inhibitors of DNA synthesis.

Our observations with the inhibitor of DNA synthesis, hydroxyurea (HU), can be used to illustrate this hypothesis. We found (COYLE and STRAUSS, 1970) that:

1. HEp. 2 cells incubated in the presence of HU continued to incorporate a small amount of thymidine into nuclear DNA.
2. Thymidine incorporated by control cells sedimented as an aggregate when lysates of more than 10^4 cells were placed on an alkaline sucrose gradient (Fig. 13). A one-hour pulse of thymidine incorporated by HEp. 2 cells incubated with HU did not sediment with the aggregate, but rather as acid-precipitable material of about 27S. HU action was reversible if inhibitor was not present for more than 20–24 hours. After a short additional incubation without inhibitor, thymidine incorporated in the presence of HU sedimented with the aggregate. After 24 hours the effect of inhibitor was not reversible.
3. After 24 hours incubation in the presence of HU, the DNA synthesized in the presence of inhibitor was found as small fragments (about 20S) in the supernatant in the Hirt fractionation (Table 2).

4. Incubation of cells with BUdR in the presence of HU led to the synthesis of a high proportion of a DNA of density only slightly greater than light DNA (Fig. 3) suggesting the formation of partially completed chains. These observations fit the hypothesis of chromosome fragmentation presented in Fig. 12.; the initial formation of small chains, the conversion into double-strand scissions, and the incomplete density shift are all in accord with the hypothesis presented.

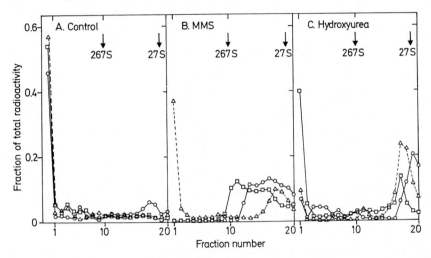

Fig. 13. Sedimentation of incorporated ³H-thymidine through an alkaline sucrose gradient. A. Control: Cells incubated an initial 30 min with ³HTdR were incubated an additional 30 min (○); 2 hours (□) or 24 hours (△) before lysis. B. MMS-treated: Cells treated with 2 mM MMS were incubated with ³HTdR and then an additional 30 min (○); 2 hours (□) or 24 hours (△) before lysis. C. HU-treated: Cells were allowed to incorporate thymidine in the presence of HU (5 mM) and were then incubated an additional 30 min (○) or 24 hours (△) before lysis. One set of cells was removed from HU after 2 hours and incubated an additional 2 hours in HU-free medium (□). Sedimentation was for 60 min at 20,000 rpm and 20° C in the SW 50. 1 rotor of the Spinco L-2 centrifuge. The gradient was 5–20% sucrose in 0.9 M NaCl + 0.1 M NaOH.

Although the myriad of facts relating to the production of chromosome aberrations in a variety of organisms can hardly be accounted for by a simple hypothesis, it seems likely that there is some close connection between DNA replication and the production of aberrations. On the other hand, it is not at all clear that chromosome aberrations are responsible for cell death.

At this stage of our work we cannot distinguish between an abnormality in the DNA which prevents its replication and some cellular abnormality of treated cells which prevents their entering and completing S periods subsequent to the first division. It has been suggested (H. SWIFT, personal communication) that alkylation might affect both chromosomal and mitochondrial DNA but that the chromosomal DNA might be more readily repaired. Cell death might then be due to some defect in the mitochondria which showed up only when preformed mitochondria were diluted by several cell divisions. Although this hypothesis was proposed as an exercise showing that there are interesting alternatives to the idea that cell death is due to nuclear events, it should be noted that Todd (1968) showed that defective chinese hamster lines resulting from radiation had no gross alterations in karyotype but did show a reduced oxygen consumption. Todd (*loc. cit.*) briefly considered the relationship between these cells and the »petit« strains of yeast.

This paper began with a description of the abnormal cells observed after treatment with alkylating agents. Although a large deletion or a chromosome loss will make any cell genetically abnormal, such chromosomal deficiencies alone will not account for all cell damage, since defective lines of cells can be obtained which have no alterations in karyotype (Terasima and Ohara, 1969). Although we can now begin to account for the production of chromosome aberrations on the basis of our knowledge of the interactions of the repair mechanisms with DNA synthesis, it is not at all certain that this knowledge, alone, is of great help in accounting for the abnormal growth of damaged cells.

Abbreviations

BUdR	5-bromodeoxyuridine
FUdR	5-fluorodeoxyuridine
^{3}H BUdR	tritium-labelled 5-bromodeoxyuridine
^{3}H TdR	tritium-labelled thymidine
HU	hydroxyurea
MMS	methyl methanesulfonate
NTG	N-methyl-N'-nitro-N-nitrosoguanidine
TdR	thymidine

References

Barranco, S., R. Humphrey: The response of chinese hamster cells to N-methyl-N'-nitro-N-nitrosoguanidine. Mutation Res. *11:* 421 (1971).

Belli, J.: Daughter cell repair by mammalian cells in culture after potentially lethal radiation damage. Nature New Biology *233:* 47 (1971).

Ben-Hur, E., R. Ben-Ishai: DNA repair in ultraviolet light irradiated HeLa cells and its reversible inhibition by hydroxyurea. Photochem. Photobiol. *13:* 337 (1971).

Billen, D.: Replication of the bacterial chromosome: Location of new initiation sites after irradiation. J. Bact. *97:* 1169 (1969).

Britten, R., D. Kohne: Repeated sequences in DNA. Science *161:* 529 (1968).

Cleaver, J.: Repair replication of mammalian cell DNA: Effects of compounds that inhibit DNA synthesis or dark repair. Radiat. Res. *37:* 334 (1969).

Comings, D.: The rationale for an ordered arrangement of chromatin in the interphase nucleus. Amer. J. hum. Genet. *20:* 440 (1968).

COYLE, M., B. STRAUSS: Cell killing and the accumulation of breaks in the DNA of HEp. 2 cells incubated in the presence of hydroxyurea. Cancer Res. *30:* 2314 (1970).

COYLE, M., M. McMAHON, B. STRAUSS: Failure of alkylated HEp. 2 cells to replicate newly synthesized DNA. Mutation Res. *12:* 427 (1971).

EVANS, H., D. SCOTT: The induction of chromosome aberrations by nitrogen mustard and its dependence on DNA synthesis. Proc. Roy. Soc. B. *173:* 491 (1969).

FUKUDA, S., N. YAMAMOTO: Effect of β-propiolactone on bacteriophages and *Salmonella typhimurium.* Cancer Res. *30:* 830 (1970).

HARM, W.: The role of host-cell repair in liquid holding recovery of U.V. irradiated *Escherichia coli.* Photochem. Photobiol. *5:* 747 (1966).

HILL, T., PRAKASH, L., B. STRAUSS: Mutagen stability of alkylation-sensitive mutants of *Bacillus subtilis.* J. Bacteriol. *110;* 47 (1972).

HIRT, B.: Selective extraction of polyoma DNA from infected mouse cell cultures. J. molec. Biol. *26:* 365 (1967).

HUBERMAN, J., A. RIGGS: On the mechanism of DNA replication in mammalian chromosomes. J. molec. Biol. *32:* 327 (1968).

IYER, V., W. RUPP: Usefulness of benzoylated naphthoylated diethyl aminoethyl cellulose to distinguish and fractionate double stranded DNA bearing different extents of single stranded regions. Biochim. biophys. Acta (Amst.) *228:* 117 (1971).

LAWLEY, P., P. BROOKES: Further studies on the alkylation of nucleic acids and their constituent nucleotides. Biochem. J. *89:* 127 (1963).

MYERS, T., B. STRAUSS: Effect of methyl methanesulfonate on synchronized cultures of HEp. 2 cells. Nature New Biology *230:* 143 (1971).

PETTIJOHN, D., P. HANAWALT: Evidence for repair replication of ultraviolet damaged DNA in bacteria. J. molec. Biol. *9:* 395 (1964).

PRAKASH, L., B. STRAUSS: Repair of alkylation damage: Stability of methyl groups in *Bacillus subtilis* treated with methyl methanesulfonate. J. Bact. *102:* 760 (1970).

RIS, H., D. KUBAI: Chromosome structure. Ann. Rev. Genetics *4:* 263 (1970).

RUPP, W., P. HOWARD-FLANDERS: Discontinuities in the DNA synthesized in an excision defective strain of *Escherichia coli* following ultraviolet radiation. J. molec. Biol. *31:* 291 (1968).

TERASIMA, T., H. OHARA: Chromosome aberration and mitotic death in X-irradiated HeLa cells. Mutation Res. *5:* 195 (1968).

TODD, P.: Defective mammalian cells isolated from X-irradiated cultures. Mutation Res. *5:* 173 (1968).

YU, C., W. SINCLAIR: Cytological effects on chinese hamster cells of synchronizing concentrations of hydroxyurea. J. Cell Physiol. *72:* 39 (1968).

WOLFF, S.: Strandedness of chromosomes. Int. Rev. Cytol. *25:* 279 (1969).

Studies on the Reactivation of Bacteria after Irradiation with Ultraviolet and Visible Light in the Presence of Acetone and Furocoumarins*

A. Wacker and P. Chandra

Scientific basis for the action of light was recognized at the end of the last century. This began with the pioneering work of Finsen (1894, 1899), whose therapeutic use of light, and other photobiological studies, had aroused a widerspread interest among biologists and physicians. Soon Raab (1900) reported that light in the presence of a sensitizer damages the living organisms. This destructive action of light was termed by Raab and his teacher Von Tappeiner as »photodynamische Erscheinung«, or photodynamic action. Thus the action of light has two aspects: its usefulness and its destructive action. The recent developments in molecular genetics have made use of light as »repair« agent for UV damages. This field has astonishingly progressed in the last ten years. The process by which light repairs UV damages is known as »photoreactivation«. Our recent results show that in addition to UV damages, photosensitized damages can also be repaired by light under similar conditions.

Repair of acetone-sensitized damage to bacteria

The electronic mechanism by which pyrimidine dimers are formed when DNA is irradiated is not yet completely understood. This problem can be attacked by studying the effects of the excitation energy transfer occurring either from a sensitizer to DNA or its isolated constituents, or from DNA to a quencher. Experiments have been performed where acetone, acetophenone and benzophenone have been used to sensitize the action of light of 315 nm (Wilucki, Matthäus and Krauch, 1967; Chandra et al., 1967; Lamola and Yamane, 1967; Krauch et al., 1967; Elad, Krüger and Schmidt, 1967; Wacker and Chandra, 1967). It has been assumed that the excitation energy transfer

---

* The lecture was delivred by Prof. P. Chandra to whom the correspondence should be sent.

which eventually will give rise to a photochemical lesion takes place at the triplett level (KORNHAUSER, HERAK and TRINAJSTIC, 1968). Since UV light of 315 nm does not excite pyrimidines, it is obvious that the ketone molecule plays the role of transferring energy. In particular, the carbonyl group is responsible for the photosensitive action. From the fact that the light of 315 nm is used in these experiments and that the efficiency of photodimerization is low these authors (KORNHAUSER, HERAK and TRINAJSTIC, 1968) conclude that the n-π transitions promote carbonyl groups from S_0 to the S_1 state.

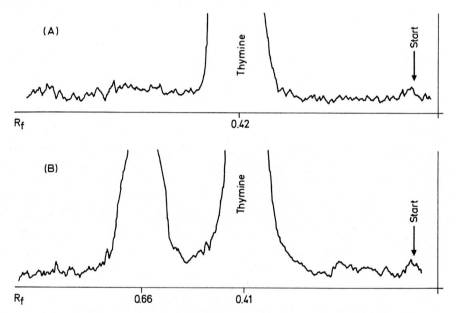

Fig. 1. Photosensitized dimerization of thymine in DNA. Thymine-labelled DNA was isolated from *E. coli* 15T⁻ cells. This DNA was dissolved in water (5 optical units/ml/ appx 10^6 c.p.m.) and irradiated at 315 nm (1.15×10^5 ergs/mm²) in the presence of 10% acetone. This was applied on an IRC-50 paper (Serva, Heidelberg) and the chromatogram was run in an ascending manner using 0.1 M acetic acid (pH adjusted to 4.5 with ammonia) as developer. Ordinate: radioactivity. (A) without acetone, (B) with 10% acetone.

The data of the sensitized reaction experiments show that the photoproducts in DNA consist almost exclusively of thymine containing dimers. These studies were carried out by irradiating thymine-labelled DNA, isolated from *E. coli* 15T⁻ cells grown on thymine-(2- ¹⁴C), at 315 nm in the presence of acetone. Paper chromatography of the hydrolyzed DNA shows a photoproduct, which on reirradiation at 240 nm gives rise to thymine (Fig. 1).

These findings suggest a new way to find out the nature of a particular lesion and its biological significance. Pyrimidine on irradiation by UV light undergoes several photochemical reactions. As a result, the specific role of dimers on UV irradiation is not easy to predict. The contribution of the total pyrimidine dimers, but not the thymine dimers alone, to the biological damage can be studied by the extent to which they are split by the photo-reactivating enzyme (SETLOW, 1964; SETLOW, 1966), or their excision by the

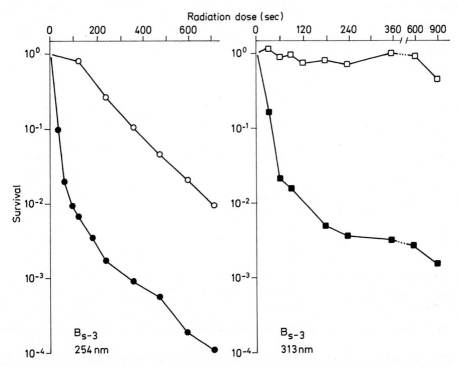

Fig. 2. Photosensitized inactivation of *E. coli* B$_{s-3}$ by acetone and its photoreactivation. Left panel: irradiation at 254 nm. Right panel: irradiation at 313 nm in the presence of 10% acetone. Closed symbols: without photoreactivation; open symbols: with maximum photoreactivation.

dark-repair system (SETLOW and CARRIER, 1964). However, using the acetone-sensitized reaction one can study the biological effects of a particular lesion, namely thymine dimers, and their susceptibility to repair processes.

The dose-response curves for the loss of colony-forming ability of *E. coli* B$_{s-3}$ are shown in Fig. 2. The left panel of the curve represents inactivation at 254 nm, whereas the right panel shows photosensitized inactivation by acetone at 313 nm. Also included in the figure (open symbols) are the survival curves after a maximum photoreactivation (45 minutes at 37° C; the irradiated culture was diluted to 10^{-2} before illumination). An obvious difference in the survival curves for the two types of irradiation is that with irradiation at 313 nm a plateau of about 0.5% survivors is reached. For irradiation at 254 nm no such plateau seems to exist. Maximum photoreactivation is lower after irradiation at 254 nm than after 313 nm. This may not be important because in the latter case cells are inactivated only to a survival level from which photoreactivating light restores viability of almost all the cells after irradiation. Therefore, it seems necessary to explain why the survival after irradiation at 313 nm does not go below 0.5%. At least two explanations are possible: For physiological reasons, a small fraction of the population a) may be impermeable to acetone, or b) may possess a greater capability for dark repair than the rest of population. If the latter were true one might expect the fraction of survivors a) to become larger if the dark-repair capacity of the otherwise inactivated part of the population can also be increased (for instance by photoprotection), or b) to become smaller if the dark-repair capacity of the otherwise surviving fractions is reduced. If the former were true, one should not be able to alter the size of this fraction by changing post-irradiation conditions. Therefore, the following experiment was performed using both methods of irradiation.

Cells were inactivated down to about 2 percent survivors, i.e. slightly above the extrapolation value. Then, maximum photoreactivation was allowed to take place. *E. coli* B_{s-3} tolerates 10% acetone for several hours without any loss in viability. But, after irradiation at 313 nm, cells die further if kept undiluted during photoreactivation at 37° C. This effect is not observed if the irradiated culture is diluted 10^{-2} or if undiluted cultures are kept at 30° C for not more than 15 minutes. Therefore, the latter procedure was used here.

The cells photoreactivated to a maximum level were reirradiated at the same dose. This cycling of irradiation and illumination has been repeated several times. The results of such experiments are given in Fig. 3 for inactivation at 254 nm and 313 nm, respectively. Closed symbols denote the inactivation after irradiation at 254 nm or 313 nm, whereas the open symbols signify the maximum photoreactivation.

It can be seen that, indeed, the influence of irradiation becomes smaller with increasing doses of light (which serves at the same time as photoreactivating and photoprotective light), so that survival after five successive doses is better than after the first irradiation. Furthermore, this effect is greater, and the photoreactivation takes place more readily after irradiation at 313 nm than after 254 nm. This result is in favour of the hypothesis that survival of the fraction in question is due to dark repair. Two other types of experiments strengthen this hypothesis: When the dark-repair capacity of *E. coli* B_{S-3} was further reduced by the addition of acroflavin to the plating medium, the lower plateau was further lowered; when the more UV-sensitive strain *E. coli* B_{S-1}, whose dark-repair capacity is much lower as compared to the one of *E. coli* B_{S-3}, is used, a lower plateau could not be observed at all. In this connection it might be of interest that the survival curve for the

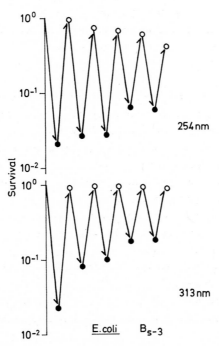

Fig. 3. Alternating inactivation and photoreactivation of *E. coli* B_{S-3}. Upper panel: irradiation at 254 nm. Lower panel: irradiation at 313 nm in the presence of 10% acetone. Closed symbols: after irradiation; open symbols: after maximum photoreactivation.

sensitized reaction after maximum photoreactivation of *E. coli* B_{S-1} is identical to that for *E. coli* B_{S-3}.

The results of these experiments may be summarized as follows: a) The lesions produced by the sensitized reaction are more uniform in the sense that the fraction of repairable lesions among all lethal lesions is considerably bigger than after direct UV-irradiation at 254 nm; b) the lowest triplett energy level of acetone is higher than those of all sensitizers mentioned above and is higher than those of all deoxyribonucleotides. Thus, if the sensitizers differ in the types of the minor photochemical lesions produced in DNA, acetone will probably give the greatest variety of photoproducts. Nevertheless, these can all be repaired by the combination of photoenzymic and dark repair. Therefore, if acetone can be used to transfer energy from light of 313 nm to DNA to produce lesions which are reversible by the above mentioned repair mechanisms, the same should be true for other presumable more selective sensitizers, provided they can enter the cells. In addition, comparisons of such sensitizers might give more information about the biological effects of the minor lesions. Since thymine dimers in any case are an overwhelming part of the lesions, such sensitized reactions allow the study of their effects on biological activities.

The role of adenosine-3′, 5′-monophosphate in the dark-repair process

The reversal of UV-induced biological damage by visible light has been discussed above. Bacterial cells under a certain set of conditions can repair the UV damage. The process, known as »dark repair«, is known to involve a number of enzymes. Bacterial cells highly sensitive to UV light are known to lack one or several of these enzymes. The first dark-repair system to be elucidated at the molecular level was the so-called »cut and patch« or excision repair system (SETLOW and CARRIER, 1964; HOWARD-FLANDERS and BOYCE, 1966; BOYCE and HOWARD-FLANDERS, 1964). These authors have shown that the dimers are extracted as whole, including the intervening phosphodiester bond, and that nucleotides were then inserted into the excised region by complimentary pairing with the intact opposite chain, and the broken phosphodiester backbone was rejoined. HOWARD-FLANDERS and BOYCE (1966), as a result of their studies with uvr mutants, believe that the repair of DNA in the dark occurs in 4 steps: a) excision by an endonuclease of a trinucleotide containing the pyrimidine dimer or other damaged nucleotides as a unit, b) widening the gap for a distance estimated to average nearly 500 nucleotides by an exonuclease acting on a free end of the chain, c) repair replication by a DNA polymerase, using the intact chain as template, to fill the gap, and d) joining the phosphodiester backbone after the last nucleotide has been inserted: an enzyme, DNA ligase, which catalyzes this reaction and has now been isolated from $E.\ coli$ and virus-infected (T_4) cells.

It is known that the inhibition of dark repair, presumably of an enzymatic nature, by caffeine and theophylline can cause mutation in bacteria (SHANKEL, 1962) and in mammalian cells (OSTERTAG, 1966). In mammalian system it is also known that caffeine competitively inhibits phosphodiesterase, which rapidly hydrolyzes cyclic AMP to 5′-AMP. This tempted us to examine the role of cyclic AMP in the dark-recovery phenomenon of UV-inactivated *E. coli* 15T⁻ in the presence of caffeine.

E. coli 15T⁻ was grown at 37° C for 20 hours in steam-sterilized glucose-salts medium containing 2 mcg/ml of thymine. At appropriate times cells were spun down at 4° C and suspended in 0.14% saline at 10^7 cells/ml. 5 ml of this suspension were irradiated with a Hanau UV lamp (Quarzlampengesellsch. Hanau, Type NN 30/89, main output at 253.7 nm). After irradiation suitable

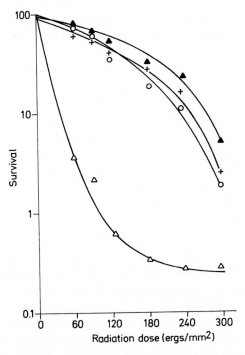

Fig. 4. Dark repair of UV-inactivated *E. coli* 15T⁻ in the presence of caffeine and cAMP. Survival of *E. coli* 15T⁻ in the presence of caffeine (△ — △), cAMP (○ — ○), caffeine and cAMP (▲ — ▲) and the control (+ — +).

aliquots were diluted with saline after each UV dose and plated on Bacto-agar. Caffeine (100 mcg/ml) was incorporated in Bacto-agar (2.0%) containing 0.5% NaCl and 0.8% nutrient broth, and 100 mcg/ml of cyclic AMP was in-stilled just before plating the irradiated suspension. After incubation at 37° C overnight, cell counts were made to calculate the percentage survivors (Fig. 4).

As shown in Fig. 4, caffeine strongly inhibits the excision repair part of the dark reactivation in *E. coli* 15T⁻ at the UV doses used. This inhibition can be reversed by cyclic AMP. A detailed examination of this reversal action of cyclic AMP has brought to our attention two facts: the sodium salt of cyclic AMP is not effective in these studies; the effects could be reproduced, also using *E. coli* K$_{12}$, only with the cyclic AMP supplied by Boehringer Mannheim GmbH, Tutzing. Under similar experimental conditions no effect could be reproduced using the preparation of Zellstoff Waldhof, Mannheim. The only difference between these two preparations, as mentioned in their respective catalogues, was that in one of the cases it was Na-salt, whereas the other was a pure substance. We are now examining this aspect in detail .If it be true, then one has to consider the differences in the cell permeability of these preparations.

Recently it was reported that, in vivo (SIDEROPOULUS and SHANK, 1968) as well as in vitro (SHIMADA and TAKAGI, 1968), caffeine depresses the excision of pyrimidine dimers, presumably by binding to the excision enzyme involved in dark repair. The reversal with cyclic AMP of the inhibition by caffeine in our experiments indicates that both compounds compete with the phospho-diesterase-like enzymes necessary for the removal of UV photoproducts, whereby cyclic AMP binds to the enzyme with a greater affinity than caffeine.

Reactivation studies on bacteria photodamaged by furocoumarins

Furocoumarins constitute a well-known group of naturally occurring and synthetic substances which, when added to several biological systems and irradiated at long wavelengths of ultraviolet light, produce various interesting effects, which are not observed without furocoumarins, or irradiation. These biological effects are due to a photoreaction between nucleic acids and furocoumarins, leading to an inactivation of nucleic acids in molecular biological processes (CHANDRA and WACKER, 1966, 1970, 1971; CHANDRA, 1969a, 1969b; RODI-GHIERO, CHANDRA and WACKER, 1970). The damage done to nucleic acids by irradiation at 365 nm in the presence of furocoumarins (linkage of a furocoumarin molecule to a pyrimidine base forming a C$_4$-cyclo-adduct) is of a different nature to that produced by irradiation in the presence of dyes, i.e. oxydation of guanine moieties, or in the presence of ketones, i.e. dimerization of pyrimidine bases.

As reported earlier the cycloaddition product of furocoumarins with thymine (MUSAJO et al., 1967) and with uridine (KRAUCH, KRÄMER and WACKER, 1967) can be split by reirradiation at shorter wavelengths. It was therefore interesting to study the repair of the photodamage by furocoumarins to bacterial cells irradiating either at shorter wavelengths (photochemical splitting) or by visible light, under conditions in which photoreactivating enzymes are active in repairing the damage due to pyrimidine dimers.

The bacterial cells (*E. coli* B) were irradiated in 1 cm quartz cuvettes in a grating monochromator (Bausch & Lomb). After irradiation at 365 nm in the presence of psoralen (mcg/ml = 5) the cells were centrifuged in the cold, washed with physiological saline and resuspended in the same solution. An aliquot of this suspension was reirradiated at the desired wavelength (290, 312, 332, 450, 500 and 550 nm) and the percent survival was determined by plating on agar.

The reirradiation of photoinactivated cells under the above conditions was ineffective, or the damage was potentiated. To compare these results the photo-splitting of a psoralen-DNA combination was studied. An aqueous solution of DNA containing ^{3}H-psoralen was irradiated at 365 nm and the DNA was precipitated to separate it from the non-reacted psoralen. The DNA-^{3}H-psoralen combination was then reirradiated at shorter wavelengths (334, 312,

Table 1. Splitting of a DNA-psoralen combination (7.5 mcg psoralen/mg DNA) by reir-radiation at various wavelengths.

Wavelength of reirradiation	Radiation dose ($\times$ 10^5 ergs/mm²)	mcg of ^{3}H-psoralen linked/mg of DNA	Splitting (%)
365	9.1	7.5	—
334	8.6	7.5	—
312	11.2	7.5	—
254	9.2	7.38	1.50

302 and 254 nm), and the amount of labelled psoralen linked to DNA was measured after each reirradiation.

As shown in Table 1, reirradiation at wavelengths 365, 334, 312 nm are completely ineffective in releasing psoralen bound to DNA. Reirradiation at 254 nm shows a very slight release of the bound psoralen, which increases by increasing the irradiated dose. However, to achieve a significant release, very high doses of radiation are needed which, under in-vivo conditions may not be applicable.

The irradiation of furocoumarins with pyrimidine bases forms a C_4-cyclo-addition of furocoumarins to the 5,6-double bond of pyrimidine bases. Furo-coumarins can photoreact either with their 4',5'-double bond or with their 3,4-double bond. Moreover, it has been shown (DALL'ACQUA, MARCIANI and RODGHIERO, 1970) that in photoreaction with DNA a third type of photoadduct is formed in which one psoralen molecule is linked to two pyrimidine bases. Thus psoralen in photoreaction with DNA may react both, with 3,4- and 4'-5'-double bonds linking to two pyrimidine bases. This possibility was in-

vestigated by examining the denaturation and renaturation capacity of DNA.
These studies were carried out with DNA before and after irradiation in the
presence of psoralen, operating under experimental conditions used for the
determination of T_m.

The results obtained with non-irradiated DNA and with DNA irradiated for
1 and 10 minutes in the presence of psoralen are shown in Fig. 5. The denaturation of DNA irradiated in the presence of psoralen takes place at temperatures

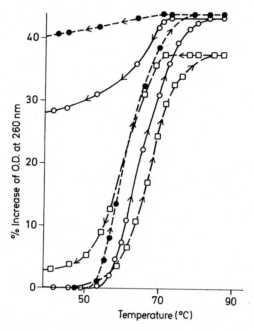

Fig. 5. Denaturation and renaturation curves of DNA. (●—●) Native untreated DNA;
(○—○) DNA irradiated for 1 min in the presence of psoralen (10 mcg/ml); (□—□)
DNA irradiated for 10 min in the presence of psoralen.

progressively higher; moreover, the total percent increase of the optical density
becomes smaller, indicating that after irradiation a fraction of DNA cannot be
denatured (1% after 1 minute and 14.5% after 10 minutes of irradiation).
By decreasing the temperature, renaturation takes place only to a small degree
in the non-irradiated DNA, while after irradiation it becomes more easy. This
behaviour is characteristic of DNA containing interstrand cross-linkings.
Using a molecular model of the double-stranded native DNA (Crystal Structure
Ltd., Bottisham-Cambridge, England) and a molecular model of psoralen on the
same scale, we have studied the various positions that an intercalated psoralen

molecule can assume. As pointed out also by COLE (1970), when psoralen is intercalated between two stacked base pairs it can assume two different positions in which it has both the 4′,5′- and 3,4-double bonds aligned with 5,6-double bonds of the two pyrimidine bases of the opposite strands. Therefore, in these two positions psoralen can form cross-linkings (Fig. 6).

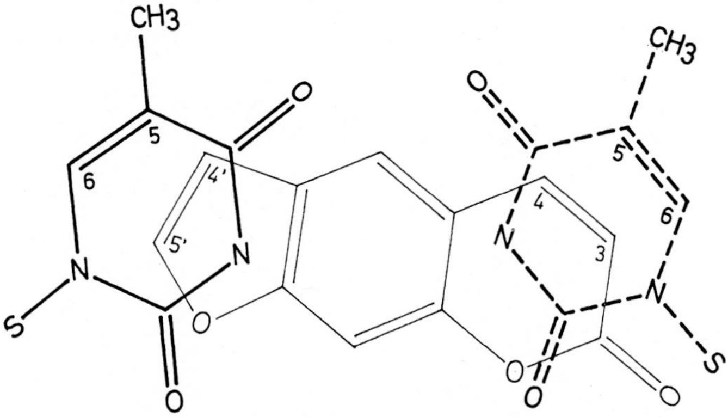

Fig. 6. Projection of a psoralen molecule intercalated between two base pairs in DNA. Only two thymines belonging to the opposite strands are shown.

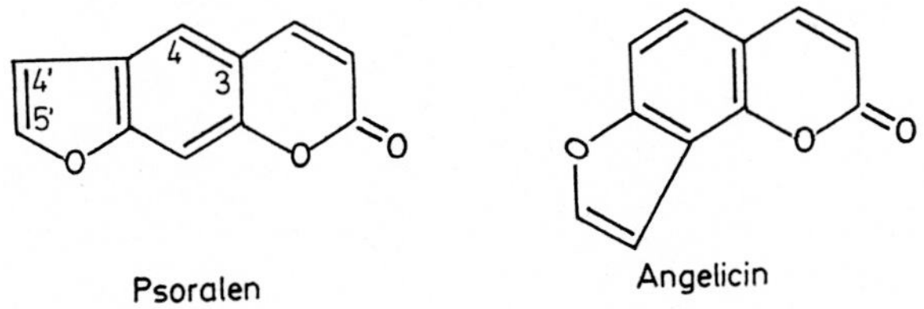

Psoralen   Angelicin

Fig. 7. Chemical structures of psoralen and angelicin.

The formation of cross-linkings by psoralen in DNA may contribute to explain why photodamage by psoralen to bacterial cells is not reactivable by reirradiation with visible light, i.e. under conditions which usually repair the damage due to pyrimidine dimers (photoreactivation).

To verify this hypothesis, we have performed experiments to study reactivation of bacterial cells damaged by irradiation in the presence of angelicin (Fig. 7). This angular furocoumarin though covalently binding to DNA by means of a C_4-cyclo-addition to the pyrimidine bases, does not form interstrand cross-linkings (DALL'ACQUA et al., 1971).

We have studied first the possibility of splitting a ^{3}H-angelicin-DNA combination under conditions employed for psoralen (see Table 1). DNA-angelicin

Table 2. Photosplitting of angelicin from a DNA-angelicin combination.

Wavelength of reirradiation	Radiation dose ($\times 10^5$ ergs/mm²)	Angelicin linked to DNA (mcg/mg)	Splitting (%)
365	15.2	8.30	—
334	16.0	8.30	—
312	13.5	8.30	—
302	16.5	7.15	13.8
254	17.3	6.14	26.0
240	15.1	6.00	27.7

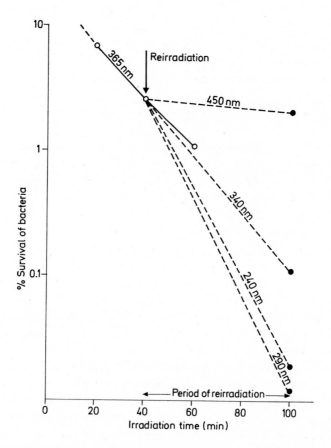

Fig. 8. Effect of reirradiation on the survival of bacteria photodamaged by angelicin. For details see text.

combination was prepared by irradiation of an aqueous solution of DNA containing ^{3}H-angelicin at 365 nm. Angelicin has a low photoreactivity with DNA, much lower than that of psoralen; however, after a long period of irradiation, we obtained a sample of DNA containing 8.30 mcg of ^{3}H-angelicin covalently bound to 1 mg of DNA, which corresponds to 15 angelicin molecules every 1000 nucleotides.

As follows from Table 2 reirradiations at 365, 334 and 312 nm are completely ineffective in releasing the bound angelicin. However, reirradiations at shorter wavelengths are able to split the angelicin-DNA combination. This is in contrast to the observations made on psoralen-DNA combination (Table 1) where little or practically no splitting was achieved under these experimental conditions.

The conditions used to split the angelicin-DNA combination were employed to reactivate bacterial cells photodamaged by angelicin. Irradiation at 365 nm for 40 minutes in the presence of angelicin (10 mcg/ml) kills about 98% population of cells. Aliquots of this suspension were reirradiated at 450, 340, 240 and 290 nm for 60 minutes, and analyzed by plating them on agar. Reirradiation at 450 nm was completely ineffective (Fig. 8), whereas reirradiations at lower wavelengths were lethal.

Conclusion

1. From the reirradiation of bacterial cells at short wavelengths one may expect to obtain a photochemical splitting of angelicin molecules bound to bacterial DNA, followed by a restoration of its functional activity. The in-vitro photosplitting of angelicin from DNA, although taking place much more easily than in the case of psoralen, requires large doses of radiation, and the more effective radiations are those which provoke a direct damage to DNA (pyrimidine-pyrimidine dimer formation). We can conclude, therefore, that the damage produced directly by the short wavelength radiations very probably is greater than the small repair produced by the same radiations.

2. Reirradiation of bacterial cells with visible light is a condition which activates the photoreactivating enzymes which are able to provoke the cleavage of the dimers between two adjacent pyrimidine bases formed in DNA by irradiation with UV light (257 nm).

The lack of reactivation of bacterial cells photodamaged by psoralen and angelicin indicates that the interstrand cross-linking of psoralen is of no importance in this process. The true explanation lies very probably in the high specificity of photoreactivating enzymes, which are able to split the pyrimidine-pyrimidine dimers, but not the photoadducts between furocoumarins and pyrimidines, even though in both cases the two molecules are bound by means of a cyclo-butane ring.

Acknowledgement

The authors gratefully acknowledge the collaborations of Profs. H. D. MENNIGMANN (Frankfurt), G. RODIGHIERO (Padova) and F. DALL'ACQUA (Padova).

References

(1) BOYCE, R. P., P. HOWARD-FLANDERS: Proc. nat. Acad. Sci. (Wash.) *51:* 293 (1964).
(2) CHANDRA, P.: NATO International Advanced Study Inst.; p. 29. Sassari (Italy) 1969a.
(3) CHANDRA, P.: Kemija Industr. *11:* 657 (1969b).
(4) CHANDRA, P., A. WACKER: Z. Naturforsch. *21b:* 663 (1966a).
(5) CHANDRA, P., A. WACKER: Biophysik *3:* 214 (1966b).
(6) CHANDRA, P., A. WACKER: Stud. Biophys. *24/25:* 437 (1970).
(7) CHANDRA, P., A. WACKER: Biophysik *7:* 245 (1971).
(8) CHANDRA, P., P. MILDNER, H. FELLER, A. WACKER: Europ. Symp. Photobiol.; p. 145. Hvar (Yugoslavia) 1967.
(9) COLE, R. S.: Biochim. biophys. Acta (Amst.) *217:* 30 (1970).
(10) DALL'ACQUA, F., S. MARCIANI, G. RODIGHIERO: FEBS-Letters *9:* 121 (1970).
(11) ELAD, D., C. KRÜGER, G. M. J. SCHMIDT: Photochem. Photobiol. *6:* 495 (1967).
(12) FINSEN, N. R.: Hospitalstidende *36:* 1069 (1894).
(13) FINSEN, N. R.: Über die Anwendung des Lichtes. Vogel Verlag, Leipzig 1899.
(14) HOWARD-FLANDERS, P., R. P. BOYCE: Radiat. Res. Suppl. *6:* 156 (1966).
(15) KORNHAUSER, A., J. N. HERAK, N. TRINAJASTIC: Chem. Commun. *1968:* 1108.
(16) KRAUCH, C. H., D. M. KRÄMER, A. WACKER: Photochem. Photobiol. *6:* 341 (1967).
(17) KRAUCH, C. H., D. M. KRÄMER, P. CHANDRA, P. MILDNER, H. FELLER, A. WACKER: Angew. Chem. *79:* 944 (1967).
(18) LAMOLA, A. A., T. YAMANE: Proc. nat. Acad. Sci. (Wash.) *58:* 443 (1967).
(19) MUSAJO, L. et al.: Photochem. Photobiol *6:* 711, 927 (1967).
(20) RAAB, O.: Z. Biol. *39:* 524 (1900).
(21) RODIGHIERO, G., P. CHANDRA, A. WACKER: FEBS-Letters *10:* 29 (1970).
(22) SETLOW, J. K.: Photochem. Photobiol. *3:* 405 (1964).
(23) SETLOW, J. K.: Radiat. Res. Suppl. *6:* 141 (1966).
(24) SETLOW, R. B., W. L. CARRIER: Proc. nat. Acad. Sci. (Wash.) *51:* 226 (1964).
(25) SHIMADA, K., Y. TAKAGI: Biochim. biophys. Acta (Amst.) *145:* 763 (1968).
(26) SIDEROPOLOS, A. S., D. M. SHANKEL: J. Bact. *96:* 198 (1968).
(27) WACKER, A.: Progr. in Nucleic Acid Res. Vol *1:* 369 (1963).
(28) WACKER, A., P. CHANDRA: Stud. biophys. *3:* 239 (1967).
(29) WILUCKI, I., H. MATTHÄUS, C. H. KRAUCH: Photochem. Photobiol. *6:* 497 (1967).

The Distribution of Chromosome Aberrations in Human Leukocytes after X-Ray Therapy and Myxovirus Infection

S. Stenman

In the present paper results are reported on the cytogenetic effect of virus infection in vitro of lymphocytes from X-irradiated patients. Dose-response curves of radiation-induced chromosome damage are presented, and the influence of lymphocyte kinetics on the frequency of chromosome aberrations in blood lymphocytes, after partial body irradiation, is discussed.

During our earlier investigations on virus-induced chromosome aberrations, we observed a morphological similarity between damage of this kind and that caused by ionizing irradiation and radiomimetic drugs or FUDR. In particular, chromosome pulverization which was caused by virus treatment and chromosome shattering in irradiated or FUDR-treated cells seemed morphologically similar. Furthermore, this type of treatment also causes less severe damage, such as chromatid or chromosome breaks and rearrangements (5, 8, 13, 16). It was therefore thought that chromosome pulverization and shattering are similar phenomena. To elucidate this we investigated whether there is a synergism between irradiation and viruses as concerns their ability to cause chromosome damage. For this purpose we infected phytohemagglutinin-stimulated peripheral lymphocytes from irradiated patients with different myxoviruses known to cause chromosome breaks and pulverization (2, 16).

After the project was started we detected that the chromosome pulverization was not the damage of metaphase chromosomes, as originally believed. The chromatin fragments of pulverized cells are condensed interphase chromosomes, and the change is caused by virus-induced cell fusion, by which mechanism an interphase nucleus is introduced into the cytoplasm of a metaphase cell (16). This results in a premature condensation of interphase chromosomes which form small fragments instead of becoming morphologically normal metaphase chromosomes (7). Our finding was therefore to be expected when we observed that pre-irradiation did not make cells more susceptible to virus-induced chromosome pulverization. These results are, therefore, not presented in more detail here.

The patients were females, 29 in all, radically operated for clinically unmetastasized cancer of the breast. They were all treated, according to the same procedure, with X-rays in four fields on the chest, the supraclavicular and the axillary lymphatic tissue. The treatment was administered in 32 fractions of 300–350 rad each, during approximately 6 weeks. The accumulated skin dose was then calculated.

Blood lymphocytes were cultured and chromosome preparations made according to standard techniques (9). Fifty to one-hundred cells from each

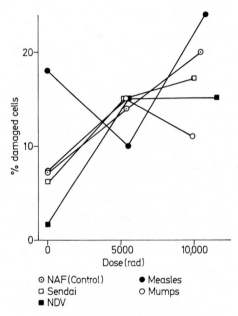

Fig. 1. Chromatid aberrations after treatment of peripheral lymphocytes from irradiated patients with myxoviruses.

culture were scored for chromatid and chromosome aberrations. In the statistical analysis a chromosome fragment was calculated as one break, a dicentric or a ring with an accompanying fragment as two breaks, and tricentrics with two fragments as four breaks.

The patients were divided into two groups. In the first group of 9 patients the cytogenetic effect of virus infection on blood lymphocytes from irradiated patients was investigated. The cells were cultured for 70–76 hours, and during the last 4 hours they were treated with different myxoviruses. Sendai, Newcastle Disease Virus (NDV), mumps and measles viruses were used, and normal allantoic fluid (NAF) was the virus control because the viruses were produced on chick allantoic membranes.

From each patient one blood sample was obtained before therapy. Two blood samples were obtained during therapy, the first after 16 treatments, i.e. after half the total treatment when the mean accumulated skin dose was 5,570 rad. The second sample was taken at the end of treatment when the mean dose was 10,540 rad. The results of similarly treated cultures were pooled.

In cultures from unirradiated patients only cells infected with measles virus had a higher frequency of chromatid aberrations than NAF-treated control cells (Fig. 1). This difference, however, was not significant. In cultures made when the patients had received half of the radiation therapy none of the viruses caused a higher frequency of chromatid damage than observed in the NAF-treated control cultures. At the end of the therapy, once again only measles caused a higher frequency of damage than in the control cultures, but the difference was not significant.

Remarkable in these experiments was that the frequency of chromatid damage in NAF-treated control cultures increased with the radiation dose. This is obviously due to the relatively long culture time of 70–76 hours (1, 3, 18), because in the second patient group no such increase occurred in cells cultured for only 50 hours.

The cytogenetic effect of virus infection on pre-irradiated cells was thus antagonistic rather than synergistic as no significant increase in chromatid aberrations or chromosome pulverization occurred but rather a decrease in most experiments. This may, however, merely reflect a lowered ability of irradiated and infected cells to enter mitosis.

The results from all virus-treated cultures were pooled when chromosome damage was scored, because a similar trend was observed in all experiments: in virus-treated cultures the frequency of chromosome aberrations was lower than in NAF-treated controls (Fig. 2). This again may reflect a mitotic inhibition of virus infection in cells damaged by the irradiation.

The second group consisted of 20 patients, and the dose-response after partial body irradiation was investigated. Blood samples were taken once before and twice during therapy. The first sample of irradiated cells was taken randomly before the patients had received 16 treatments, and the second sample when they had been given an additional 4500 rad of X-irradiation. The cells were harvested after 50 hours.

The dose-response curves were calculated separately for single-hit aberrations (fragments) and double-hit aberrations (dicentrics and rings). The aberration yield was tested by the simplified formula $y = bDx$ (17), but the coefficient x did not exceed 1 and linear dose-response curves gave better

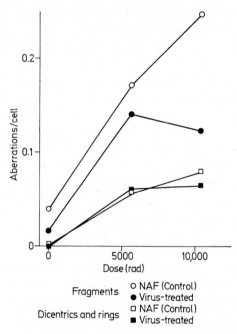

Fig. 2. Chromosome aberrations after treatment of peripheral lymphocytes from irradiated patients with myxoviruses.

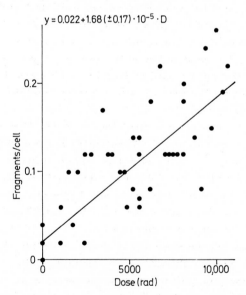

Fig. 3. Frequency of fragments in peripheral lymphocytes of X-irradiated cancer patients.

coefficients of correlation. The yield of fragments (Fig. 3) was thus $y = 0.022 + 1.68 (\pm 0.17) \times 10^{-5} \times D$ aberrations/cell/rad where D is the accumulated skin dose in rad ($r = 0.82$). The yield of dicentrics and rings (Fig. 4) was $y = 0.0086 + 1.53 (\pm 0.15) \times 10^{-5} \times D$ aberrations/cell/rad ($r = 0.83$).

The linear yield of double-hit aberrations, dicentrics and rings results from the fractionated radiation. Treatment was given for ten minutes, with intervals of at least 24 hours, which by far exceeds the longest calculated »rejoining time«, which is 30 minutes for double-hit aberrations, i.e. the longest time interval allowed between two breaks which can form an exchange aberration (17). The response in our experiment is therefore expected to follow the simplified formula $y = nD'^2$, where D' is the dose of each fraction and n the number of treatments, since after a single exposure the yield of double-hit aberrations is proportional to the square of the dose. As D'^2 is a constant, the response is linear.

When the chromosome damage was scored as the percentage of damaged cells, the yield increased until a dose of 6000 rad was achieved, but then levelled off at a plateau of 22%. The yield of damage, calculated as aberrations per cell, continued to increase above this dose (see above) which indicates that cells which had been damaged at low dose ranges became proportionately more damaged at high dose ranges, whereas relatively few new cells got damaged. Because of this observation we made the following statistical analysis.

It is known that in a uniformly irradiated cell sample cells with different amounts of chromosome aberrations will have a Poisson distribution (11, 12). We scored only 50–100 cells from each patient, and we were unable to test this individually. The results were therefore pooled according to the accumulated skin dose, and five groups were obtained. The dose ranges of the groups were 0–2500 rad, 2500–5000 rad, 5000–7500 rad, 7500–10,000 rad and 10,000 to 10,800 rad. The number of breaks in each damaged cell was calculated and the obtained distribution was tested.

The cells did not have a Poisson distribution in any of the 5 groups (Fig. 5). In all groups there were too many undamaged cells, as well as cells with two breaks, and too few cells with only one break. This uniform deviation from the expected distribution suggested that the sample might form a Poisson distribution if the number of undamaged cells was decreased. This would cause an increase in the mean and a shift in the expected distribution. Our hypothesis was, therefore, that part of the undamaged cells had not been irradiated. This would mean that the examined blood sample contained two populations of cells: one which had been exposed to irradiation and one which had not. The cells in the irradiated population could be expected to form a Poisson distribution and we therefore calculated a size (N) of this as follows.

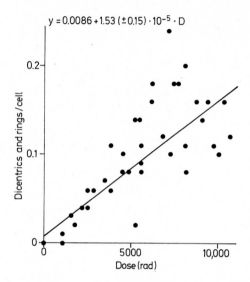

Fig. 4. Frequency of dicentrics and rings in peripheral lymphocytes from X-irradiated cancer patients.

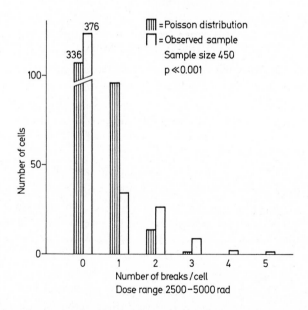

Fig. 5. Comparison between the observed sample and the expected Poisson distribution of breaks in peripheral lymphocytes from X-irradiated patients. Pooled results of cell cultures from patients who had received an accumulated skin dose of 2500–5000 rad.

Denote $y = x/M$, where x is the total number of breaks and M the total number of damaged cells in the sample. The maximal likelihood estimate $\hat{\lambda}$ of the parameter λ (the mean) of the sample N truncated at zero (i.e. the un-damaged cells are omitted from the calculation) is given by the formula $y = \hat{\lambda}/(1 - e^{-\hat{\lambda}})$. $\hat{\lambda}$ was calculated by iteration from y which was known. By definition $\hat{\lambda} = x/N$, giving the value of N, which is the size of a Poisson distribution with the same total number of breaks and damaged cells as the observed sample. The »corrected« number of undamaged cells is then N—M.

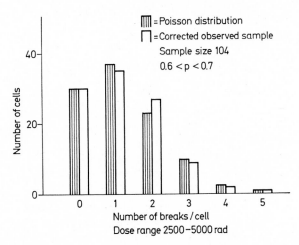

Fig. 6. Comparison between the »corrected« observed sample and the corresponding Poisson distribution of breaks in peripheral lymphocytes from X-irradiated patients. Pooled results from the dose range 2500–5000 rad. The »corrected« sample was obtained by omitting undamaged cells from the observed sample. The results were tested by the χ^2-test without using the zero class.

In the »corrected« cell samples obtained in this way, only the number of undamaged cells had changed. Three of these »corrected« samples did not deviate significantly from a Poisson distribution (Fig. 6), but the samples between 5,001–10,000 rad did so.

The results show that there is a definite possibility that the blood of the patients contained cells which had not been irradiated at all. These cells were scored as supernumerous undamaged cells, and they caused a shift from the expected Poisson distribution. One explanation for this must be that the patients were subjected to partial body irradiation. The chromosome damage observed in the blood lymphocytes, namely, reflects the situation in the lymphatic tissue of the whole body. After partial body irradiation only the cells in the irradiated regions are damaged. Cells which are irradiated in the blood of this region are relatively few, because probably less than 10% of the lymphocyte pool is in the blood (14, 15). In our calculation the size of the »corrected« sample as a percentage of the observed sample corresponds to the relative amount of lymphatic tissue in the irradiated part of the body as compared to the total amount of lymphatic tissue. At lower dose ranges this is 17%, and at higher ranges about 30%. The increase is caused by the recirculation of lymphocytes, which causes the damaged cells to move out of the irradiated region to other parts of the body, while new undamaged cells repopulate the irradiated lymph nodes. In the »corrected« sample 80% of the cells were damaged at the higher dose ranges, which indicates that most cells in the irradiated region had been damaged.

Other factors can also influence the size of the »corrected« samples. Repair of chromosome damage is important (6), but elimination of damaged cells, as of normal lymphocytes, also occurs (4, 10).

Our results indicate that the quantitative effect of ionizing irradiation on the yield of chromosome aberrations in peripheral blood lymphocytes must vary in proportion with the relative amount of lymphatic tissue irradiated. Therefore, the size and site of the radiation fields, the length of each treatment, and the interval between successive treatments, are important factors which contribute to the variation of the results in different investigations. It is important to keep this in mind when one attempts to use chromosome aberrations of peripheral lymphocytes as a biological measurement for radiation dose.

References

(1) AMROSE, A. P., E. J. PLOTZ, A. A. STEIN: Residual chromosomal aberrations in female cancer patients after irradiation therapy. Exp. Mol. Pathol. 7: 58 (1967).

(2) AULA, P.: Virus-associated chromosome breakage. Ann. Acad. Sci. Fennicae Ser. A. IV. 89: 78 (1965).

(3) BENDER, M. A., P. C. GOOCH: Somatic chromosome aberrations induced by human whole-body irradiation: The »Recuplex« criticality accident. Rad. Res. 29: 568 (1966).

(4) BUCKTON, KARIN E., W. M. COURT BROWN, P. G. SMITH: Lymphocyte survival in men treated with X-rays for ankylosing spondylitis. Nature 214: 470 (1967).

(5) CANTELL, K., E. SAKSELA, P. AULA: Virological studies on chromosome damage of HeLa cells induced by myxoviruses. Ann. Med. exp. Fenn. 44: 225 (1966).

(6) HUMPHREY, R. M., D. L. STEWARD, B. A. SEDITA: DNA-strand breaks and rejoining following exposure of synchronized Chinese hamster cells to ionizing radiation. Mutation Res. 6: 459 (1968).

(7) JOHNSON, R. T., P. N. RAO: Mammalian cell fusion: Induction of premature chromosome condensation in interphase nuclei. Nature 226: 717 (1970).

(8) KIHLMAN, B. A.: Actions of chemicals on dividing cells. Prentice-Hall, Englewood Cliffs 1966.

(9) MOORHEAD, P. S., P. C. NOWELL, W. J. MELLMAN, D. M. BATTIPS, D. A. HUNGERFORD: Chromosome preparations of leukocytes cultured from human peripheral blood. Exp. Cell Res. 20: 613 (1960).

(10) NEFF, R. D., B. CASSEN: Relative radiation sensitivity of circulating small and large lymphocytes. J. Nucl. Med. *9:* 402 (1968).

(11) NORMAN, A.: Multi-hit aberrations. In: Human Radiation Cytogenetics (Ed. H. J. EVANS, W. M. COURT BROWN, A. S. McLEAN), p. 53. North-Holland Publishing Company 1967.

(12) NORMAN, A., M. S. SASAKI, R. E. OTTOMAN, A. G. FINGERHUT: Elimination of chromosome aberrations from human lymphocytes. Blood *27:* 706 (1966).

(13) OCKEY, C. H., T. C. HSU, C. RICHARDSON: Chromosome damage induced by 5-fluoro-2′-deoxyuridine in relation to the cell cycle of the Chinese hamster. J. Nat. Cancer Inst. *40:* 465 (1968).

(14) REVILLARD, J. P., J. BROCHIER, A. DURIX, J. P. BERNHARDT, P. A. BRYON, J. P. ARCHIMBAUD, D. FRIES, J. TRAEGER: Drainage du canal thoracique avant transplantation chez des malades atteints d'insuffisance rénale chronique. Nouv. Rev. Franç. Hémat. *8:* 585 (1968).

(15) SHARPE, H. B., G. W. DOLPHIN, K. B. DAWSON, O. E. FIELD: Methods for computing lymphocyte kinetics in man by analysis of chromosomal aberrations sustained during extracorporeal irradiation of the blood. Cell Tissue Kinet. *1:* 263 (1968).

(16) STENMAN, S., E. SAKSELA: Susceptibility of human chromosomes to pulverization induced by myxoviruses. Hereditas *62:* 323 (1969).

(17) United Nations Scientific Committee on the Effect of Atomic Radiation: Report of the United Nations committee on the effect of atomic radiation. General Assembly. Official Records: Twenty-fourth Session. Supplement No. 13 (A/7613). United Nations, New York 1969.

(18) WARREN, S., L. MEISNER: Chromosomal changes in leukocytes of patients receiving irradiation therapy. J. Amer. Med. Assoc. *193:* 351 (1965).

DNA-Repair Inhibitors and Carcinogenesis:
Inhibition of Post-UV Irradiation Growth in the Dark of Tetrahymena Pyriformis by Caffeine and the Oncogenic Mycotoxin Luteoskyrin

R. F. Mouton

A simple and reliable method for investigating the in-vivo action of agents capable of inhibiting selectively (i.e. at sub-toxic levels) the dark repair of DNA (UV or γ lesions) is to compare their action on survival of wild type or mutants of the same bacterial strain. Mutants with specific DNA sites where enzymic repair synthesis is blocked (e.g. HCR$^-$, UVR$^-$, EXR$^-$ mutant in E. coli K_{12}) are useful for such studies.

The genetic and biochemical data on the action of caffeine (CAF) and iodo-acetamide on dark repair (UV and γ lesions) of E. coli K_{12} and phage λ were reported at the »International Conference of Evian on Radiation Research« (1).

Fig. 1 illustrates the effect of sub-toxic levels of CAF added after UV irradiation of phage λ vir, to the growth medium of the infected E. coli K_{12} wild (A_{15}) and HCR$^-$ (A_{16}) strains respectively. It is important that CAF must be introduced after irradiation, otherwise the irradiated buffer would lead to UV physical protection as illustrated in Fig. 2.

While using CAF as an anti-repair (anti-HCR) agent we must not overlook the possibility that in other systems than E. coli (2), CAF may act as an inhibitor of the phosphodiesterase enzyme, converting cyclic AMP (3′, 5′) into 5′ AMP. This could enhance the glycogenolytic action of adrenalin as observed in higher organisms (Fig. 3) (3).

Experiments with CAF and iodoacetamide (4) attracted the interest of another research group in Saclay – in particular Dr. FROMAGEOT who had observed, independently in vitro, a specific interaction of luteoskyrin with denatured DNA, in presence of Mg^{++}, as shown in the next 3 figures.

Fig. 4 shows the peculiar stereochemical structure of luteoskyrin (Ls). It is chemically a bis-8-hydroxy-anthraquinone, synthesized by *Penicillium islandicum Sopp* which grows on rice (yellow rice).

Fig. 5 shows various modes of interactions of Ls in vitro in the presence of denatured and native DNA. Complex I shows a specific absorption spectrum at 435 nm, reflecting an interaction between single-stranded purine DNA bases −Mg −Ls (5). No difference is observed if heat-denatured DNA is treated with hydrazine (i.e. becoming pyrimidine-less), complex I being unaffected.

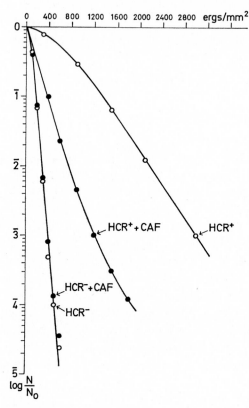

Fig. 1. Reactivation of phage λ vir after UV irradiation of *E. coli* K_{12}, A_{15} and *E. coli* K_{12}, A_{16}.

Fig. 6 shows the stoechiometry of complex I (1 denatured DNA purine base −$^1/_2$ Mg^{++} equivalent −1 Ls when the $\div$ of Mg/Ls is modified). These detailed physico-chemical studies are still continued at present in Dr. FROMAGEOT's laboratory by Dr. P. PHAM VAN and J. C. BOUHET. Since during the dark repair of UV lesions single-stranded DNA might become accessible due to action of the endo- and exonucleases, it was tempting to see how Ls would behave in comparison to the known DR inhibitor CAF.

Preliminary toxicity studies of Ls on HCR$^+$ and HCR$^-$ strains of E. coli K_{12} showed that 10^{-6}M − 10^{-4}M of Ls inhibit the growth of non-irradiated cells if Ls is introduced at the time of inoculation.

Survival curves of both strains after post-UV treatment with Ls (around 10^{-5} M) did not reveal the differences expected on the basis of the observation made previously with CAF under similar experimental conditions. Fig. 7 shows a lower UV survival for HCR$^-$ strains, but the Ls effect is just a toxic effect, as it remains the same for both strains in un-irradiated cells.

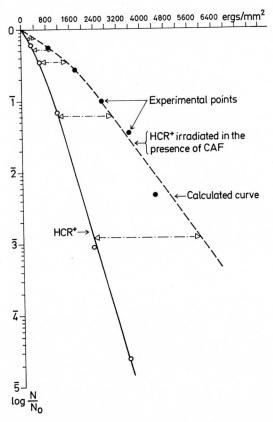

Fig. 2. Reactivation of phage λ vir after UV irradiation of *E. coli* K$_{12}$, A$_{15}$.

The above-mentioned toxicity studies indicate that Ls might not penetrate easily into the bacterial cells, presumably because of the presence of Mg^{++} in the cell wall and the concurrent formation of the insoluble Ls-Mg complex.

BRUNK and HANAWALT (6) have reported studies on the DNA dark repair in *Tetrahymena pyriformis*. This soon appeared a fascinating biological system, intermediary between bacteria and mammalian cell culture, with regard to sensitivity to drugs including Ls. Fig. 8 shows the anatomy of this eucaryote presenting a large macronucleus governing nonsexual reproduction by fission (whereas the small micronucleus governs sexual recombination). We used the strain GL, an amicronucleate mutant, for which fission can be observed under favorable conditions every 5 hours.

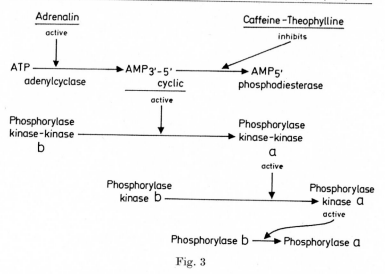

Scheme of activation of the glycogenolytic action of adrenalin by phosphorylase.

Fig. 3

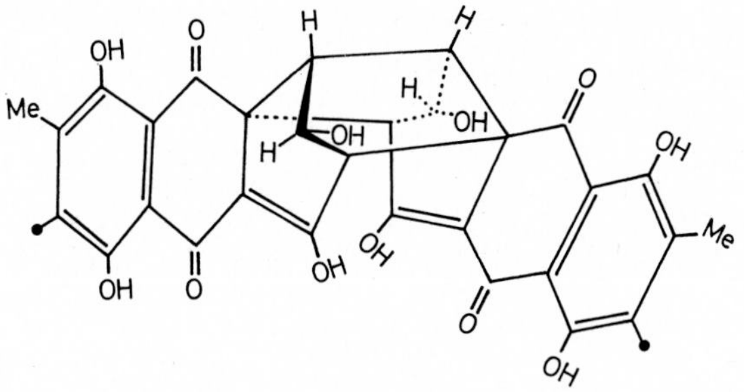

Fig. 4

I cannot enter in the details of the adaptation of radiobiological techniques used in order to experiment with this protozoan studied as early as 1932 by A. Lwoff (7). The important fact was that I could see visually through the microscope that the yellow pigment Ls would penetrate quickly through the cytostome of this animal and, accordingly I could expect that no problem of membrane permeability would interfere with the anticipated anti-repair effect of Ls after UV irradiation.

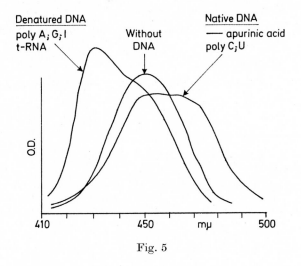

Fig. 5

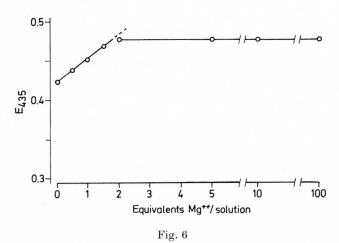

Fig. 6

In axenic conditions, combining absorption (546 nm) and counting cell measurements, described in details elsewhere (8), I got indeed very clear toxicity growth curves, always proportional to the concentration of the drug tested. Sub-toxic levels were determined for CAF and Ls as shown in the next two figures (Fig. 9, Fig. 10). Accordingly CAF 10^{-3} M (0.02%) and Ls 2.6×10^{-7} M (0.117 γ/ml) could be considered safely as sub-toxic, showing that the sensitivity of our strain to these drugs was higher than in the case of E. coli (CAF = 0,1%): in fact closer to that found for mammalian tissue culture cells (Ls = 0.1 γ/ml) for HeLa BB cells of mice (9).

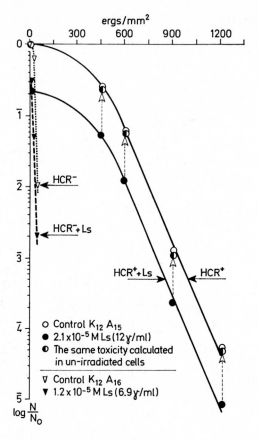

Fig. 7

Using sub-toxic concentrations of CAF and Ls, we were thus in a position to see whether or not these agents were enhancing the effect of a sub-lethal exposure to UV. We exposed *Tetrahymena pyriformis* suspension in a sterile buffer to 450 ergs/mm² UV and found indeed delay in the rate of multiplication, and decrease in the number of generations as previously reported by CHRISTENSEN and GIESE (10). (Fig. 11.)

As can be seen, Ls and CAF added immediately after the irradiation become toxic at concentrations found noninhibitory in previous control experiments. Ls inhibits post-UV irradiation growth to roughly the same extent as CAF, but at a sub-toxic molar concentration 5000 times lower.

Fig. 12 shows the increasing effect observed when the primary irradiation dose is increased from 250 to 500 ergs.

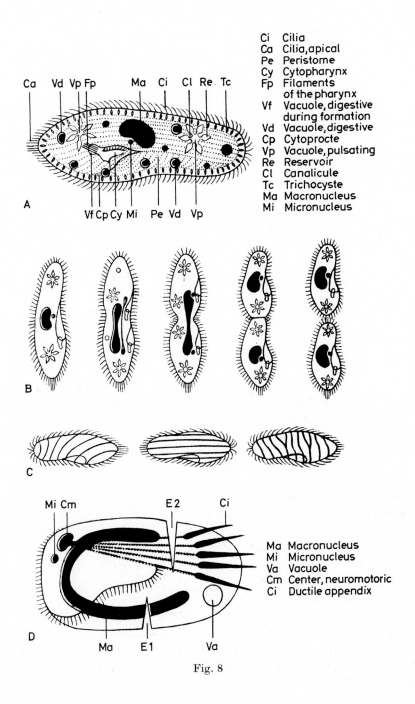

Ci   Cilia
Ca   Cilia, apical
Pe   Peristome
Cy   Cytopharynx
Fp   Filaments
      of the pharynx
Vf   Vacuole, digestive
      during formation
Vd   Vacuole, digestive
Cp   Cytoprocte
Vp   Vacuole, pulsating
Re   Reservoir
Cl   Canalicule
Tc   Trichocyste
Ma   Macronucleus
Mi   Micronucleus

Ma   Macronucleus
Mi   Micronucleus
Va   Vacuole
Cm   Center, neuromotoric
Ci   Ductile appendix

Fig. 8

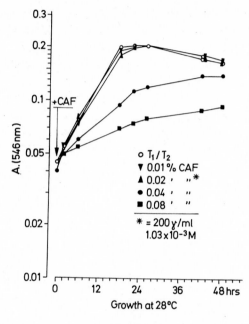

Fig. 9

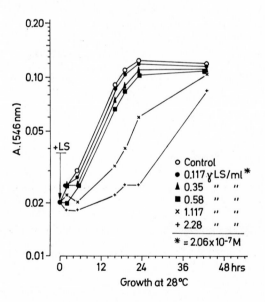

Fig. 10

On the basis of our results with CAF and Ls, we expected that Ls may interact in vivo with single-stranded DNA. This would inhibit dark repair at a later stage than does CAF, namely by interfering with the repolymerization step, whereas CAF is known to interfere specifically with the early exonuclease step of repair as illustrated in Fig. 13. This was checked in an in-vitro nicked DNA repolymerization test using DNA polymerase I of Kornberg in the presence of both repair inhibitors. Fig. 14 confirms that indeed Ls interacts with the repolymerization step which is not affected by CAF up to 5×10^{-3} M.

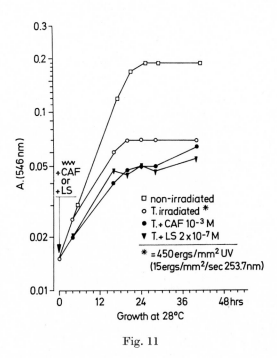

Fig. 11

Conclusion: The preliminary experiments have established at least the first correlations we were looking for:

1. in vitro, physico-chemical interaction of Ls with denatured DNA.

2. in vivo, biological inhibition by Ls of post-UV irradiation growth of *Tetrahymena pyriformis*.

3. in vitro, biochemical inhibition by Ls of the DNA repair polymerization step in nicked calf thymus DNA by the Kornberg's polymerase I enzyme.

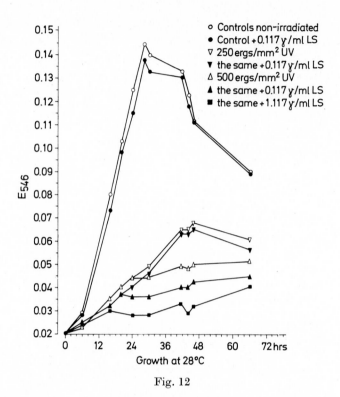

Fig. 12

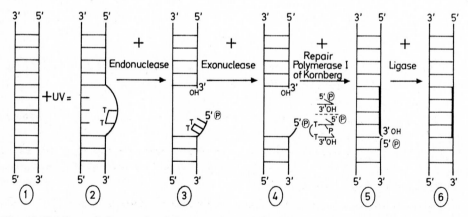

Fig. 13. Scheme of the repair of thymine dimers (GROSSMAN et al., 1968). 1. Intact DNA helix; 2. Formation of athymine-dimer due to UV irradiation, deformation of the helix. 3. Incission at point of the damage by endonuclease »enzyme of palpation«. 4. Elimination of the damaged DNA segment by exonuclease. 5. Repolymerization of the removed DNA by replication of the helix complementary to repair of polymerase I of Kornberg. 6. Recombination of the repolymerized chain by a ligase, restoration of the intact helix.

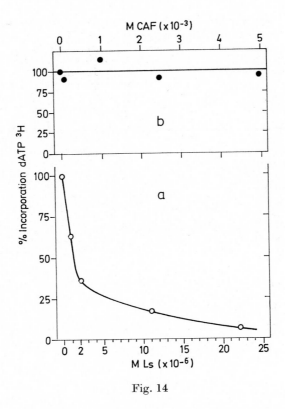

Fig. 14

Oncogenicity of Ls

Caffeine is known to be mutagenic for man (11). Luteoskyrin has been found oncogenic when administered at sub-toxic concentrations in the food to mammals, e.g. mice (12).

At whole-organism level, Fig. 15 shows an adenoma of the liver in a mouse having received Ls (0.5 mg/10 g body weight) per os for 604 days.

Fig. 16 shows survival diagrams of 2 groups of mice having received respectively 0.15 and 0.5 mg Ls/10 g body weight per os for 800 days. We have here many forms of liver cancer.

At the cellular level, Ls seems to concentrate in mitochondria, microsomes and nuclei where DNA is present. In cell cultures some studies have been recently published (13) using mice ascites tumor cells of Ehrlich (hyperdiploids 41–46 chr.), Ls being added after 36 hours (exponential phase) at a dose of 1 γ/ml (10^{-6} M). These authors (13) observed a »disequilibrium syndrome bound to DNA«, similar to »thymine death« in bacteria.

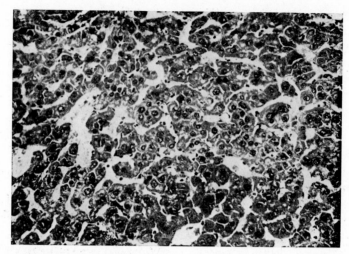

Fig. 15. Liver cell adenoma developing in the liver of mouse fed with 500 μg/10 g body weight/day of luteoskyrin for 604 days (H. and E., × 200).

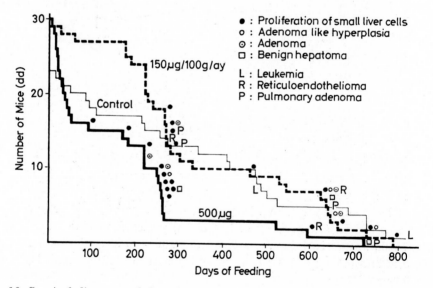

Fig. 16. Survival diagrams of the mice groups administered with luteoskyrin [MIYAKE and SAITO (12)].

When DNA replication is stopped by Ls, RNA and protein syntheses continue at half-rate. Thus replication appears to be more sensitive to the toxic action of Ls than does transcription.

Fig. 17 shows chromosomal aberrations observed when Ls-resistant sub-clones are isolated. One can see abnormally long chromosomes at metaphase pointing out to abnormal replication, an observation to be compared with that of YU (1960) after X-ray exposure. The authors (13) conclude that these in-vivo effects on replication are the result of the direct binding of Ls with DNA – in agreement with our earlier observations.

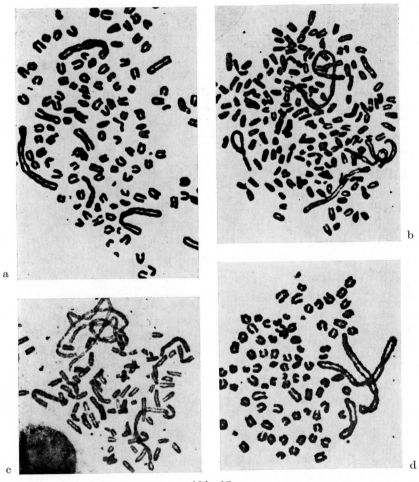

Abb. 17

Even if at a 10^{-6} M concentration, Ls affects transcription in the above system, as reported by UENO (14), in no case the energetic metabolism of these tumor cells is inhibited by Ls, the aerobic or anaerobic production of lactic acid remains unaffected.

Conclusions: The observations on the oncogenicity and effect of Ls on cell cultures brings further conclusions:

4. in vivo, the oncogenic effect of Ls is observed in whole animal, but only after long-term feeding tests.
5. in vitro, in the toxic range of concentration of 10^{-6} M, sub-cloning of Ls-resistant Ehrlich ascites tumor cell cultures leads to chromosomal abnormalities.
6. in vivo, in the toxic range of concentration of 10^{-6} M of Ls, the energetic metabolism of the Ehrlich ascites tumor cells remains unaffected.

These conclusions added to the former ones observed in our laboratory (see above), are indeed in good agreement with our basic working hypothesis that inhibition of repair, a mechanism which normally protects DNA exposed to radiation or chemical damage, could explain the cocarcinogenicity of some compounds capable of interacting specifically and only with damaged DNA. The discovery that in xeroderma pigmentosum the human fibroblasts are indeed defective in one step of dark-repair function brings a general genetic support to our proposition (15).

I am contemplating to resume my research work to confirm these preliminary findings by direct analysis of repaired DNA, extending my survey to other anti-repair potential cocarcinogens or to carcinogens like aflatoxin B_1, which is already known to interact in vitro with denatured better than with native DNA (16). It may also be interesting to study luteoskyrin analog like rugulosin (Rg), the non-oncogenic pigment (bis-6-hydroxyanthraquinone) (Fig.

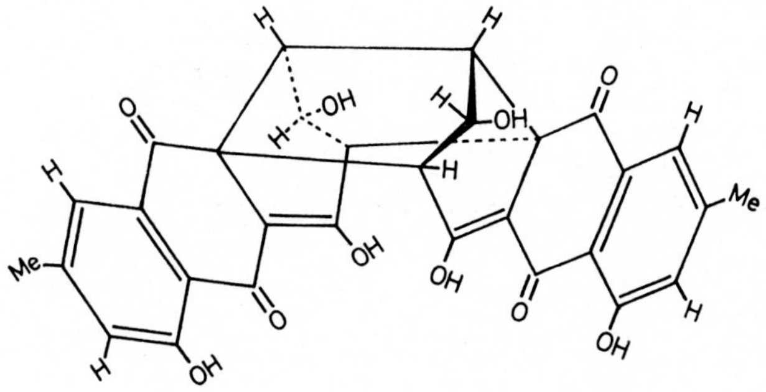

Abb. 18

18), which differs stereochemically and interacts differently with the damaged double helix. In this particular case we have found a negative correlation between lack of in-vivo UV-repair inhibition and lack of oncogenicity. Fig. 19

shows that 1.85×10^{-6} M Rg is sub-toxic for *Tetrahymena pyriformis*. Fig. 20 shows that 2.23×10^{-6} M Rg does not affect the post-UV irradiation growth of *Tetrahymena pyriformis*.

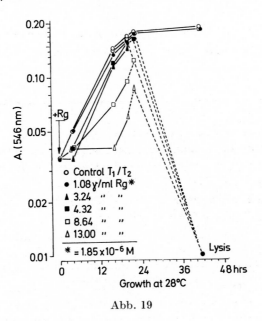

Abb. 19

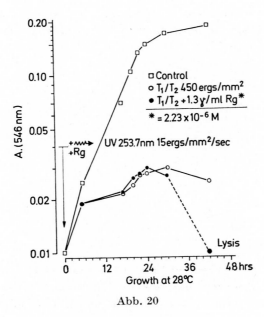

Abb. 20

On the basis of our results (8, 17) I may stress the relevance of such work in environmental carcinogenesis where *combined effects* of radiation and substances introduced artificially or naturally to our food and drugs may mimic better the true risk encountered by man. On the curative side, proper use of well localized anti-repair agents may greatly benefit radiation or chemotherapy of cancer.

References

(1) MOUTON, R. F.: Proc. IVth Int. Congress of Radiation Research, Evian 1970.
(2) BRANA, H., F. CHYTIL: Folia Microbiol. *11:* 43 (1966).
(3) SUTHERLAND, E. W., T. W. RALL: J. Amer. chem. Soc. *79:* 3608 (1957).
(4) MOUTON, R. F., O. TREMEAU: Int. J. Rad. Biol. *15:* 369 (1969).
(5) UENO, Y., A. PLATEL, P. FROMAGEOT: Biochim. biophys. Acta (Amst.) *134:* 27 (1967).
(6) BRUNK, C. F., P. C. HANAWALT: Radiat. Res. *4:* 241 (1969).
(7) LWOFF, A.: Recherches Biochimiques sur la Nutrition des Protozoaires; p. 42. Masson, Paris 1932.
(8) MOUTON, R. F., P. FROMAGEOT: FEBS-Letters *15:* 45 (1971).
(9) UMEDA, M.: Acta path. jap. *14:* 375 (1964).
(10) CHRISTENSEN, E., A. C. GIESE: J. gen. Physiol. *39:* 513 (1956).
(11) KUHLMANN, W., H.-G. FROMME, E. M. HEEGE, W. OSTERTAG: Cancer Res. *28:* 2375 (1968).
(12) MIYAKE, M., M. SAITO: Mycotoxins in Foodstuffs. Proceedings M.I.T. symposium (G. N. Wogan, ed.); p. 133. Cambridge, Massachusetts, 1964.
(13) SCHACHTSCHABEL, D. O., F. ZILLIKEN, M. SAITO, G. E. FOLEY: Exp. Cell. Res. *57:* 19 (1969).
(14) UENO, Y., J. UENO, K. ITO, T. TATSUNO: Experientia *23:* 1001 (1967).
(15) CLEAVER, J. E.: Proc. nat. Acad. Sci. (Wash.) *63:* 428 (1969).
(16) SPORN, M. B., C. W. DINGMAN, H. L. PHELPS, G. N. WOGAN: Science *151:* No. 3717, 1539 (1966).
(17) MOUTON, R. F.: Proc. Ist Europ. Biophys. Congress; Vol. *II*, p. 241. Baden near Vienna 1971.

Discussion

BOYLE: Before opening this discussion, I feel there may be questions pertaining to this morning's presentations. Does anyone have a question for Dr. OKAZAKI?

CHANDRA: WERNER [Nature New Biol. *233:* 99 (1971)] has recently reported that DNA replication and repair utilize different types of nucleotide precursors. He believes that TTP may not be the precursor for replication process. The postulated precursor for this process, TMP-X, is synthesized from TDP, which is in complete equilibrium with TTP, the precursor for repair synthesis. Unfortunately, he does not mention in this paper more about TMP-X. Since you are now coming from the Cold Spring Harbor Meeting, I would like to ask you, if you heard more about the nature of TMP-X. What does »X« precisely denote?

OKAZAKI: WERNER has two papers in »Nature« [Nature *230:* 570 (1971); Nature New Biol. *233:* 99 (1971)]. The second paper has appeared very recently and I have not read it very carefully. As I mentioned in my talk we could not confirm his results presented in his first paper. His data in the second paper may be interpreted in various ways. In the Cold Spring Harbor Meeting he suggested that X of dTMPX could be PP. There might be two pools of dTTP, one preferentially utilized for replication and the other for repair. Thymine is converted to thymidine by thymidine phosphorylase, and because of special intracellular location of the phosphorylase thymine might go preferentially to the first pool, while thymine may be incorporated into both pools.

CHANDRA: I do not quite understand the conclusions drawn by WERNER in his paper. It is to me upsetting, how one can speak of replication in a saturated suspension of bacterial cells (2×10^{10} cells/ml), used by him in these experiments.

In one of your slides, if I correctly remember, you showed some mutants with various amounts of ligase. Do these mutants have different kinetic behaviour during replication in your sedimentation experiments?

OKAZAKI: The slide showed that in two mutants, P3478 and R15, polymerase activity is very low but ligase activity is normal. So the slow joining in these mutants could not be due to ligase but due to DNA polymerase I.

BOYLE: Following UV or X irradiation of *E. coli* polA⁻ DNA is degraded very extensively [BOYLE, PATERSON and SETLOW: Nature *226:* 708 (1970); PATERSON, BOYLE and SETLOW: J. Bacteriol. *107:* 61 (1971)]. Degradation appears to be due to an exonuclease which acts on single-strand breaks in DNA. I wonder whether the slow rejoining you see in the polymerase mutants could be due to inhibition of normal rejoining by the same exonuclease activity that we see after irradiation?

OKAZAKI: It is quite possible that exonuclease and polymerase are competing at the gaps and that the slow joining of the short pieces in the DNA polymerase I-deficient mutants may be due to uncompensated exonuclease action.

KLEPPE: Dr. OKAZAKI, can you tell us anything more about the distance between these pieces? How many nucleotides do you guess that there would be? Another question: Have you done any experiments with the DNA polymerase I *in vitro* to see whether or not it can fill the gaps?

OKAZAKI: We have not measured the size of gaps but we are going to. HURWITZ and his coworkers [Proc. Natl. Acad. Sci. (Wash.) *61:* 1199 (1968)] have shown that short pieces in a normal strain can be joined *in vitro* by polymerase and ligase plus four dXTP's and DPN or ATP.

TRAUT: I would like to ask two questions to Dr. STRAUSS, one concerning the chromosome model he has proposed, the other concerning the mechanism of chromosome breakage. What happens to this model if chromosomes are not single-stranded but multi-stranded as many people believe? And the second question: What happens to the protein component of the chromosome when the chromosome is broken? I would like to ask this question especially with regard to the work of SHELDON WOLFF and his coworkers [WOLFF, SH.: Radiation studies on the nature of chromosome breakage. The American Naturalist, Vol. XCIV, 85 (1960)]. They demonstrated that in the process of rejoining of chromosome breaks protein synthesis, but no DNA or at most very little DNA synthesis is involved.

STRAUSS: A multi-stranded chromosome model requires that chromosome aberrations should not be produced until a sufficient number of generations have occurred to permit the damaged strands to segregate along with newly synthesized strands as chromatid breaks.

It is necessary to consider the difference between ionizing radiation which may break a number of strands simultaneously and monofunctional alkylating agents. The alkylation of a single base results in depurination and eventual breakage of a single chain by hydrolysis. In contrast to ionizing radiation, alkylation will only break one strand. The problem in considering the mechanism by which alkylating agents cause aberrations is therefore one of segregation which is the reason most geneticists prefer to think of chromosomes as double-stranded. Although there are observations which also imply that chromosomes are multi-stranded, there is sufficient reason, both theoretical and experimental, to continue to suppose that many chromosomes have a single DNA molecule as their backbone. If this hypothesis should turn out to be incorrect, many of our explanations will have to be revised.

I have looked at Dr. WOLFF's paper on the relationship between DNA synthesis and chromosome rejoining [WOLFF, S. and D. SCOTT: Expt. Cell Res. 55: 9 (1969)]. The data are very interesting but the question is partly one of how much DNA synthesis does occur. At the present moment, however, I would have to say that I have no idea what happens to the protein component of chromosomes during repair.

CHANDRA: Did I understand correctly that FUdR causes chromosomal aberrations?

STRAUSS: It is my understanding that chromosome aberrations are observed in cells inhibited by FUdR. This observation was made in the early 1960's by TAYLOR and his colleagues [Proc. Natl. Acad. Sci. (Wash.) 38: 190 (1962)].

CHANDRA: What is the mechanism of this chromosome aberration by FUdR? Is it possible to say that any inhibitor of DNA synthesis causes chromosome aberration, or is it due to some mechanism by which the RNA is modified so that the synthesis of some chromosomal proteins is blocked. Could someone suggest any other mechanisms for chromosome aberrations?

STRAUSS: It is more than just speculation to say that any inhibitor of DNA synthesis which acts either directly or indirectly (i.e., cycloheximide) will turn out to break chromosomes. Unfortunately. I think that it is just too early to say what the general mechanism(s) may be because of the diversity in the action of those inhibitors which have been reported to produce breaks.

MENNIGMANN: I am referring to some experiments with bacteria and FUdR. [MENNIGMANN, H. P. and W. SZYBALSKI: Biochem. biophys. Res. Commun. *9:* 398 (1962)]. You find the same, namely that you get single-strand breaks, if you inhibit DNA synthesis with FUdR or, if you are afraid of the drug, with bacteria which are genetically inhibited in the same enzyme (viz. thymidylate synthetase) which is inhibited by FUdR.

BOYLE: Are not single-strand breaks also produced by nalidixic acid?

MENNIGMANN: Yes.

PAINTER: There is only one problem and that is that FUdR causes chromosome aberrations in G_2 phase. I meant chromosome aberrations in general.

STRAUSS: I think that what seems to be contrary cytological evidence can be easily misinterpreted. Clearly the bulk of DNA synthesis occurs during the S period. At some stage however, the individual replicons will have to be joined. Now we do not know what the configuration of the DNA is at that stage and we cannot tell whether some sort of repair synthesis may not occur at the G_2 stage. I think it is impossible to decide with the data we have at present, even though I admit that they appear to support the point you made. In the same way, WOLFF's data [Amer. Naturalist *94:* 85 (1960); Exp. Cell Res. *55:* 9 (1969)] seem to show that protein but not DNA synthesis is important for chromosome rejoining. I think that with the accumulation of more facts about the biochemistry of DNA replication, WOLFF's data will turn out to fit a more conservative hypothesis of chromosome structure.

PAINTER: I agree with you. But I think at the same time one can't neglect the fact that inhibitors of DNA synthesis don't affect rejoining, but protein synthesis inhibitors do. You can say it's such a small amount that the inhibitors of DNA synthesis are not effective. On the other hand I think you cannot ignore the evidence that WOLFF has for protein synthesis. It means something and you must handle it within your final construction as a model of chromosome aberration.

STRAUSS: I'd like to say that there is evidence that inhibitors like hydroxyurea do inhibit ligase or some joining reaction. Although I do not know whether hydroxyurea inhibits ligase activity *in vitro*; our data [COYLE, M. and B. STRAUSS: Cancer Res. *30:* 2314 (1970)] and the data I mentioned yesterday published by BEN-HUR and BEN-ISHAI [Photochem. Photobiol. *13:* 337 (1971)] indicate that it can inhibit the joining of breaks *in vivo*.

BOYLE: Are you talking about mammalian systems or bacteria?

STRAUSS: About mammalian systems. BEN-HUR and BEN-ISHAI studied breaks occurring as a result of the repair of UV-induced damage. In our own work [COYLE, M. and B. STRAUSS: Cancer Res. *30:* 2314 (1970)] it appeared that newly synthesized DNA formed in the presence of hydroxyurea was not joined to larger fragments.

REGAN: We have hydroxyurea present at 3×10^{-3} M in our UV experiments and in our gamma experiments. There is no inhibition of UV repair or gamma repair by this compound.

STRAUSS: By this sucrose gradient method?

REGAN: The BU insertion and photolysis method. I mean hydroxyurea does not inhibit the shift back to higher molecular weight after gamma irradiation.

PAINTER: I think it is a very strong point on the BEN-HUR and BEN-ISHAI paper that nobody else doing sucrose gradients has got even close to these results. I mean not even close. You look after UV and you don't see anything like that.

STRAUSS: Hydroxyurea has been reported to induce chromosome breaks [YU, C. and W. SINCLAIR: J. Cell Physiol. *72:* 39 (1968)]. We have also observed the degradation of the DNA of HEp. 2 cells incubated in the presence of hydroxyurea. This degradation can be observed on alkaline sucrose gradients and also by the HIRT [J. molec. Biol. *26:* 365–369 (1967)] technique. We supposed, as an explanation for this degradation, that over the long term there is some inhibition of a joining process by hydroxyurea. Now I am sorry to have brought in the paper by BEN-HUR and BEN-ISHAI because the authors are not here to discuss their work. However, I did quote it because their results support the ideas we derive from the experiments I have just described.

BOYLE: I think the action of these various drugs is a topic that we may come back to later. Are there any other comments about this morning's papers?

TRAUT: Dr. STENMAN, how did you obtain the number of breaks and were all breaks involved in aberrations? I would especially like to know how you distinguished between breaks and achromatic lesions.

STENMAN: The number of breaks was calculated from the total number of fragments (1 break), dicentrics and rings with accompanying fragments (2 breaks) and tricentrics with two fragments (4 breaks). This is an underestimate, but the distribution of damage between the cells is correctly scored. This distribution of breaks was also the basis for our observation that only part of the lymphocytes had been irradiated. This indicates that the frequency of chromosome aberrations in peripheral lymphocytes is not a good measure of the radiation dose after partial body irradiation. We regarded a lesion as a break when the distance between the broken ends was more than the width of the chromatid.

TRAUT: But you are aware that many so-called breaks are really no breaks but are, in fact, achromatic lesions?

STENMAN: Yes, but this influences the results of virus treatment only, since in experiments in which the cells had been irradiated and not virus-treated, only fragments and exchange aberrations were scored.

ERNST: I have a question to you, Dr. Stenman. You fitted a Poisson distribution by this additional zero values to your results. Did you try other distributions as well? For instance a negative binomal one, which could yield different results?

STENMAN: No we did not. According to previous experiments *in vitro* (EVANS, H. J.: Human Radiation Cytogenetics; p. 20. North Holland Amsterdam 1967) and *in vivo* [NORMAN, A. et al.: Blood *27:* 706 (1966)] this kind of chromosome damage has a Poisson distribution.

LUCAS: What I should like to ask you, Dr. CHANDRA, is the following: because of the environmental importance of psoralens I am very interested to know whether the cross-links they form with DNA are excised. Do you know if there is still agreement that psoralens are mutagenic?

CHANDRA: I think, I made it quite clear that photochemical splitting and photoreactivation are completely different processes. The photochemical splitting called short-wavelength reversal, involves the interaction of photons and nucleic acids only. On the other hand, photoreactivation is an enzymatic process requiring visible light, or radiations in the range 3100–4400 A.

Now to your second question, regarding the repair of photodamage by psoralen. I have presented data to show that psoralen is intercalated between two thymine molecules on opposite strands of DNA, whereas the angular furocoumarin, angelicin, does not possess this property of intercalation. This was shown by the fact that angelicin-DNA complex could be dissociated photochemically, whereas psoralen-DNA complex was photochemically rather resistant. The failure to photoreactivate damages by angelicin and psoralen under *in-vivo* conditions, indicate that intercalation may not be the only reason for this damage (biological damage). However, our preliminary studies show that in bacterial system one can dark-reactivate these damages, and as I heard from Dr. PAINTER, CLEAVER has also found dark-reactivation of HeLa cells damaged by psoralen.

ERNST: A short question to you, Dr. CHANDRA. Did your bacteria really survive 10% acetone in the nutrition solution?

CHANDRA: Well, they do. May be, Dr. MENNIGMANN can comment on this.

MENNIGMANN: I have been asked this question several times. I think I am the only person that ever did these experiments because I dared to put bacteria into 10% acetone. They survived about two days in this solution. But they will start to die in the dark above 15% acetone and above 30 degrees centigrade. But, I would now give the advise to use acetophenone instead of acetone because it has several advantages. One of the disadvantages of acetone is that it unfortunately gives a number of other lesions. If one uses pure DNA, one produces obviously radicals which are fairly long-lived. One has to scavenge these radicals because they produce single-strand breaks. But this is not the case if one uses acetophenone so that the results are more clear-cut, at least within the »biological dose range«. That I obtained such nice results with acetone and bacteria is probably due to the fact that within the bacterial cell you have so much material which can scavenge the radicals that it works here; but it does not work with transforming DNA and also not with viruses because in the latter case in addition you get protein damage.

AVERBECK: During the 8th Annual Meeting of the European Society for Radiation Biology in Basko Polje, Yugoslavia, H. S. KAPLAN gave a paper concerning »Chemical inhibitors of the repair of X-ray induced single-strand breaks in cellular DNA«. Using the method of alkaline sucrose gradient centrifugation described by McGRATH and WILLIAMS it was demonstrated that there are three types of repair of single-strand breaks in *E. coli*.

1. The first type of repair can take place in complete growth medium, not in buffer. Recombination-deficient strains of *E. coli* (rec⁻) are unable to carry out this type of repair. This recombination or post-replication repair is a very slow repair process. More than 30 minutes are needed in *E. coli*. Hydroxyurea (impure, i.e. contaminated with an unknown compound) can act as an inhibitor [KAPP, D. S. and K. SMITH: The chemical inhibition of the repair of single-strand breaks in DNA: post-irradiation sensitization to X-rays. Int. J. Radiat. Biol. *19:* 255 (1971)].

2. The second type of repair is faster than the first type. It can take place in buffer and is complete in about 15 minutes. This type of repair is absent in *E. coli* polA mutants which are lacking the Kornberg polymerase I. In wild-type cells it can be inhibited by NaCN and EDTA. It is also temperature-dependent.

3. The third type of repair is an »ultrafast« repair process. It is inhibited in air-irradiated cells. Heat, cold, oxygen, N-ethyl-maleimide and hydroxyurea can act as inhibitors. It was suggested that this type of repair is dependent on a DNA ligase. This repair process can take place in less than 2 minutes.

Since it has been suggested by H. S. KAPLAN (8th Annual Meeting of the European Society for Radiation Biology in Basko Polje, Yugoslavia, 1971) that there exists a third repair process (perhaps related to the DNA ligase) which is very fast in wild-type cells but inefficient in cells irradiated in oxygenated conditions, it can be assumed that oxygen can act (directly or indirectly) as an inhibitor of the activity of repair enzymes. Perhaps in this aspect the oxygen effect can be interpreted in terms of equal lesions but different repair ability of X-irradiated cells in oxygenated or hypoxic conditions.

BOYLE: May we now turn to the scheduled discussion which concerns the influence of drugs and environmental factors on repair mechanisms. I would like to make a few general comments at the outset. This subject can be discussed, of course, at a number of different levels, depending on the type of approach one wishes to use. For example, the biologist studying the effect of temperature on the shape of radiation survival curves of cells may find a completely different value for the temperature optimum to that of the biochemist studying the effect of temperature on the in-vitro properties of a particular repair enzyme. The problem is, of course, one of biological complexity: in order that repair processes can work within the cell, other ancillary processes must also be operative. Thus one must attempt to differentiate between effects caused by the direct action of a drug on repair enzymes, and indirect effects operating via ancillary processes. Although this is an obvious statement to make, it is one that appears to be frequently forgotten, particularly when biological data are being interpreted using facts derived from in-vitro biochemical data.

We should therefore attempt to ask:

1. What factors specifically affect repair processes?
2. What ancillary processes affect the efficiency of DNA repair, and what factors affect repair either by their indirect action on these processes, or by combined action on both repair and ancillary processes.

As an example of the latter case, I would like to take up 10 min of your time in reviewing some work which has been done in collaboration with Dr. PAUL SWENSON of Oak Ridge National Laboratory [BOYLE, J. M., R. L. SCHENLEY, and P. A. SWENSON: J. Bacteriol. *106:* 896 (1971)]. Most of what I have to say has recently come into print. Incidentally, I think these data may have some relevance to what Dr. POHLIT was saying yesterday.

These data will show that metabolic events occurring after irradiation of DNA can affect the survival of cells, a factor which I think is not considered in Dr. POHLIT's theory which considers only the effects on the cytoplasm at the time of irradiation. We have been looking at the responses of *E. coli* B/r to ultraviolet (UV) light of 254 nm wavelength. This organism is radiation-resistant and can perform excision and presumably post-replication repair. Yet despite having these repair systems, when B/r cells are grown on minimal medium containing glycerol as the sole carbon source, 99.5% of the cells are inactivated by a dose of 520 ergs/mm². We argued that the most likely cause of death of most of the cells was due to metabolic disturbances occurring after irradiation. If this were true then it might be possible to identify events that were critical to survival and prevent their occurrence. Since available chemical energy is an obvious necessity for cell survival we have studied the respiration of cells following UV.

Fig. 1. – The survival of B/r is dependent on the carbon source on which the cells are grown. The slopes of the survival curves for cells grown on glycerol are parallel but displaced by a shoulder on the glucose grown cells.

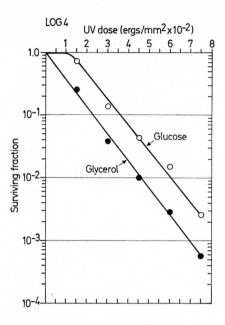

Fig. 1. Ultraviolet survival curves of E. coli B/r. Cells grown on glucose (○—○) or glycerol (●—●).

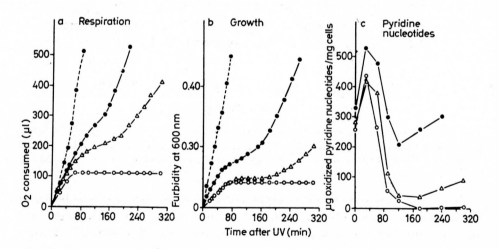

Fig. 2. a) Respiration, b) growth and c) pyridine nucleotide content of E. coli B/r cells irradiated with 520 ergs/mm². Non-irradiated cells: dashed line; irradiated cells: solid lines. Cells grown in minimal medium continuing glucose (●—●), glycerol + casamino acids (△ — △), or glycerol (○—○) as carbon sources.

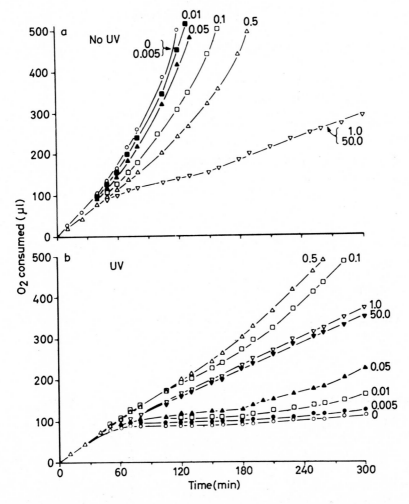

Fig. 3. Effect of FU on respiration of E. coli B/r. Upper panel: non-irradiated; lower panel: cells irradiated at 0 min with 520 ergs/mm². After irradiation respiration of cells at 2×10^8/ml was measured, in the presence of 0 to 50 μgm/ml FU as indicated.

Fig. 2. – In this slide panel a shows the respiratory patterns of cells grown before and after irradiation in minimal medium containing glycerol, glycerol and casamino acids, or glucose. As you can see, respiration after UV is very dependent on the carbon source, and is paralleled by the pattern of cell growth (panel b). The subsequent work I will discuss concerns cells grown in glycerol-containing medium, chosen because such cells gave the largest effect on respiration when irradiated. – In this case, after 520 ergs/mm² respiration ceases after one hour. SWENSON and SCHENLEY [Mutation Res. *9:* 443 (1970); J. Bacteriol. *104:* 1230 (1970)] have shown that the cessation of respiration is associated with the loss of two cell components, glycerol kinase, the pacemaker for glycerol metabolism, and pyridine nucleotides, the respiratory coenzymes. The loss of pyridine nucleotides is shown in panel c. By the use of metabolic inhibitors it was shown that respiratory turnoff occurs as a result of transcription of the irradiated genome.

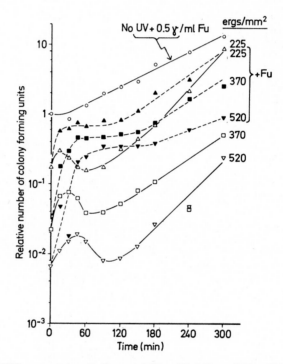

Fig. 4. Effect of FU on post-irradiation viability. Viability of E. coli B/r cells irradiated with various UV doses. Solid lines: no FU; dashed lines: 0.5 μgm/ml. FU added at zero time.

Two methods which we have used extensively to prevent respiratory turnoff are the additon of 5-fluorouracil (FU) to the post-irradiation incubation medium (presumably the FU is incorporated into those species of mRNA which would, except for their fraudulent character, be involved in the process of turning off respiration) and elevation of the temperature of irradiated cells to 42 °C after irradiation (presumably one or more of the proteins involved in respiratory turnoff are thermolabile).

Fig. 3. – This figure shows the effect of different concentrations (μgm/ml/ 2×10^8 cells) of FU on the respiration of non-irradiated (upper panel) and irradiated (lower panel) cells. With 0,5 μgm/ml respiration continues at a linear rate.

Fig. 4. – We compared untreated cells with those treated with FU after irradiation and this slide shows the viability kinetics of both cultures. During the first hour after irradiation the viability of the treated cells increased dramatically from about 0,5% to about 25%. The UV dose response of cells treated with various amounts of FU for one hour after UV is shown in Fig. 5.

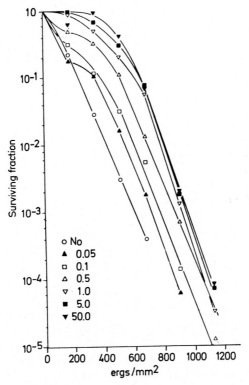

Fig. 5. Effect of FU concentration on ultraviolet survival curves. Cells irradiated and plated immediately (curve labelled No) or after 60 min incubation with various concentrations of FU as described in Fig. 3.

Fig. 5. – If we measure the viability of the treated cultures at 60 min as a function of FU concentration and UV dose we can obtain survival curves for the effect of FU on UV-irradiated cells, and we see that the effect of FU

treatment is to enlarge the shoulder of the survival curves, in the same way
that growth of cells in glucose medium enlarges the shoulder.

Fig. 6. – We have also looked at excision-associated events occurring in both
untreated and FU-treated cells, and found only marginal differences in the
rate of dimer excision (lower panel) and DNA degradation. There is, however,
a difference in the pattern of rejoining of excision-induced strand breaks (upper
panel). More strand breaks are closed at times longer than one hour in treated
cells than in untreated cells.

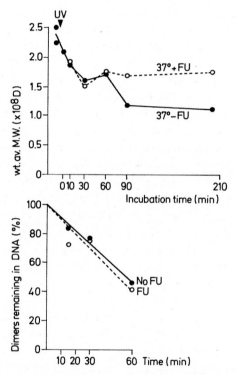

Fig. 6. Excision of dimers and strand-break repair. The effect of 0.5 μgm/ml. FU on the
kinetics of dimer excision (lower panel) and on the repair of single-strand breaks (upper
panel) was observed following 520 ergs/mm².

We believe that the explanation of these phenomena is that in FU-treated
cells pyridine nucleotide levels remain high: one of these respiratory coenzymes,
nicotinamide adenine dinucleotide (NAD), is also the coenzyme of the putative
rejoining enzyme of *E. coli*, polynucleotide ligase. Thus in this system we have
a situation in which the nutritional and drug factors that alter the radiation
survival responses of B/r, do so (at least in part) by a mechanism that affects

both cellular respiration and, more directly, the activity of one of the DNA repair enzymes.

I was talking last night and today with one or two other people about the energy requirements for repair. I think Dr. KIEFER has some comments to make.

KIEFER: We have been interested in the relation between split-dose recovery (sometimes also called »Elkind-type of recovery«) and cellular energy metabolism (Fig. 1). A normal wild-type diploid yeast *Saccharomyces cerevisiae* was used for the investigations. Experimental details are given in the published paper, so I need not bother you with that here. [KIEFER, J.: Int. J. Rad. Biol., 325–336 (1971)]. Since yeasts are facultative anaerobes they are able to grow with or without oxygen, provided a fermentable substrate is available. We started always with normally grown stationary phase cells, irradiated them with X-rays or UV and incubated them in medium containing either glucose or lactate (Fig. 2). After variable intervals a second dose of radiation was given and the effect on colony forming ability plotted as a function of time between exposures. If glucose is the carbon source in the medium we do not find any significant difference between samples kept in air or in nitrogen during the interval. This was not surprising to us since we know that yeast cells can synthesize sufficient amounts of energy-rich metabolites only by fermentation of glucose. This is not true for most other cell types and therefore a strong dependence of the split-dose sparing effect was often found [see, e.g., HOWARD, A.: Int. J. Radiat. Biol. *1968:* 341] as a function of oxygen pressure.

The situation is different if lactate is the carbon source in the medium. This compound cannot be fermented and energy is only provided by respiration. As you see from Figs. 3 and 4 split-dose sparing can only be found in the aerated sample. In our mind, this is quite conclusive evidence that a functioning energy metabolism is a necessary prerequisite for split-dose recovery. It has to be admitted, of course, that until now nobody knows, what split-dose sparing means at the molecular level, particularly, whether there is any relation to the kind of DNA repair mechanisms we were talking about mainly at this meeting.

Since we had demonstrated that energy metabolism plays an important role in the course of events after irradiation we also measured respiration and anaerobic fermentation in irradiated cells. I should like to show you some preliminary results: As unirradiated controls and the exposed samples have a different proliferation behaviour, we related all our measurements to cell number in the sample, i.e. respiration and fermentation are given as relative values *per cell*. Also, since we were interested in the effects in surviving cells, we chose doses so that the surviving fractions were relatively high – normally about

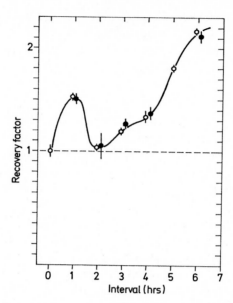

Fig. 1. The time course of split-dose sparing after X irradiation. »Recovery factor« is the ratio between surviving fractions with split doses and an interval as indicated on the abscissa and that after exposure to the total dose without interval. Glucose was given as carbon source. Open circles: incubation in air; closed circles: incubation in N_2.

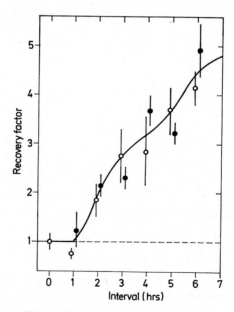

Fig. 2. As in figure 1, but with UV.

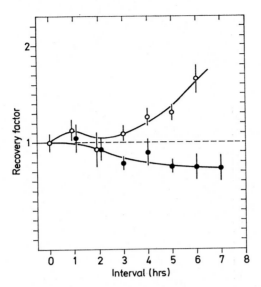

Fig. 3. As in figure 1, but with lactate as carbon source.

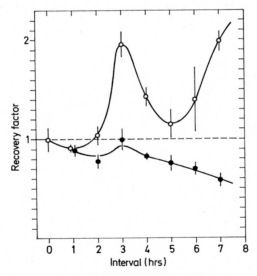

Fig. 4. As in figure 1, but with acetate as carbon source and with UV irradiation.

50%. The time course is given up to six hours in Figs. 5 and 6. If we integrate these curves, i. e. plot the areas under them, we arrive at the kind of picture as given in Figs. 7 and 8. You see, that both respiration and fermentation per cell

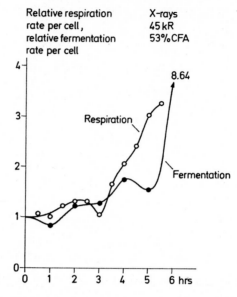

Fig. 5. Relative respiration and fermentation rates as function of time after X-ray exposure to a colony forming ability of about 50% (values calculated *per cell*).

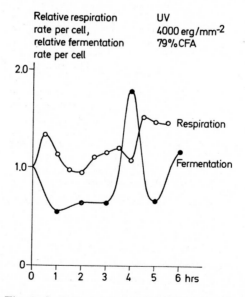

Fig. 6. As in figure 5, but after UV exposure.

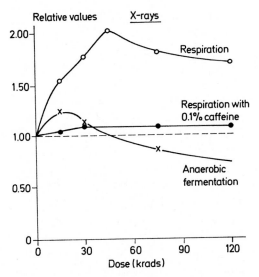

Fig. 7. Dose dependence of total respiration or fermentation per cell within six hours after irradiation.

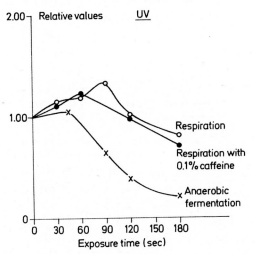

Fig. 8. As in figure 7, but after UV exposure. The dose rate was 44 ergs/mm^{-2}/sec^{-1}.

are increased with low doses of radiation although the behaviour is different, and also there are big differences between X-rays and UV. Since these results are preliminary, I do not want to embark on a detailed discussion but like to stress only that obviously surviving cells have an increased demand for energy which fits nicely into the split-dose studies. The exact kind of regulation, however, has still to be elucidated.

RÉVÉSZ: Without wishing to complicate the issue further, as an analytical approach to the problem I suggest to distinguish between 1) the functional integrity of the components involved in the recovery and repair processes; 2) the functional integrity of the energy generating system which supplies the energy required by these processes; and 3) a factor which I will term »recoverability« or »repairability« of the damage. Let me refer to one of Dr. SHELDON WOLFF's experiments from the fifties to explain what I mean with these terms. Dr. WOLFF [WOLFF, S., H. E. LUIPPOLD: Science *122:* 231 (1955) and Genetics *43:* 493 (1958)] showed that rejoining of broken chromosomes is also an energy requiring process. No rejoining occurs in anoxia, but it does occur in the presence of oxygen which permits the generation of the required energy. However, there is a time limit after the induction of the damage within which oxygen must be available for rejoining to occur. If oxygen becomes available later than about 15 min after the damage had been inflicted, the broken chromosomes do not rejoin. The damage becomes fixed, the breaks are not »rejoinable« any longer. Analogously, it is conceivable that the reparable state of the DNA damage, or the recoverable state of the sublethal damage is limited in time. Some of our findings on the effect of cysteamine on cellular recovery from radiation damage could be explained by such an assumption [cf. LITT-BRAND, B., L. RÉVÉSZ: Acta Radiol. *10:* 257 (1971)]. If the assumption is correct, information on the factors which influence recoverability or repairability, i.e. the fixation of the damage, is of the greatest importance for the correct interpretation of the repair and recovery phenomena.

BOYLE: In our experiments we found that you must have transcription and translation of the irradiated genome within the first hour after UV irradiation. In order to prevent cessation of respiration one can interfere with normal transcription by adding 5-fluorouracil immediately after irradiation, and under these conditions one sees a large increase in viability over the first hour after irradiation. With reference to Dr. KIEFER's work I would add that the behaviour of our system after X irradiation is very like that after UV. One difference is that although cessation of respiration can be prevented by fluorouracil, in the case of X-rays this does not result in an increase in viability.

RÉVÉSZ: Could this last comment of yours be considered as a direct evidence for the time limitation of the recoverability or repairability just to introduce this new term?

Boyle: I do not know.

Ernst: A short report on some side results of one of our experiments on green plant cells. Primarily we were looking for photoreactivation. If you have a green plant cell, the light which is given after the X-ray damage will do two things: 1) It causes real photoreactivation. 2) It allows photosynthesis to work and so it is difficult to differentiate between these two processes. If you restrict the wavelength of your reactivating light by filters to the range at about 400 nm which is known to allow photoreactivation you may suppress photosynthesis. In Funaria hygrometrica (moss) we did not find real photoreactivation. But if we use the same (mercury-arc) lamp without these filters and we can be sure that the photosynthesis was working, we got something like a reactivation or repair. So this, I conclude, is due to the energy supply by the photosynthesis.

Averbeck: I would like to comment on what Dr. Révész was saying. The gassing conditions during X irradiation may interfere with subsequent repair mechanisms and not only produce different radiation damage.

The current status of the discussion about the sensitizing effect of oxygen during X irradiation is that the effect is primarily due to:

1. radical damage to the DNA and other cell components, but includes the possibility

2. that oxic damage could affect the DNA in such a way that the action of repair enzymes in the cell is prohibited or inefficient.

I like to show some of our data about the effect of oxygen in radiation sensitive strains of Saccharomyces which could possibly favour the second possibility.

We have measured the X-ray survival curves for different strains in oxygenated and hypoxic conditions. The experiments were performed using a haploid wild-type strain and three mutants out of our collection of radiation sensitive mutants carrying the genes r_1^s and r_2^s which confer increased sensitivity to UV and X irradiation and the allele r_{3-1}^s which confers high sensitivity to UV [Laskowski, W., E. R. Lochmann, S. Jannsen u. E. Fink: Zur Isolierung einer strahlensensiblen Saccharomyces-Mutante. Biophysik 4: 233 (1968); Averbeck, D., W. Laskowski, F. Eckardt and E. Lehmann-Brauns: Four radiation sensitive mutants of Saccharomyces. Molec. gen. Genetics 107: 117 (1970)]. Several spore clones of each genotype were used.

The colony-forming ability of the X-irradiated cells (using an X-ray Siemens machine at 300 kVp, 10 mA with 0.2 Al filter) was determined in the usual way by plating the irradiated cells immediately after irradiation on complete growth medium (AVERBECK et al., 1970).

Fig. 1 shows the dose-response curves after X irradiation for the haploid wild-type strain (full lines). The ratio of the doses in hypoxic and oxygenated conditions at the 10% survival level, i. e. $D_{10}(N_2)$ over the $D_{10}(O_2)$ is 2.5.

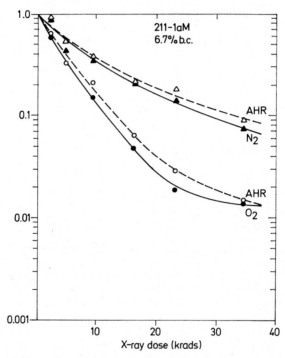

Fig. 1. Typical survival curves of the haploid wild-type strain 211-1aM after X irradiation in oxygenated (points) and hypoxic conditions (triangles) after immediate plating (full lines) and 48 hours agar-holding (AHR, dotted lines). Percentage of budding cells in the irradiated sample 6.7%.

An oxygen enhancement ratio is not given because the oxygen enhancement ratio does only apply when oxygen is strictly dose modifying in all dose ranges. Figs. 2 and 3 show the dose-response curves of the haploid spore clones carrying the gene r_2^s and the allele r_{3-1}^s. The ratio of the doses required to give 10% survival in the two irradiation conditions are similar to the values obtained with wild-type cells although r_2^s-cells exhibit increased sensitivity to X irradiation and r_{3-2}^s-cells do show only little differences in their X-ray sensitivities compared to wild-type cells.

Fig. 4 shows the survival curves of a haploid spore clone carrying the gene r_1^s. In contrast to wild-type cells the ratio of the doses at the 10% survival level in the two irradiation conditions is only about 1.4. Similar low values of the ratio $D_{10}(N_2)$ over the $D_{10}(O_2)$ are found in other spore clones carrying the r_1^s-gene.

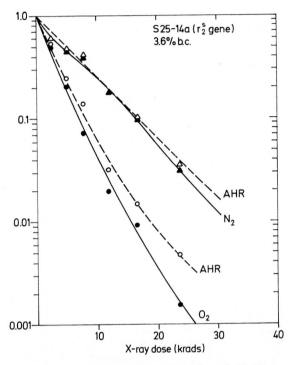

Fig. 2. Typical survival curves of the haploid spore clone S 25-14a carrying the r_2^s-gene after X irradiation in oxygenated (points) and hypoxic conditions (triangles) after immediate plating (full lines) and after 48 hours agar-holding (AHR, dotted lines). Percentage of budding cells in the irradiated sample 3.6%.

r_1^s-cells show similar sensitivities to X irradiation in oxygenated and hypoxic conditions as wild-type cells in oxygenated conditions. This perhaps can be interpreted that r_1^s-cells are unable to repair hypoxic X-ray damage which, when repaired in wild-type cells, leads to resistance to X irradiation.

Since it is known that r_1^s- and r_2^s-genes confer increased sensitivity to UV and the r_{3-2}^s-allele high sensitivity to UV the overall picture reported by ALPER [A characteristic of the lethal effect of ionizing radiation on »hcr⁻« bacterial strains. Mutation Res. *4:* 15 (1967)] that there exists a negative correlation between oxygen enhancement ratio and UV sensitivity in radiation sensitive bacterial mutants does not apply to the strains of Saccharomyces used.

The differences in the responses to X irradiation in hypoxic and oxygenated conditions seem to be correlated to the genetically controlled sensitivity changes of the strains of Saccharomyces used.

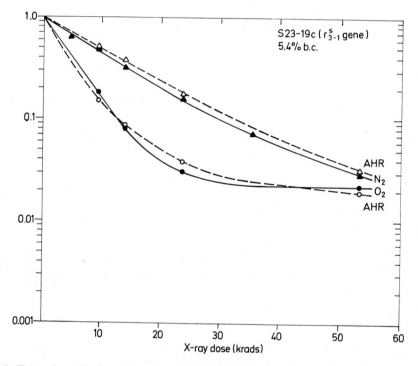

Fig. 3. Typical survival curves of the haploid spore clone S 23-19c carrying the r_{3-1}^s-allele after X irradiation in oxygenated (points) and hypoxic conditions (triangles) after immediate plating (full lines) and 48 hours agar-holding (AHR, dotted lines). Percentage of budding cells in the irradiated sample 5.4%.

BOYLE: How soon do your anoxic cells return to oxic conditions?

AVERBECK: One should assume that yeast cells return quickly to normal conditions since they are used switch back to aerobic or anaerobic metabolism. On the other hand we compare different strains under the same conditions and the onset of replication after irradiation is expected to occur in all strains at a similar time scale.

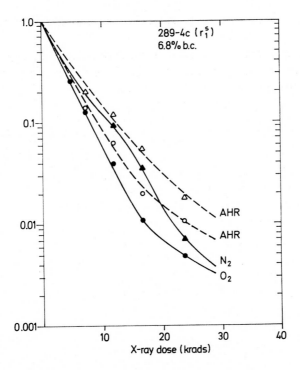

Fig. 4. Typical survival curves of the haploid spore clone 289-4c carrying the r_1^s-gene after X irradiation in oxygenated (points) and hypoxic conditions (triangles) after immediate plating (full lines) and 48 hours agar-holding (AHR, dotted lines). Percentage of budding cells in the irradiated sample 6.8%.

LINDAHL: DNA-repair mechanisms have presumably evolved in response to the most common types of damage to intracellular DNA. One such form of damage is probably that due to heat. On heating DNA in solution at a temperature below the T_m, a slow degradation of the primary structure takes place, mainly due to depurination [GREER, S. and S. ZAMENHOF: J. molec. Biol. *4:* 123 (1962)]. The temperature dependence of this inactivation of double-stranded DNA has been determined by following the rate of loss of transforming activity at different temperatures, and by direct measurements of the rate of release of purine bases from DNA radioactively labelled in these residues [LINDAHL, T. and B. NYBERG: Biochemistry, in press (1972)]. For the latter type of experiments, DNA was isolated from a purine-dependent mutant strain of *B. subtilis* grown in the presence of ^{14}C-adenine. The data available so far indicate that at neutral pH and ionic strength 0.15, 1 purine base is released per 10^6–10^7 base pairs per hour at 37°C. It seems likely that this type of specific acid-catalyzed hydrolysis would occur at a similar rate *in vivo* as *in vitro*. In a mammalian cell, the rate of degradation would then correspond to the loss of 10^4–10^5 purine residues from the DNA of a cell during one generation time of 20 hours. As depurination causes loss of genetic information, it appears that cells should be able to repair depurinated sites in DNA. In considering how heat lesions in DNA may be repaired, it is useful to draw a parallel with UV-repair systems. Thus, in analogy with photoreactivation, a direct repair event could conceivably take place by enzymatic replacement of a missing purine residue. Further, apurinic sites could be removed by a post-replication type of repair mechanism, but this would at present be difficult to prove, as no good method exists to selectively introduce depurinated sites into DNA *in vivo*. Finally, repair by excision and repair replication would presumably require an endonuclease that attacks at apurinic sites and thereby would allow exonuclease and polymerase action.

In a search for endonucleases of this type, it was observed that cell extracts from several bacteria and mammalian tissues contain an activity that rapidly inactivates preheated, but not unheated, transforming DNA of *B. subtilis* at pH 8.0 in the absence of divalent metal ions. The active factor(s) in the cell extracts chromatographed as a macromolecule on gel filtration. In an *E. coli* extract, the active principle appears to be identical with the DNA endonuclease II, which has recently been shown to catalyze the formation of strand breaks at depurinated sites [HADI, S. M. and D. A. GOLDTHWAIT: Fed. Proc. *30:* 1156 Abs. (1971)]. The active factor from calf thymus shows alkaline endonuclease activity with preheated DNA after 100-fold purification by standard enzymological techniques. However, at its present stage of purification it also contains acid DNase activity towards unheated DNA.

BOYLE: You have presumably looked at the specificity of this enzyme. Does it work on UV-irradiated DNA or anything else?

LINDAHL: We have tried UV-irradiated DNA and normal DNA. There is no selective attack at pyrimidine dimers.

BOYLE: Have you looked at alkylated DNA in which there may be some depurination?

LINDAHL: We have not done that. Dr. STRAUSS has pointed out previously that this is a rather complicated experiment to do, because the alkylated purines are quite unstable, and are split off.

PAINTER: Is there some way to do this experiment with DNA in a dry state because the DNA in the cell is in some state which may not be in solution? Therefore these depurination events would not occur under those circumstances (in vivo) because it may not be really in a water solution at all.

LINDAHL: I assume that in living cells the DNA is in a hydrated form.

PAINTER: Well, I am not sure that you can make that assumption because there is a considerable amount of evidence from irradiation inactivation experiments that many molecules in the cell do not »see« water products.

STRAUSS: I think I should point out that when cells are alkylated one gets the same sort of products in not too different amounts that one sees if DNA is alkylated *in vitro*.

PAINTER: I didn't object, I ask the question whether it can be done with dry DNA.

LINDAHL: WILKINS [WILKINS, M. H. F. and J. T. RANDALL: Biochim. biophys. Acta (Amst.) *10:* 192 (1953)] found that DNA has the fully hydrated B structure *in vivo*.

STRAUSS: Didn't ZAMENHOF measure depurination in dry DNA?

LINDAHL: Yes. GREER and ZAMENHOF have done some experiments with spores, and also heating dry DNA. Then the question is, what is *dry* DNA? Dry DNA is very hygroscopic, and some of the water is never removed by conventional drying methods.

ROBERTS: Does your apurinic acid exhibit the same alkali instability as the apurinic acid formed following loss of alkyl purines from alkylated DNA?

LINDAHL: Yes, the time required for chain breakage at a depurinated site in DNA, at 37° and neutral pH, has been estimated to be 2000 hours [LAWLEY, P. D. and P. BROOKES: Biochem. J. *109:* 433 (1968)].

PARTSCH: In the sessions yesterday and today many problems on repair mechanisms after X-ray and UV-ray were discussed. There is yet another problem, namely the synthesis of nucleotides needed to replace the excised nucleotides of the damaged DNA, which was not discussed till now, but seems to be of great importance.

In organisms two ways are possible to synthesize nucleotides (Fig. 1). One of these is the de-novo synthesis using small precursors such as C-1 units, the other way is called »preformed pathway«, a process where pyrimidine and purine bases released by catabolism of nucleic acids are reutilized. Purine bases are converted to the corresponding nucleosides by purine-phosphorylases and

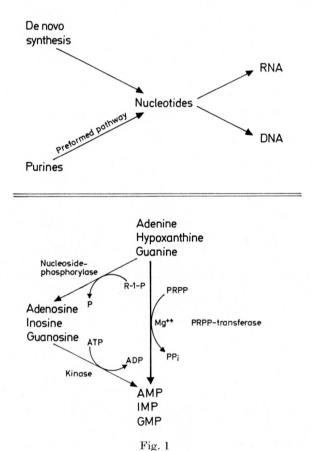

Fig. 1

then to nucleotides by kinases or directly by 5-phosphoribosyl-1-pyrophosphate-transferases (PRPP-transferases). Investigating these enzyme activities in the cell-free homogenate of the radioresistant *Pullularia pullulans*, we measured different enzyme activities depending from growth conditions (Figs. 2 and 3). The activities were not reduced after irradiation up to 1.5 Mrad. The LD_{99} of anaerobically grown blastospores was about 860 Krads.

Since some authors have reported that the de-novo synthesis of nucleotides is much more affected by ionizing radiation than the preformed pathway, especially at high radiation doses, we studied this fact in *Pullularia*. For this purpose, ^{14}C-formic acid and ^{3}H-adenine were incorporated in unirradiated and irradiated blastospores of *Pullularia*. Comparing the formation of adenosine mononucleotide over the two synthesis ways we found that the de-novo pathway was much more sensitive than the preformed pathway (Table 1).

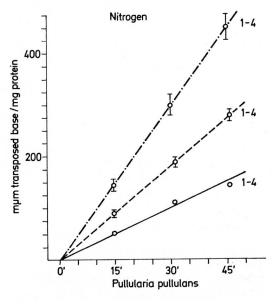

Fig. 2. The purine-PRPP-transferase activities in anaerobically cultivated Pullularia.

——— guanine
– – – – hypoxanthine } -PRPP-transferase activities
– · – · – adenine

1 = control, 2 = 0.5 Mrad, 3 = 1.0 Mrad, 4 = 1.5 Mrad.

Table 1. The de-novo synthesis and the formation of AMP over the preformed pathway in *Pullu'aria pullulans*.

	De-novo synthesis	Preformed pathway
Control	3.370 DPM	10.191 DPM
500 Krad	1.389 DPM	6.422 DPM
Reduction to	41.22%	64.02%

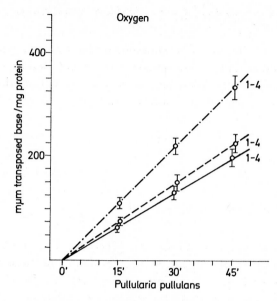

Fig. 3. The enzyme activities were also determined in cells of the same culture as described above, but aerated for four hours.

$$\left.\begin{array}{l} \text{———— guanine} \\ \text{– – – – hypoxanthine} \\ \text{– · — · – adenine} \end{array}\right\} \text{-PRPP-transferase activities}$$

1 = control, 2 = 0.5 Mrad, 3 = 1.0 Mrad, 4 = 1.5 Mrad.

This indicates that after irradiation, especially at higher radiation doses, the nucleotides may be formed mainly over the preformed pathway. Since, for example, lymphocytes are affected by much lower doses than this radioresistant organism (they also do not possess so many protective substances), the preformed pathway may be a way to form purine-nucleotides for the repair replication.

KIEFER: Just a simple question: What was the colony forming ability after 500 Krads?

PARTSCH: In the nitrogen grown cells 500 Krads were approximately LD_{50}. In nitrogen grown cells, they were cultivated in a pH constant culture, the LD_{99} was 860 Krads and after change to the oxygen growth conditions we found an increase in the colony forming ability of the cells. The LD_{99} was about 1.4 Mrads.

REGAN: What is the generation time of this organism?

PARTSCH: I haven't studied it, but I think it is not known in the literature.

MOUTON: I would like to get some comments on diseases resulting from the combined action of radiations and molds. I think for instance on the inception of pulmonary cancer (the so-called Jáchymov cancer) studied presently by M. ADAMEK in the Czechoslovak uranium mines?

KIEFER: Prof. SCHRAUB investigated this disease which we refer as »Schneeberger Krankheit«; the present knowledge has been reviewed recently [SCHRAUB, A.: Radiological health and safety in mining and milling of nuclear materials. IAEA-Symposium, Vol. I, p. 3 (1964)]. As far as I know, no interaction between radiation and molds has been found.

ALTMANN: Perhaps I can answer your question, Dr. MOUTON. A colleague from Prague was working in our laboratory for some time and he told me that a mold called *Aspergillus fumigatus* grows on the wooden parts in Joachimsthal. We have isolated also a toxin from this mold. But we have no direct evidence that there is an interaction between Schneeberger Krankheit and the inhibition of repair by this toxin.

KLEPPE: I wish to review briefly the various types of DNA which arise during irradiation and the manner in which the repair enzymes act on these. In particular I want to focus on some of the properties and functions of DNA polymerase I from *E. coli*.

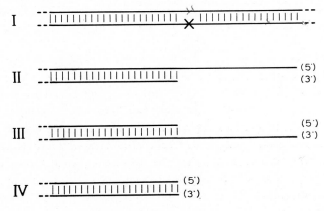

Fig. 1. General structure of irradiation damaged DNA. The vertical bars are meant to represent several base pairs.

It would appear that within a given region on the chromosome irradiation can give rise to basically four different types of DNA structures. The general structure of these DNA's are given in Fig. 1. The damage occurring most frequently can be represented by DNA I where alterations have occurred in one of the strands. Examples of this type are thymine dimers, base modification and single-strand breakage etc. If both strands of the DNA are broken within a more narrow region of the chromosome then three different types of DNA may be formed, namely DNA II, DNA III and DNA IV. DNA II contains a protruding single-stranded 5′ end, DNA III a single-stranded 3′ end whereas type IV possesses no free single-stranded ends. In addition to these structures DNA with crosslinking should also be considered. However, crosslinked DNA is formed mostly in the presence of certain alkylating agents and furthermore the mechanism of repair is not fully known. Therefore this type of damage will not be considered here.

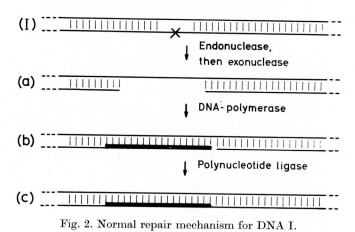

Fig. 2. Normal repair mechanism for DNA I.

The normal excision repair mechanism for DNA I is shown in Fig. 2. Nucleases excise a portion of the damage chain, DNA polymerase I then fills the gap, and joining of the last phosphodiester linkage is catalyzed by polynucleotide ligase [HOWARD-FLANDERS, P.: Ann. Rev. Biochem. *37:* 175 (1968); KORNBERG, A.: Science *163:* 1410 (1969); KELLY, R. B., M. R. ATKINSON, J. A. HUBERMAN and A. KORNBERG: Nature *224:* 495 (1969); KAPLAN, J. C., S. R. KUSHNER and L. GROSSMAN: Proc. Nat. Acad. Sci. (Wash.) *63:* 144 (1969)]. If, however, polynucleotide ligase has been inactivated or the concentration of the necessary cofactor (NAD or ATP) severely decreased, then a different situation may arise. Recent studies by RICHARDSON et al. [MASAMUNE, Y., R. A. FLEISCHMAN and C. C. RICHARDSON: J. Biol. Chem. *246:* 2680 (1971);

Masamune, Y. and C. C. Richardson: J. Biol. Chem. *246:* 2692 (1971)] have shown that DNA polymerase I can initiate syntheses of DNA at single-strand phosphodiester bond interruptions as shown in Fig. 3. Initially the DNA polymerase I hydrolyzes a small portion of the original DNA from the 5′ end.

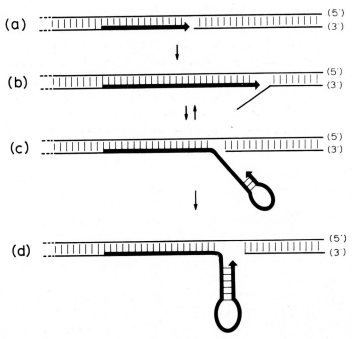

Fig. 3. DNA polymerase catalyzed synthesis of DNA at single phosphodiester bond interruption.

This hydrolysis is then followed by repair from the 3′ end and when a portion of the DNA helix is reached which is less stable, then the 5′ end will be displaced and DNA repair continued as shown in Fig. 3 (b). Structure (b) is thought to be in equilibrium with structure (c), Fig. 3, where the newly formed chain is partially single-stranded. If the 3′ end of this newly formed DNA can fold back on itself (see Fig. 5), i. e., if it is partially selfcomplementary, then this new 3′ end can itself serve as a primer for DNA polymerase I and repair will proceed as shown in Fig. 5 (d). The result will be a new branched DNA, the branched part being a selfcomplementary structure. It is doubtful whether such a DNA would be biologically active. Nature must therefore have enzyme systems which efficiently can repair such »overrepaired« DNA. From the above considerations it therefore follows that merely measuring incorporation of thymine or thymidine may not always give the true picture with regard to repair in a given cell. The state of polynucleotide ligase and its cofactor must also be known if the correct conclusions are to be drawn.

Repair of DNA of the general structure II has been extensively investigated in KHORANA's laboratory using duplexes with known sequences, part of the gene for alanine t-RNA [KLEPPE, K., E. OHTSUKA, R. KLEPPE, I. MOLINEUX and H. G. KHORANA: J. molec. Biol. *56:* 341 (1971)]. DNA polymerase I will repair such DNA's to completion, i. e., the very last nucleotide is also incorporated as shown in structure (a), Fig. 4, which is identical with DNA IV. The minimal size of the primers was found to be an oligonucleotide of approximately 5–7 nucleotides in length.

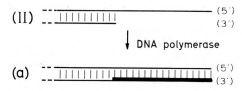

Fig. 4. Repair of DNA II by DNA polymerase I.

Concerning DNA III, DNA polymerase will act on this type of DNA in two different ways, depending on whether or not the 3′ end possesses a complementary structure on the single-stranded portion, such as shown in Fig. 5 (a). Experiments with single-stranded DNA of known sequence (KLEPPE et al., 1971) have revealed that DNA's capable of looping back on themselves can be repaired by various DNA polymerases, as shown in (b), Fig. 5. On the other hand if the 3′ end is not capable of looping back on the single-stranded regions then the 3′ end most probably will be degraded by the exonuclease II activity of DNA polymerase I to give structure (d), Fig. 5, which is identical with DNA IV.

It has recently been shown that DNA of type IV with no single-stranded ends can be joined end to end by T4 polynucleotide ligase [SGARAMELLA, V., H. VAN DE SANDE and H. G. KHORANA: Proc. Nat. Acad. Sci. (Wash.) *67:* 1468 (1970)]. Whether or not polynucleotide ligases from other sources also can carry out such a joining is not known. However, this finding raises many questions regarding the mechanisms of recombination and rejoining of damaged DNA molecules.

ALTMANN: The selection of invited speakers for this symposium was done in the way, that in the first papers presented a review on DNA-repair mechanisms

– including new results – was given, and in the second part a connection was made between the research from more theoretical standpoints with possible practical applications.

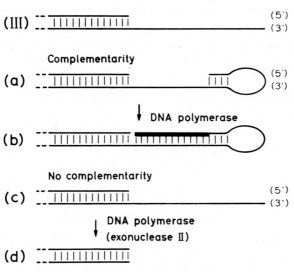

Fig. 5. Repair of DNA III by DNA polymerase I.

I believe, that only the first part was fully successful and many new aspects, especially the relationship between DNA repair, chromosome aberrations and cell death, including many new reaction mechanisms and methods, were discussed in details. In the second part very rare information was gained on DNA-repair inhibitors. Some new results were also reported on diseases which are based on DNA-repair enzyme defects. In xeroderma pigmentosum as well as after incorporation of certain mycotoxins which also inhibit DNA repair it is known, that »late effects« like leucaemias or other different types of cancer normally occur. But there is still a lack of information on the problem if certain cytostatic or immunosuppressive drugs which produce also these »late effects« are DNA-repair inhibitors.

Some environmental contaminants beside mycotoxins – like detergents and pesticides – seem also to have this side-effect. On the other side the question arises if it is possible to use DNA-repair inhibitors which are not strong immunosuppressive drugs – to avoid undesirable side-effects – in combination with irradiation in cancer therapy. The increase of secondary cancers can possibly be reduced and lower local irradiation doses may be necessary. Normally there is a more or less long delay between the time in which basic results are obtained and the practical application of these results. Possibly this symposium can help to shorten this lag phase and we hope, not only the scientist attending this symposium but also the pharmaceutical industry and last not least mankind will have some profit from this line of research.

In conclusion I hope you agree with me that this symposium was successful and we thank the Medical Department of the Hoechst AG for their kind invitation and excellent hospitality.